Soviet Social Policies
WELFARE, EQUALITY, AND COMMUNITY

THE DORSEY SERIES IN POLITICAL SCIENCE

EDITOR   Norton E. Long   *University of Illinois*

Soviet Social Policies

WELFARE, EQUALITY, AND COMMUNITY

ROBERT J. OSBORN, Ph.D.
Associate Professor of Political Science
Temple University

1970 | THE
DORSEY PRESS HOMEWOOD, ILLINOIS
IRWIN-DORSEY LIMITED, GEORGETOWN, ONTARIO

Library of Congress Catalog Card No. 75-124169

Printed in the United States of America

Preface

This book is quite simply the result of wondering whether or not we have anything to learn from the Soviet Union, or the Soviets from us, in motivating people to fill useful roles in modern society. Do people who live in highly urban surroundings and work in large factories and organizations respond to similar prods and incentives in the same way? Are there limits to the way in which a central government can influence the important choices which people make in finding their places in an urban and industrial society?

The "convergence" idea both attracts and repels. What is the purpose in maintaining our distinctively American or Western notions of man and his political order if this political order of ours is being driven inexorably toward some sort of midpoint—location as yet unknown—between ourselves and the communist world? Our American reaction is that the whole notion smacks of Marxist determinism, anyway. For us it is more reassuring to assume that the "midpoint" is rather close to our own political system. An urban and industrial system, we like to think, will thrive in the long run only when its men enjoy the kind of choices which we like to claim as our own. As for our problems—urban crime, the generation gap, anonymity and anomie, the threatening deterioration of the environment, misuse of social manipulation, and many others—we reassure ourselves with the unproven notion that every industrializing society will sooner or later have to face these anyway.

If there is one theme which unites the policy areas dealt with here, it is the double theme of equality and opportunity. These two principles may be combined harmoniously in some situations, but they stand opposed to each other elsewhere. If equal opportunity means the opportunity to gain extra rewards for performance, it becomes a means to inequality. Every society that seeks consciously to manipulate career paths and rewards, security, environmental influences, and all the rest, whether it is private corporations or government agencies that do this, must find its own answer to the equality problem and in so doing reveal some of the assumptions about human nature held by the men who run it.

The Soviet ideological vision of a society based upon its own particular version of equality and opportunity was a dream long delayed. Inequality and denial of opportunity had to be maintained as policies in different ways and different situations for long decades. The real tragedy of the Soviet industrialization drive has not been in the delay of welfare goals, since this planned lag is now being made up by stages. The tragedy has been, rather, in the political repression upon which Stalin and others embarked in order to secure their rule against the discontents that their policies evoked at every level. Consumer austerity can be erased by reallocating resources, but the habit of repressing political dissent has sunk deep psychological roots which cannot be dealt with so easily. That Stalin's successors, while refraining from massive repression, have lacked the resolve to alter decisively his style of political management is a sad fact that could not be offset even by sizable future increases in the Soviet standard of living.

While Soviet resources still are not nearly enough to meet today's needs even in some of the policy areas where the greatest breakthroughs have been made, yet the shape of much of the future is visible from what has been done with the resources now available. Each of the policy areas described in this study represents an unfinished story, and the reader is asked to bear this in mind. Whether the sum of Soviet social policies 25 or 50 years from now will be something resembling our own social policies, something vastly different, or anything acceptable to American preferences at all, I must leave to the reader's speculations.

I am much indebted to the Inter-University Committee on Travel Grants for the opportunity to spend 10 months in the Soviet Union in 1963-64 doing research on many of the topics dealt with here, as well as to the University of Pennsylvania for research funds subsequently. A month of travel in the Soviet Union during the summer of 1969 made it possible for me to check on the recent application of most of the policies with which this book deals. Among the many persons with whom I have consulted on various problems, special thanks are due to Professors William W. Brickman and Thomas A. Reiner of the University of Pennsylvania.

June, 1970   R. J. O.

Contents

ix

.1. Policy Decisions and Social Values

Part of the early fascination of many foreign observers with the Soviet Union lay in their belief that political and social purposes had been made explicit by deriving them from a single ideology. Whatever they thought of these values personally, at least they found no need to waste time searching for them or attempting to define them. It was no matter that realization of a number of them was postponed, and that realization of others was hampered by conflicting priorities and administrative inexperience; for when the opportunity came, they too would be translated into policy. Thus, according to this widespread early view, a political system had at last arisen which was capable of carrying out true social experiments because it had closed the gap between values and legislation. If the means by which this was accomplished were not themselves acceptable to most observers from the West, nevertheless the Soviet Union had thrown out a challenge to the industrialized West to make its social values explicit.[1]

This early optimism about prospects for social experimentation was tempered not only by Stalin's style of social management, but also by gaps in the array of values derived from Soviet Marxist ideology, and by even greater gaps in social research and the prediction of human response. More important than these drawbacks

[1] See, for example: George S. Counts, *The Soviet Challenge to America* (New York: The John Day Co., 1930); Samuel N. Harper, *Civic Training in Soviet Russia*, (Chicago: University of Chicago Press, 1929); Sydney and Beatrice Webb, *Soviet Communism: A New Civilization?* (2 vols.; New York: Charles Scribner's Sons, 1936).

is the fact that any kind of social ideology has serious pitfalls. It can be a hazard for legislation if it serves as substitutes for research, or if it serves to block experimentation. Furthermore, there is no guarantee that the actual values of policymakers actually do correspond, in any given case, to officially stated values. Ideology cannot be taken as synonymous with political and social values; hence some purposes may happen to be rooted in values other than those which enjoy official support. An ideology, in fact, may serve as an invitation to policymakers to cover their application of their own values with inappropriate ideological statements. Unforeseen problems may be dealt with haphazardly if they have no place in ideological assertions about society. In short, explicit long-range social goals which are embedded in an official ideology may themselves be a hazard to the makers of policy. If indeed the Soviet use of an ideology of society constitutes a challenge of some sort to the noncommunist world, an appropriate response to the challenge certainly is not to set up an explicit counterideology. If anything, we should feel challenged to be clear about the values undergirding social legislation in the present, to be aware of what experience and research have to say about these values, and thus to be mindful of where they will lead if we intend to maintain them over a number of years.

Actually, the derivation of legislation from ideology in the Soviet Union has been carried out flexibly, and this is particularly true in the field of social legislation. The formal programmatic expression of ideology can be found in only two documents, the Party Programs of 1919 and 1961; and the first of these was long outdated even by the 1930's. To be sure, statements by Stalin, Khrushchev, and other leaders took care of part of the long gap, as did Party resolutions elaborating these statements. The Khrushchev era also saw several major ideological statements drawn up under high-level Party supervision, notably the *Fundamentals of Marxism-Leninism,* compiled in 1959. Both the 1919 and 1961 Party Programs dealt with limited time periods, and what they included was mainly programs already under way or contemplated for the near future.[2] Take, for example, the question of income distribution as the 1961 Program deals with it (Chapters 2, 3, and 5 treat this in detail). Its 20-year projections call for rounding out existing programs, starting with the

---

[2] For reliable translations of the texts of these two programs, see Jan F. Triska (ed.), *Soviet Communism: Programs and Rules* (San Francisco: Chandler, 1962).

extension and improvement of a wide variety of free public services. The Program's prediction that the rate of growth of the value of these services will exceed the rate of growth of earnings was simply a projection of the trend of the latter 1950's. This was also true of the prediction of a gradually lessening disparity between high and low incomes. At the same time, references to distribution based wholly on need rather than labor, a state of affairs which presumably will be attained by the 1980's, is not elaborated save for the suggestion that it is a still further projection of current trends. The whole definition of "need" as a basis of planning consumption is left open. Unanswered too is the question of whether money distribution will continue into the period of full communism which lies beyond the current 20-year transition period (1961-80).

Nonetheless, ideology does limit policy alternatives to the extent that it is translated into policies and programs. In the policies just described, it bars the repetition of any dramatic increase in earnings differentials such as the Soviet government introduced in the early 1930's. The 1961 Program forbids the reintroduction of charges for education, medical treatment, and other free public services which are wholly or partially subsidized. Ruled out likewise is any policy that would require Soviet citizens to bear amortization costs for the state apartments they occupy. This has not, however, prevented the Soviet government from pushing for the expansion of cooperative housing, whose occupants do pay full construction costs with the help of state loans, and cover full maintenance as well.

So the limitation of policy alternatives is one thing, and the prescription of policies another. Every political system imposes limits on the conduct of its leaders and administrators through the values which help sustain the system. The narrowness of these limits is not necessarily determined by whether or not an effort has been made to coordinate values in an official ideology. Actually, the behavior of policymakers may be more constrained where values are not formally expressed, since one is less sure where the limits lie and testing them may be politically risky. The caution of Soviet policymakers below the level of the Politburo and Party Secretaries may be explained not so much by ideological or programmatic restraints as by the top leadership's customary preemption of policy initiatives.

So merely possessing an official ideology, and working with programs said to be derived from the ideology, does not necessarily make policy decisions easier in the Soviet Union. The one major advantage which the Soviet policymaker enjoys is that he is probably less troubled than his noncommunist counterparts about the validity of his long-term goals, and about the philosophical justification of what he is doing. But in defining current purposes and then translating them into laws and administrative acts, his problems are comparable to those of policymakers anywhere. Nowhere is this more evident than in policy areas which have seen a long succession of efforts to motivate ordinary people to make the desired choices. Legislative and administrative inertia are much in evidence too: If the most conspicuous American example of this is the present welfare system, a comparable Soviet example is *Orgnabor,* the national employment service, described in Chapter 5, which was finally overhauled in 1967 after experiencing many years of bureaucratic decay.

There is no way of fitting all the legislative programs in effect at any given time into a system. It would be a mistake to try to see legislative planning where legislation represents an accumulation of decisions, many of which were not coordinated with the others. If the 1961 Party Program represents a solid effort to maintain legislative planning, its broad language leaves plenty of room for interpretation. It is the contention of this study that policy, in the sense of basic intent, must be sought in the decisions of the present by finding out what the makers of policy intended to accomplish in the present and the near future. Since we are looking at social policies, the intent is of two kinds: what human behavior is desired, and how the human being is expected to react to the manipulation of his environment.

At this point the writer must confess that this approach rests partly on his own feeling about how values are formed. What men really believe about human reactions, and the values they hold about their own society, should be sought first of all in the decisions they make from day to day. Men in positions of responsibility reveal their values in the decisions they make under pressure, sometimes when they are too busy to reflect adequately on where they are going. The "gut reaction" may not tell everything, but it tells much. Verbalized expressions of belief, if they differ from the beliefs which are implied in today's actions, may indeed show dispositional values, which the study of actions alone does not usually show. At the same time, repeated actions of the past and present are perhaps the strongest shapers of dispositional values.

What led the writer to select the policy areas covered in this book is the growing importance of various "convergence" theories. These theories assert that as different societies become more urbanized, they also become more alike in other respects as well. So far these are simply theories, of course. Among those who claim to see convergence in some form as between the Soviet Union and the United States, for example, opinions differ widely as to just what else is converging or is going to converge, and why. Opinions differ likewise as to where the meeting point will occur: Are "they" going to become more like "us," or the reverse?[3]

The writer does not propose to try to answer any of these questions here. The purpose, rather, is to describe the answers which Soviet policymakers have been finding to problems in several policy areas which are central to the urban and industrial segment of society in any industrially advanced nation. The policy areas selected are the following: (1) security and the individual's claim to assistance and benefits as against the system which has made him wholly dependent upon its complex survival relationship; (2) the motivations which are offered to the individual to find the level and type of education suited to his capacities, to select appropriate and meaningful employment, and to remain committed to his work; and (3) the shaping of the physical environment of the city dweller in such a fashion as to promote meaningful social interaction, and to furnish him with a sense of identity within his largely man-made environment.

Within each of these policy areas, emphasis is placed on those choices which became available to Soviet policymakers as new resources became available during the 1950's and 1960's, with particular attention to the 1960's. Allowance is thus made for the fact that many decisions of the first three decades of Soviet rule were the product of resource scarcities, and that the effects of these scarcities are still reflected in decisions of the recent past. For

---

[3] An example of a positive answer to the convergence question is that of John Kenneth Galbraith in *The New Industrial State* (1967); Raymond Aron in *The Industrial Society* (New York: Praeger, 1967) gives a qualified positive answer.

Qualified negative answers may be found in Samuel P. Huntington and Zbigniew K. Brzezinski, *Political Power US/USSR* (New York: Compass Books, 1963), and in Gunnar Myrdal, *Beyond the Welfare State* (New Haven, Conn.: Yale University Press, 1960).

Other proponents of convergence include the following: Gunnar Adler-Karlsson, "Functional Socialism," *Peace Research Society: Papers,* VI, 1966, pp. 87-100; Pitrim A. Sorokin, "Soziologische und kulturelle Annäherungen zwischen den Vereinigten Staaten und der Sowjetunion," *Zeitschrift für Politik,* VII: 4 (1960), pp. 342-69; Andrei D. Sakharov (the eminent Soviet physicist), *Progress, Coexistence and Intellectual Freedom* (New York: W.W. Norton, 1968). Vigorous opposition was furnished by Peter Wiles, "Will Capitalism and Communism Spontaneously Converge?" *Encounter,* XX:6 (June, 1963), pp. 84-90.

example, the legislation of the 1950's on pensions and on the minimum wage (both discussed in Chapters 2 and 3) set levels for both which were below what an ordinary individual—let alone a family—needed to live on in the cities and towns. Consequently, this legislation is treated from the point of view of the direction and principles which it established, and not as an expression of what Moscow ultimately wants by way of living standards for the elderly.

If any kind of "convergence" is occurring among the social policies of industrial nations, socialist and nonsocialist, surely these are areas in which the convergence ought to be very evident. Or if, as Soviet Marxist ideology claims, capitalism and communism lead to radically different ways of life, it is in these same areas that the differences should stand out. In official doctrine, the industrial city is the place where communist society of the future is being born today; the countryside will follow behind, to the degree that the circumstances of agricultural workers come to resemble those of city dwellers. Whichever is the case, the Soviet experience in shaping the urban and industrial environment bears continued watching.

Other policy areas might have been added: population policy, family law, criminology and the treatment of offenders, ethnic relations, the use of leisure time, policy toward religions, and the social aspects of public health. Even narrower fields which require a good deal of special knowledge to understand, such as the treatment of mental illness, display interesting features which may reflect some kind of national policy. Likewise omitted from this study is the Soviet rural population. The efforts made during the 1960's to make agricultural pursuits attractive and stem the flow of youth and talent from the villages are turning into a whole new chapter in Moscow's efforts to substitute persuasion and motivation for compulsion. Finally, the role of organizations in influencing behavior would deserve much attention in any comprehensive survey of social policies. While the Soviet social scientists who have worked on the problem of job changing and migration patterns among Soviet youth (see Chapter 5) have said little about the role of the Komsomol (Young Communist League), surely the Komsomol itself has to deal actively with these and other problems.

THE SEARCH FOR VALUES AND INTENT IN POLICY DECISIONS

In identifying the values behind policy decisions, the first attention is given to the decisions themselves as expressed in legislation and in authoritative statements. Statements of political leaders and high-level administrators in various fields are important too, as are scholarly debates and press commentary. Where the policy action taken was very specific, as for example in the new social security law of 1956, these statements and debates may help clarify intent. But where the top policymakers in a given field are still searching for a direction, or experimenting with several policies at once, as in the urban planning problems dealt with in Chapters 6 and 7, professional debates and newspaper commentary assume much greater importance.

There are other ways of attempting to identify policy intent, and some recent experiments deserve attention. One approach focuses on verbal expression of intent and assumes that these, if properly understood, can be taken as a reliable indicator of values. The shortcomings of this approach do not stem from the problems of studying verbal expression as such. Rather, in the Soviet case, ideological constraints and practical obstacles may seriously impede the collection of any significant number of verbalizations that do not coincide with those having official sanction. Such an obstacle may be surmountable in the politically less volatile policy areas.

The 1964 study of values held by Soviet and U.S. elites in equivalent fields, which was carried out at the University of Michigan by Robert C. Angell and others, suffers from both conceptual and methodological shortcomings.[4] This survey and analysis used newspaper statements on given topics as stand-ins for the values assumed to be held by the highly-placed members of various occupational groups; the editors of given newspapers were assumed to speak for one or another elite. Thus, the "Government-Party" elite, a designation which itself ignores the distinction made by most Soviet area specialists between the governmental and Party hierarchies, was represented by *Pravda, Kommunist,* and *Voprosy filosofii;* the "economic" elite was assumed to speak through *Voprosy ekonomiki, Sovetskaya torgovlya,* and *Planovoye khozyaistvo;* and so on. The survey failed to distinguish between value statements in materials furnished by the same central sources, and statements emanating from a prominent member or organization of a given elite group.

There is ample evidence testifying to the use of the press by different individuals and organizations for the purpose of promoting their particular claims and emphases by publishing them in careful

---

[4] Angell, 1964.

but unmistakable terms. Until the mid-1950's, study of these differing emphases required line-by-line study of the central press organs, the most conspicuous example of which remains the Malenkov-Khrushchev disagreement over economic priorities in the fall of 1954, *Izvestiya* supporting Malenkov's view, *Pravda* that of Khrushchev. In the 1960's, by contrast, Soviet newspapers and journals have more or less openly taken sides on a number of practical domestic issues, including most of the issues which this study deals with.

Hadley Cantril made some initial progress towards identifying official Soviet social values in his *Soviet Leaders and Mastery Over Man* (1960).[5] His study of the Soviet leadership's assumptions about human nature, drawn up on the basis of published materials and some interviews, set forth 55 propositions concerning "manipulation" of the Soviet population. Of these propositions, nearly one third are designated as implicit rather than explicit; that is, they find no formal public expression in the Soviet Union. For example: "That human beings are rather simple creatures; there is no need to have much respect for them or much awe of their complexities and capacities. Nearly all people are like children in that they need to be led and can be led by the hand, being conditioned to ask no questions about where they are going. (Implicit.)"[6] Cantril dealt only with the outlook of Soviet political leaders, not with that of social scientists and others professionally concerned with human relations.

May we assume, as Cantril did, that the attitudes of Soviet leaders are congruent? Such an assumption naturally led Cantril and his associates to prefer congruent statements, and possibly to reject others which did not fit the pattern. One must ask here also to what extent public statements can be regarded as the equivalent of values. We are dealing with a society which places great stress not only on its official ideology, but on the highly stylized conformity to ideology of all public statements on important issues.

A more satisfactory method of arriving at elite social values—if far more limited in its application—is to study the political leadership's demands made upon the professions which develop and apply specific social theories in their work. Psychologists, educators, and criminologists are among those most exposed to these demands. The

---

[5] Cantril, 1960.

[6] *Ibid.*, p. 23.

demands occur in several forms in the Soviet system: one can speak of an overall demand for the conformity of professional findings to relevant points of ideology, of demand imposed via allocation of substantial resources to the solution of a given social problem, and of the specific demand which may come in the form of a Central Committee directive or in statements by Party leaders.

Raymond A. Bauer's landmark study *The New Man in Soviet Psychology* (1952), published at a time when specific Party demands on psychology and biology had reached an incredible extreme, relates in detail the impact of all three types of demand on Soviet psychologists. The environmentalism and mechanistic personality models of the 1920's, concepts within which the debates of the psychological profession took place in that era, were themselves the product of the acceptance by Soviet psychologists of broadly stated Marxist premises about man and society. The 1930's saw a specific Party demand for the abandonment of those environmentalist assumptions which discouraged the active reshaping of the personality through training. And during this time resources were directed to the appropriate educational reforms, and away from undesired psychological and pedagogical research. Both intelligence and aptitude testing were banned from Soviet education, and so far neither has been reinstated.

One of the most refreshing things about the Bauer study is that fuzzy and excessively general ideological premises suddenly come into focus when they are translated into theories of psychology and pedagogy. Here might seem to be the best place to look for the real meaning of a number of doctrinal Marxist statements in their Soviet application, that is to say, what values the political leaders actually have in mind when they justify their policies with ideology. Unfortunately, this approach has one serious difficulty. Bauer, who was concerned much more with the impact of elite demands on psychology than with the intent of those who devise the demands, wrote that one cannot assume that the makers of the demands have any precise theory in mind at all. The Soviet policymaker is concerned with the practical effect of a theory much more than with its adequacy as a theory. He is inclined, reasons Bauer, to a common-sense approach to human behavior, and complicated theories make it more difficult for him to select means of shaping behavior. Once committed to a policy, he is not likely to be receptive to making allowances for difficulties arising from flaws in the theory he has chosen by way of justification for his policy.[7] Thus, the professions entrusted with the task of elaborating and applying a policy may, in pursuing their task, devise refinements and supporting theories which never occurred to the policymakers. The analyst of these policies is then tempted to read too much into the policy-makers' intent.

Robert C. Tucker's account of the neo-Pavlovian revolution of 1950-51 in Soviet psychology deals directly with the intent of Soviet policymakers, in this case the intent of Stalin himself.[8] The dictator's mentality during the last years of his life had led him back to the notions of environmental determinism and social causation which had dominated Bolshevik philosophy in the 1920's. To Stalin, the postwar apathy of the Soviet people, who were not responding to Zhdanov's propaganda campaign, called for more scientifically calculated stimuli. The "New Soviet Man" of the 1930's, "inner-directed" man, the model of conscious purposefulness achieved through training, was now abandoned in favor of a model built on predictable reflexes guided from the outside. As the link between environment and man, a minor and neglected feature of Pavlov's psychology was approved by Stalin, the "second signal system" or conditioning to verbal stimuli. Stalin's propositions on the role of language in social processes, set forth in his curious treatises on linguistics in *Pravda* in the summer of 1950, depicted a society regulated by verbal symbols. Immediately after these had appeared, *Pravda* announced a major scientific conference on Pavlovian psychology, which convened less than a week later.[9]

Tucker's picture of these events is that of the direct personal intervention by Stalin, who had in mind a specific psychological doctrine and made a specific and restrictive demand on psychologists and educators. This 1950 episode was the culmination of a long series of increasingly arbitrary demands, which have not been repeated in the post-Stalin era in any such drastic form. At the same time it displays the features of policymaking by a regime which is the custodian of a philosophy which purports to explain all important social phenomena: If behavior stands in apparent contradiction to the philosophy, then the philosophy must be amended as regards external stimuli, or as regards patterns of response, or both. In Tucker's interpretation, the manipulation of stimuli had gone on

---

[7] Bauer, 1952, pp. 191-6.
[8] Robert C. Tucker, *The Soviet Political Mind* (New York: Praeger, 1963), Ch. 5.
[9] *Pravda,* June 20, 22, and 28, 1950.

long enough to convince Stalin and others that the "new Soviet man," for all his training in correct motivation, had to be made more immediately responsive to those stimuli which were and are preeminently the business of the political system, namely, mass communication. The same problem can easily confront any regime whose leaders rely, by professed ideology or simply by inner conviction, on a fixed notion of behavior.

Today, nearly 20 years after the short-lived revolution which Stalin imposed on psychology, both psychology and the social sciences are experiencing a period of strong growth and change. Crude intervention in these disciplines from the present political leadership seems unlikely. The output of Soviet sociologists, particularly, conveys the impression of a discipline that has been assigned certain broad areas of investigation in order to discover new methods of motivating the Soviet populace to work better, gain new skills, and maintain order. If Soviet Marxist ideology has been used in past decades as a substitute for social research, the experience of the 1960's suggests that it can also be used as a justification for this research.

Whatever may be the benefits from social research for the Soviet political leadership, the fruitful development of this research in the present and near future requires that the leadership abstain from imposing specific doctrines of its own. But the direction of social research, its areas of concentration, are in fact strongly conditioned by the priorities of the political leadership, and rather likely these priorities are shared by the new and fast-growing fraternity of social researchers. It is no surprise, for example, that the growing edge of Soviet sociological research lies very largely in the sphere of work relationships. The two-volume collection *Sociology in the USSR,* published in 1965, the first major effort to set a direction for sociology as a whole, reflected this vividly. The articles in the section entitled "The Class Structure of Soviet Society" actually deal with *occupational* structures and interrelationships, which is the accepted Soviet definition of "class" as applied to Soviet society. The section on "Social Groups and the Individual" deals with interactions in work collectives and with variations in work attitudes within given collectives. The items dealing with the use of leisure time concentrate on the relationship between work and leisure, the influence of leisure time use on work.[10]

[10]*Sotsiologiya v SSSR,* 1964, *passim.* See also the comments by Fischer, 1964, Ch. 4, and Paul Hollander's evaluation of the new sociology of leisure in Simirenko, 1966, pp. 314-16.

Even the quite new interest of Soviet urban planners in patterns of living and consumption apart from work, which is discussed in Chapters 6 and 7 below, is frequently justified in terms of increasing the availability of women for employment by reducing further the time spent on domestic chores and errands. All of this research is valid in itself, of course. The point is that the overwhelming emphasis on work relationships is among other things a means whereby sociologists justify their usefulness to the nation. Within the boundaries they have set for this research, sociologists do not necessarily avoid publishing results which are negative or unfavorable from the point of view of the Soviet Union's self-image as expressed in its ideology and publicity. Vladimir N. Shubkin's report from Novosibirsk (see Chapter 4) on the influence of parents' occupations on the occupational choice of their sons and daughters is one of the clearest examples of this.[11]

What is more important about these boundaries of research may be the questions and research areas which they exclude. Lewis S. Feuer found some of the excluded areas to be research in the possible psychoanalytical roots of social attitudes, in modern concepts of alienation, in political sociology, and in attitudes toward the causes of shortcomings in economic organization.[12] Whether these blank areas of research are the result of self-limitation by sociologists, or of limits imposed by the Party, or both, they are definitely a reflection of the priorities of inquiry suggested by official ideology and programs. Thus, the results of current social research cannot be said to be subject to arbitrary interference from the Party, but at the same time the direction of research does certainly show the effect of official policy preferences.

The development of Soviet social research will continue to be a fascinating field to watch, not only in the sociology of work, but in criminology, family relations, educational psychology, and certain other areas. As a guide to the meaning of policies, however, the political guidance of the social sciences is only a rough indicator of policy preferences. Consider, for example, how deeply divided are the counsels of American political leaders with regard to research into the causes of urban rioting and violence, and the policies which should be employed to deal with violence. There are those who resist research conclusions when they endanger long-established opinions,

---

[11] Shubkin, 1964.

[12] Feuer, 1964.

and there are others who suspect that social research is biased from the beginning in favor of certain policies. Even among those who respect the inquiries that have been made, there can be honest differences of opinion as to what policies the results suggest. There is no reason to believe that Soviet policymakers, at the very top level or lower down in specialized policy areas, are immune to these same differences when the results of research lie on the table before them.

The approach to policy which this study represents is by no means new. Among the most successful attempts to identify the values which support policies are the studies of Soviet law done by John N. Hazard, Harold J. Berman, Rudolph Schlesinger, and others.[13] Law is the hand of the state intervening directly in the affairs of individuals and combinations of individuals; it prescribes, prohibits, and motivates. The problem of discovering the link between the paragraphs of the law and the intent of the lawmaker is quite manageable by comparison with the problems presented by other policy areas. Specifically, the lawmakers' idea of what motivates human beings stands forth clearly in the paragraphs of the law, even if this idea is based on nothing more than guesswork. Another area of fruitful investigation has been that of wage and salary incentives, the most outstanding of which are Abram Bergson's studies and further studies derived from his work.[14] While it is not necessarily the work of economists to inquire deeply into problems of motivation, the policies underlying wagesetting stand forth rather clearly from the data alone. The complications in studying wage policy arise from attempts to take account of nonwage motivations in an effort to form an overall picture of Soviet policymakers' philosophy of work motivation.

The following chapters are concerned with policies rather than the makers of policy. But because they deal with values and intent, something must be said about *whose* values and intent. The days when political leaders and officials at every level had to reckon with the often unpredictable whims of one omnicompetent policymaker are not likely to return. The difference is not only that we now have reasonably good evidence of well defined differences of opinion among the members of the Politburo and the Party Secretaries, or of

---

[13] See, for example, John N. Hazard, *Law and Social Change in the U.S.S.R.* (London: Stevens and Sons, 1953), Harold J. Berman, *Justice in the U.S.S.R.* (New York: Vintage, 1963), and Rudolph Schlesinger, *Changing Attitudes in Soviet Russia: The Family* (London: Kegan Paul, 1949)

[14] Bergson, 1944; Galenson, 1963; Schroeder, 1966.

cases in which the Party leader's proposals were defeated or seriously modified by his colleagues. Some policies were ultimately defeated by the ministries which they affected, or by Party and governmental chiefs at the provincial and local levels. Their efforts have frequently been supported by criticism of official policies by specialists, academic and otherwise, and by the foot dragging of those whose occupations were directly affected. The 1958 educational reforms described in Chapter 4, together with their ultimate reversal in the 1960's, provide a case history in which all these forms of opposition played a role. Efforts to limit the growth of the large cities, described in Chapter 6, stumbled not on high-level disagreement, as far as we know, but on the resistance of industrial and other ministries in Moscow which did not want their preferences in location of new investment to be restricted in this fashion.

The voices of specialists and functional groups have been increasingly evident in the major domestic policy debates of the last 15 years. Every policy discussed in this study has been debated vigorously by specialists and middle-level administrators not only in professional journals, but in the daily press as well. Just how much influence do they have? A recent study of the factors influencing the 1958 educational reform law concluded that "the more problematic and technical the issue, the more dependent on expert judgment elites will be. Consequently, they will be more likely to consult policy groups, who will thereby be more influential on such issues."[15]

The writer recalls several conferences at Moscow University Law School during 1963-64 in which the professors, instructors, and graduate students of a given academic department met with government specialists to go over the latest draft of a proposed law or code. There were a number of these conferences in various other legal research institutions. Usually the content of the discussion would be reflected in articles by the participants published in specialized periodicals. In the case of conferences on a new family code and a new land-use code, the daily press gave only sporadic attention to these subjects until—four years later, in 1968—the time apparently was ripe to act on the codes. At this point, *Izvestiya* published the full drafts of both codes and followed these up with many signed items supporting and criticizing various provisions. A study of the major extension of governmental tort liability under the

[15] Schwartz and Keech, 1968. p. 848.

new civil legislation of 1961 concluded that this step "grew largely out of exchanges (published and unpublished) between Soviet jurists."[16] Peter H. Juviler's research in recent family law suggested to him that, in general, "legislation by consultation" has replaced the earlier "legislation by cabal." He distinguished groupings of opinion rather than interest groups in the Western sense, "cutting across bureaucratic and professional lines."[17]

The writer recalls that several of the most prominent professors in the Moscow University Law School were regular visitors in the Central Committee Secretariat building during the last year of Khrushchev's administration. (One of the more ambitious of them apparently instructed his secretary-receptionist to tell callers "He's not here, he was summoned to the Central Committee offices"—this in a society where such information is very seldom given out gratis.) Actually, Khrushchev in the last years of his administration overemphasized consultation to the extent that sessions of the Central Committee were subdivided into workshop sessions in which Committee members were obliged to receive instruction at the hands of specialists. This practice was apparently dropped or at least greatly modified by Khrushchev's successors.

If this study pays a good deal of attention to the writings of Soviet professors, research institute personnel, and others who certainly do not belong to the circle of top policymakers on a given issue, it is not just because their values and interpretations happen to be accessible. In most of the policy areas dealt with here, they have emerged in he 1950's and 1960's as originators of proposals, as compared with their former public role of elaborating—often in the most wooden fashion—proposals already decided upon. Industrial societies have become major consumers of new ideas, even if their realization is often long delayed, and the Soviet Union will be no exception. For this reason the writer is inclined to apply to the making of Soviet social policies the rule which John Maynard Keynes in his *General Theory* (1935) applied to Europe and America:

... The ideas of economists and political philosophers, both when they are right and when they are wrong, are more powerful than is commonly understood. Indeed the world is ruled by little else. Practical men, who believe themselves to

---

[16]Donald D. Barry, "The Specialist in Soviet Policy-Making." *Soviet Studies* XVI:2 (October, 1964), p. 164.

[17]Peter H. Juviler, "Family Reforms on the Road to Communism" in Juviler and Morton, 1967. p. 54.

be quite exempt from any intellectual influences, are usually the slaves of some defunct economist. Madmen in authority, who hear voices in the air, are distilling their frenzy from some academic scribbler of a few years back. I am sure that the power of vested interests is vastly exaggerated compared with the gradual encroachment of ideas. Not, indeed, immediately, but after a certain interval; for in the field of economic and political philosophy there are not many who are influenced by new theories after they are twenty-five or thirty years of age, so that the ideas which civil servants and politicians and even agitators apply to current events are not likely to be the newest. But, soon or late, it is ideas, not vested interests, which are dangerous for good or evil."[18]

---

[18] John Maynard Keynes, *The General Theory of Employment, Interest and Money* (New York: Harcourt, Brace and World, 1964), pp. 383-4.

.2. *The Soviet Welfare Concept*

*THE PROBLEM OF EVALUATING THE SOVIET COMMITMENT TO
WELFARE*

Welfare in the sense used here is the commitment by governments
to enhance the well-being of their citizens. The American definition
of welfare as a specific type of governmental programs has little
application to Soviet circumstances. For example, many of the same
effects that our country seeks through transfer payments can be
achieved in the Soviet system through direct manipulation of wage
rates and employment patterns. What is central here is the overall
goal rather than the choice of means.

There are critics of Soviet policies who maintain that one cannot
speak of welfare in this sense where a state measures its own
accomplishments in terms of building steel mills and intercontinental
missiles, or, for that matter, erecting pyramids in ancient Egypt, or
any other giant program whose end result is not to feed, clothe, and
house its citizens. Only where states seek to enlarge public well-being
as an end in its own right, possibly at the expense of missile building
and the like, can one speak of a true philosophy of welfare. The
critics concede that no state will survive which does not pay at least
minimal attention to sustaining its population. The crucial factor,
they say, is the emphasis placed on nonwelfare purposes.

To the writer, the problem of measuring the emphasis among basic
national purposes in order to compare state against state and
economy against economy is almost insuperable. The purpose in this
chapter and the next is not to attempt to untie this knot, but rather

17

to look closely at the quality of welfare which is reflected in Soviet policies.

Western theories of totalitarianism have treated welfare as a function of other purposes rather than as a purpose in its own right. One of the best known of these theories, that of Carl J. Friedrich and Zbigniew K. Brzezinski, relegated economic goals of every variety to a position far subordinate to the overriding cluster or syndrome of political goals. The vitality of the industrial process, they wrote, is the key to political success, and the distribution of rewards is of minor significance, for "what is decisive is the overpowering reality of totalitarian central control by the dictator and his party."[1] Promises of future abundance—the welfare component of a totalitarian regime's chiliastic claims—are instrumental in establishing and building the regime, but are not in themselves a goal or operating principle. W. W. Rostow, the economist and former White House policy planner, pointed out that a minimum level of economic welfare is necessary in order to maintain a labor force and avoid any rebellion which might result from desperation. The same considerations, he concluded, may lead to a rising level of welfare, the "increasing minimum" which is necessary in order to sustain growth of a type which was at first achieved by "mining" existing human resources to the utmost.[2]

According to Milovan Djilas, the Yugoslav writer and former political leader, the Soviet emphasis on heavy industrial investment and their sacrifice of the standard of living were the result of "the power-holders' need to be independent internally and externally." Not even defense needs justified the policies that were chosen, since Russia could have obtained the same quantity of armaments had it been willing to establish closer links with foreign markets. The problem was that "greater dependency on foreign markets would have necessitated a different foreign policy."[3]

Admittedly, one may conceive of a political system which is committed to high investment and consumer austerity as a permanent policy, as a means of guaranteeing its security through scientific and industrial preeminence, or in pursuit of some intangible goal such as "greatness." Such was the policy of the hypothetical

---

[1]C. J. Friedrich and Z. K. Brzezinski, *Totalitarian Dictatorship and Autocracy* (2d ed.; New York: Praeger, 1956), p. 244.

[2]W. W. Rostow *et al.*, *The Dynamics of Soviet Society* (New York: Mentor, 1954), pp. 80-89.

[3]Milovan Djilas, *The New Class* (New York: Praeger, 1957), p. 116.

21st-century Britain portrayed in Michael Young's *The Rise of the Meritocracy* (1961):

A great country needs great investment. In the middle of last century investment was still pitiably low in Britain, far more so than in Russia, where economic power was securely in the control of an elite who knew that to make their country rich the citizens had to be kept poor. We [British] at last learnt the lesson that productivity and poverty are inseparable. Since 2005 the annual productivity increment has been ploughed back, primarily in human resources, that is, spent upon higher education and upon the maintenance at concert pitch of the people who are its products; and secondarily, upon mechanical equipment of all kinds.[4]

Interestingly, this future society had dealt with the public cry for economic equality by paying everyone an equal flat wage but at the same time added a system of lavish nonmoney benefits for brain workers and the managerial class strictly in proportion to individual contributions to productivity.

Such judgments may be criticized for failing to deal with the ambiguity attending every definition of governmental purposes. Alec Nove, a British economist, pointed out that judging consumption to be merely instrumental to heavy industry and weapons simply is not meaningful because this begs the question. "One could reverse it," he wrote, "and say that they devote as much as possible to improving the citizen's lot, subject to the necessary investment in heavy industry and weapons. . . . Is the glass half-full or half-empty?"[5]

Alfred G. Meyer of the University of Michigan argued that the Soviet industrialization drive has commingled means with ends. Referring to communist systems generally, he singled out "entrepreneurship as the overriding motive force of Communist rule; that means that the chief aim (or, perhaps, the chief effect) of communism is perhaps the promotion of industrialization." Secondary aims and effects include "strict consumer austerity, dictatorial rule, and an ambitious attempt to reeducate peasants and other preindustrial cultures for the twentieth century and the industrial way of life." These aims change in time, of course, and in the case of the Soviet Union Meyer even stands prepared to argue that there has been in fact "a succession of political systems differing from each other in purpose, structure, and functioning."[6] His thesis echoed

---

[4]Young, 1961, pp. 160-61.

[5]Alec Nove, *Was Stalin Really Necessary?* (London: Allen and Unwin, 1964), p. 234.

[6]Alfred G. Meyer, "The Comparative Study of Communist Political Systems," *Slavic Review* XXXVI:1 (March, 1967), pp. 6-7.

Rostow's conclusion (see below) about the inappropriateness of overall Soviet allocative strategy to the needs and possibilities of the present, but it was a more tentative statement than Rostow's. Rostow said that industrialization itself cannot continue indefinitely to be an overriding national purpose. Eventually the growing industrial capacity must be used either for the benefit of its own society or as a weapon against other societies. The merits of this judgment aside, Rostow's use of the term "end" is interesting in that he refused to bestow it on any kind of major national activity which cannot be sustained indefinitely without giving way to a different kind of major activity.

Can one establish a more specific definition of welfare than one based on an impression of a government's broad policy purposes? Such a definition must include, at the very least, criteria of low and high levels of consumption. To compare consumption levels as between two countries with roughly equivalent total resources and population, one naturally looks first to the proportionate share of consumption in the GNP. One American comparison of U.S. and Soviet allocation of the GNP showed that the Soviet consumer's share in the GNP, including communal services, fell from 70 percent in 1928 to 61 percent in 1940, and that it reestablished itself at approximately 60 percent in the 1950's after wartime exigencies had reduced it temporarily to 45 percent. An analysis of U.S. consumption for 1955 showed the level at 75 percent, a figure which includes the services of government to final consumers and thereby embraces a rough equivalent of the benefits of Soviet consumers from the "social wage" *(obshchestvennye fondy potrebleniya),* which is discussed below. However, U.S. Commerce Department figures for the following year (1956) show a level of 67.6 percent.[7] Figures by Simon Kuznets of Harvard University showed a far more dramatic drop in Soviet consumption for the 1928-55 period, from 84.1 percent to 56.7 percent. At the same time, his computations of consumption as a proportion of GNP for the United States and Western Europe for the post-World War II years showed a range of 60 to 67 percent for the industrialized nations of the noncommunist world, with the U.S. consumption level at 64 percent.[8] Whichever

---

[7]Janet G. Chapman, "Consumption," in Bergson and Kuznets, 1963, pp. 262-63.

[8]Simon Kuznets, "A Comparative Appraisal," in Bergson and Kuznets, 1963, pp. 358-60.

figures one accepts, the narrowness of the range of percentage points which they occupy makes difficult any clear imputation of policy choices to U.S. and Soviet policymakers.

A look at the other side of the coin, capital formation as a proportion of GNP, shows the same problems from a different vantage point. During the 1950's, for example, while the Soviet Union was reinvesting nearly one fourth of its GNP as opposed to 15 percent for the United States, the Soviet proportion was surpassed among the noncommunist industrial nations by Norway, Japan, Australia, Israel, Finland, Canada, The Netherlands, and South Africa.[9] Both these figures and the history of Soviet capital formation over the past two decades likewise throw doubt on the usefulness of Alexander Gerschenkron's proposed criterion that the distinctive Soviet political choice in economic development is that "a larger and larger portion of national output is allocated to the production of nonconsumable goods."[10] Among Soviet economic policymakers the view was long held as dogma that the rate of growth in output of the means of production should exceed the rate of growth of consumer goods output. In 1968 the opposite at last came to pass, the output of consumer goods having increased by 8.3 percent as opposed to 8.0 percent for producer goods. However, these figures are hard to evaluate for several reasons, including the vagaries of Soviet prices, and the fact that since the early 1950's, the value of annual consumer goods output has sunk from approximately 30 percent of all output to about 25 percent.[11]

Rostow suggested a criterion of welfare based on a sequence of evolution toward a given high level of consumption. It does not matter whether one accepts Rostow's five-stage scheme of economic development as "natural" or simply as desirable. In either case, "welfare" defines a choice which must be made at a given stage ("maturity") if a further stage ("postmaturity") is to ensue. Rostow

---

[9]Bruce M. Russett *et al., World Handbook of Political and Social Indicators* (New Haven: Yale University Press, 1964), pp. 168-69.

[10]Alexander Gerschenkron, *Economic Backwardness in Historical Perspective* (New York: Praeger, 1965), pp. 150-51. See also Stanley H. Cohn's survey of GNP growth and uses in U.S. Congress, Joint Economic Committee, *Dimensions of Soviet Economic Power* (1962). Admittedly Gerschenkron was directing his attention in this essay to the early five-year plans, yet he proposed this as a long-term distinction.

[11]*Ekonomicheskaya gazeta,* No. 5 (January, 1969), p. 4. *Narodnoye khozyaistvo SSSR,* 1965, p. 123.

placed the Soviet Union in the "maturity" stage even if political reasons, he wrote, have led its leaders to make some basic allocative choices which do not fit this stage (e.g., maintenance of a low-productivity agriculture, concentration of capital and technology in sectors other than consumers' goods output). The "postmaturity" stage opens up the possibility of giving priority to one of three overriding national purposes: pursuit of external power and influence, welfare defined as the purposeful ordering of employment and distribution by governments with humane motivation, and mass consumption of goods and services. As the Soviet approaches postmaturity, according to Rostow, its continued allocation of what he estimated at 20 percent of GNP to military purposes (as opposed to 10 percent in the United States) indicates a persisting preference for the first of these.[12] At the same time, he asserted that the choice of vastly expanding welfare and/or consumption by cutting military investment at least in half is still open to the Soviet Union. Its realization rests on the possibility of substituting international for national security arrangements. But at present, according to Rostow, the Soviet Union is a prototype of a system which may be called "nonwelfare," not because welfare and consumption are not promoted, but rather because they are kept at levels well below what is presently attainable by allocative choices which are unnecessary.

Why were these choices made, and why are they being upheld over decades? Here Rostow shifted from a substantive criterion to a procedural criterion: High national security allocations can be sustained only as long as the Soviet leaders are able to convince themselves and their population of "the case for hostility, for the secret police, and for austerity"; but in the face of an effective arms control agreement "the case for democracy and welfare would be overwhelming." Full entry into the age of high mass consumption, for which Soviet society is now technically, educationally, and psychologically ready, is delayed ("the regime is straining to hold the dam") because the leadership is trying to convert its present economic maturity into world primacy. The leadership's choice represents not only an unnecessary denial of the goals of welfare and/or mass consumption, according to Rostow, but an economic

---

[12]Rostow, 1960, chs. 6 & 8. Kuznets, using 1937 factor costs, gave the following levels for "General administration and defense" as proportions of the Soviet GNP: 1928–3.4; 1937–11.1; 1940–21.2; 1950–17.2; 1955–15.2 Bergson and Kuznets, *op. cit.*, p. 359.

strategy appropriate only to the transition from the earlier "take-off" stage to the stage of economic maturity.[13]

Here too, the reader who seeks clear comparisons of national purpose in a cross-national comparison of defense expenditure levels and the share of defense expenditure in the GNP is invited to look at the figures.[14] He will soon realize that information about defense expenditures by other industrialized nations outside of the two great powers does not give a meaningful background against which to measure these two giants. They are in a league of their own, and the one clear policy which emerges from a look at long-term Soviet military expenditures is the Soviet Union's determination to stay in this league. If one thing stands out in these figures it is that the nations which have spent more than 10 percent of their GNP on national defense are mainly the smaller nations whose security has been under some kind of direct threat. During the 1960's the two nuclear giants followed next in this list with expenditures of 8 to 10 percent, which if correct would mean a Soviet arms budget considerably smaller than that of the United States. If one takes instead the proportion of GNP *per capita* which is spent on defense, the United States is in the lead according to most calculations of Soviet GNP and military expenditure levels. The Soviet Union would not have equalled the U.S. level in this respect even by spending an overall 20 percent of GNP on armaments, which Rostow suggests was being spent in the 1950's. Any yardstick one chooses is ambiguous, therefore.

Another criticism of Soviet defense expenditures is that Moscow has been striving to equal our defense outlays in absolute terms, using a GNP which by the mid-1960's had just attained half the size of the American GNP (by most American calculations) or at most was a bit over three fifths of ours (by official Soviet calculations). It is one thing, the argument goes, for a country to maintain a first-class nuclear striking force which can afford great consumer prosperity on top of it; it is another thing for a country to try to equal this force which in so doing has to depress its people's living standards far below the economy's potential for maintaining satisfactory standards. Here the reader is invited to take still another look at the GNP's of other countries to see which ones devote an even greater

---

[13]Rostow, *op. cit.*, pp. 132-3.

[14]These are handily summarized for the 1950's in Russett, 1964, pp. 79-80, and for the 1960's in Institute for Strategic Studies, *The Military Balance 1968-1969*, pp. 55-56.

portion of their output to armaments than do the two titans. To try to pass judgment on their allocation decisions is to try to pass judgment on who is justified in feeling very nervous about national security: objective criteria just do not exist. As between the two superpowers, the search for a justification for the present military expenditures of both or either must start with the old insoluble problem of who started the cold war. So what a judgment based on the Soviet Union's smaller GNP boils down to is that nations less rich than the United States have no business trying to rival us in military strength.

Americans are probably more tempted than others to see the choice between guns and butter as a clear choice resting on clear alternatives. Our attitude is influenced by the fact that until World War II, our security choices did not involve drastic consequences one way or another. For most of the history of our country, up to 1941, U.S. leaders were free to choose or reject important military outlays: a two-ocean navy, the geographical extension of the U.S. security interests into Latin America and the Pacific, and the defense of Western Europe during 1914-17 and again in 1939-41. The alternative to these choices was not insecurity in any immediate sense, but only the restriction of our security concept to the safety afforded by two oceans.

Rostow made no mention of the argument that large military establishments, properly organized, can be a valuable catalyst for the transition from "maturity" to "postmaturity" stages. For example, a case of sorts can be made for the thesis that American prosperity since the turn of the century has rested upon international commercial advantages which have been gained and sustained through the long-term growth of a large, and now perhaps permanently large, military establishment. One might argue further that the low level of our military outlay during most of this period was made possible by the military cooperation of Great Britain. There are critics of the U.S. military establishments who believe, rightly or wrongly, that the choice to reduce our military budgets and commitments, for whatever reason, would mean less of both guns and butter. Wrote one such critic:

We have a need, as a nation which consumes two thirds of the world's wealth every year and lets the rest of the world have the other third, we have a very strong need of access to raw materials and so forth. . . . I think the principal function of the Armed Forces is to ensure that access, rather than defense. . . . A good many [pacifists] would not give up the standard of living which would be involved in giving up our military.[15]

Although it may be difficult to demonstrate such a view in the case of U.S. military commitments during the post-1945 period, still one might find other examples of the association of military investment with domestic prosperity in the history of the past four centuries of European expansion. While Stalin's stationing of large military forces in Eastern Europe was doubtless based more on security considerations than on the prospect of economic gain for Moscow, the terms of trade which the Soviet Union imposed during the first postwar decade certainly displayed an exploitative pattern.

Soviet commentators contend that the military establishments of a number of Western powers were used from 1917 on to deny the Soviet Union normal economic relations with much of the world's territory. In their view, post-1945 Soviet political gains can justifiably be sustained through high security outlays in support of expanded economic ties. Soviet promotion of the "camp of socialism" idea from 1946 on has embraced the idea of a socialist sphere of trade through which the Soviet Union could overcome its handicaps in maintaining economic relations with the nonsocialist world.

For all these reasons, no sure criterion of national purposes may be found in the familiar assumption that a nation which greatly enlarges its military outlays at a time when its security is not immediately threatened is choosing military power as its primary purpose. It would be safer to assume that the value choices which great powers make have sometimes been choices between lesser or greater effort in enlarging their resources in *both* military capacity and consumer satisfactions. There is also the argument that, quite aside from any question of security, maintenance of substantial armed forces may at certain times, and in certain economies, be useful as an economic pump primer or guarantor of full employment. But this line of reasoning is hard to apply to the Soviet Union at any point in the 50 years of its history. In short, Rostow's charge that the Soviet Union made a senseless, externally needless and internally disadvantageous choice in devoting a substantial part of its GNP to military purposes, must remain an impression rather than a verifiable statement.

[15] Arlo Tatum in James Finn (ed.), *Protest: Pacifism and Politics* (New York: Vintage Books, 1968), p. 395.

Another possible way of assessing the dedication of a government to welfare is to look first at the way it decides on consumption levels and goals. To what extent is the public permitted to determine, as consumers and voters (and under capitalism, as investors), the magnitude of investments in the means of production, defense, and other activities which bring no immediate returns to the consumer?

The "new welfare economics," according to Michael Kaser of the University of Oxford, rests upon a combination of the sovereignty of the people as consumers with their sovereignty as voters. The interaction of consumer choices, including employment choices, with allocation of resources by a popularly elected government, produces "social choice." Social choice, said Kaser, requires no justification as a value other than the circumstance that it is the end-product of individual choices. Soviet planning practice even today leaves little room for welfare theory, according to Kaser, because it fails to meet either of these criteria. This failure, he maintained, can be seen particularly in the persisting belief of Soviet economists that scientific norms can be established for consumption.[16] Here Kaser was referring not to the consumption requirements of individuals and households, but to the much debated problems of finding an optimal ratio of accumulation to consumption. The near impossibility of finding a "golden mean" among many possible ratios is well known to economists, as Kaser amply demonstrated. Soviet economists did not neglect this problem during the formative years of socialist planning in the 1920's, and the research of G. A. Fel'dman in particular showed promise.[17] Fel'dman's work ceased around 1930—he may have been an early purge victim—and the riddle of optimal proportions lay neglected during three critical decades of Soviet economic growth. Soviet discussion of the relative growth over time of "Group A" output (producer goods) and "Group B" output (consumer goods) was not resumed until the 1960's.

Kaser's main criticism, however, does not turn on the success or failure of fixing growth ratios for accumulation and consumption. Unless, he wrote, the public is allowed a decisive voice in determining the growth of consumption and the array of goods which is offered, governments will have no usable criteria for organizing the economy

---

[16]M.C. Kaser, "Welfare Criteria in Soviet Planning," in Jane Degras and Alec Nove (eds.), *Soviet Planning: Essays in Honor of Naum Jasny* (Oxford: Blackwell, 1964), pp. 144-72.

[17]Spulber, 1964, pp. 40-44.

to meet consumer needs. Neither norms based on social observation nor the substitution of the sentiments of a party or a leadership group for those of the consuming public will do. The fact that consumers themselves can be irrational, by whatever standard, is of secondary importance.

One might fortify Kaser's argument by applying the seven criteria proposed by Robert A. Dahl and Charles E. Lindblom as a means of pursuing welfare. These can serve as a yardstick for both consumers and governments: freedom, rationality, democracy, subjective equality, security, progress, and appropriate inclusion. Such criteria can be both instruments and ends, Dahl and Lindblom proposed. They need not be defined sharply, since their value consists in their being accepted by governments and populations in a very general way.[18] One problem with this list is that in multiplying criteria, Dahl and Lindblom have come up with three—rationality, security, and progress—of which the public is probably a worse judge than well-informed governments. If governments are unable to persuade their people to support the agonizing decisions which find their justification under one of these three headings, then we are back at the familiar dilemma: Who is capable of deciding what will benefit the people?

Kaser did concede that the irrationality of consumers can frustrate the satisfactions they seek, and that this irrationality must be placed in the balance against the inevitable irrationality of planners in those economies where consumer satisfactions are planned centrally. But he did not take into account the manipulation of consumer choice itself by producers and governments. Manipulation in one form or another lies at the very root of consumption in the United States. Corporations must plan at long range in order to prosper, and they cannot do so unless to some extent they can plan their markets. The very notion of "demand" hangs upon what is supplied; the notion of "need" is so conditioned by our changing culture and quick-moving advertising that the term might as well be dropped from the economic vocabulary. Even some situations in which the American public apparently had a clear choice between one thing and another have been manipulated, for example the apparent choice of the 1945-55 decade between rail and air passenger transportation.

The choices made by governments concerning the size, composi-

---

[18]Robert A. Dahl and Charles E. Lindblom, *Politics, Economics and Welfare* (New York: Harper and Row, 1953), pp. 26-28.

tion, and purposes of investment in producers' goods and national security raise the question of public rationality in even more acute form. A government which cannot be removed by any process related to public opinion, according to Kaser, is able to contemplate and carry out investment policies which in democratic systems it could not. No democratic government supported by a society and economy like those of Soviet Russia in the 1920's could have carried out the investment decisions made in 1928-29.

While one cannot deny the extra limitations faced by popularly elected governments in making or influencing investment decisions, is it possible to talk of any immediate connection between public opinion and decisions as to what portion of the GNP to reinvest? In the United States, a major governmental lever for influencing reinvestment decisions is the Federal Reserve Board's adjustment of the rediscount rate; this, however, is performed by a group of specialists whose actions are deliberately insulated from any immediate pressures by either the White House or Congress. As to the corporate investment decisions made as a result of government contract awards, even if a substantial portion of the American public understood their economic import, what could the public do to influence them?

One school of American economic thought does indeed support the view that the American public's influence on the nations's capital investment decisions is negligible. John Kenneth Galbraith, its best known exponent, argued as follows: Decisions on both savings and investment are made largely by a few hundred corporations, and no market mechanism links the two types of decisions. What the public saves as individuals is too small to make a difference, and the public as consumers is manipulated to the extent that these corporations can plan their markets as well. Galbraith, while he cites these factors in support of the idea of "convergence" of U.S.-type and Soviet-type economies, also points out the differences in the extent to which savings and investment decisions are centralized, and differences in the means by which savings are obtained.[19] Naturally, one might argue against Galbraith's view of American investment that American business and political leaders are limited seriously by their perceptions of what the American public will or will not stand for.

What can be said of harsh economic sacrifices whose necessity is

---

[19]John Kenneth Galbraith, *The New Industrial State* (New York: Signet Books, 1968), p. 52.

not apparent to the public at the time they begin, but which seem justified much later in view of events? The attitude of middle-aged and elderly Soviet citizens with whom the writer has discussed the experience of the first three five-year plans (1929-41) is that the German invasion which followed made the dozen years of economic deprivation appear as a harsh necessity which the nation's leaders understood far better than the populace.

Thus, there seems to be no suitable scale for weighing the desirability of high national security expenditures against the desirability of major consumer goods expansion. The latter can be justified in terms of definite goals of consumption and distribution; the former finds its justification only in the perception by a smaller number of knowledgeable men of the intentions and capacities of foreign governments. These perceptions, in spite of recent attempts to find a way of testing their accuracy or unreality, are themselves incommensurable as between one government and another. Arthur C. Pigou, a pioneer in the study of welfare economics, understated the case considerably when he wrote that resource reallocations for national security purposes "cannot be decided by reference to economic considerations alone."[20] Even reading the minds of policymakers may be of little help. One proponent of the convergence idea expressed it this way:

In reality, given institutions with vested interests attached are a most important restraint on any experimentation with society. I do not think any politicians, not even ministers of finance who may have been professors of economics, actually think in terms of maximizing any welfare. It seems much more probable that they start out from the existing institutions, observe the strains and stresses arising from them, and try to change the institutions as much as is politically possible in the direction indicated by the political valuations that they stand for. Whether all the resulting actions taken in combination maximize "welfare" for society at large, is, to say the least, an open question.[21]

In the writer's view, Soviet allocation policies of the late 1950's and the 1960's convey the impression of a national leadership which, like that of the United States during the same period, has been determined to have an ample supply of both guns and butter. The Soviet concept of welfare within the sphere of consumption begins,

---

[20] Arthur C. Pigou, *Economics of Welfare* (4th ed.; New York: Macmillan, 1952), pp. 18-20.

[21] Gunnar Adler-Karlsson, "Functional Socialism," *Peace Research Society: Papers*, VI, 1966, p. 96.

today as in the 1930's, with the idea that most consumer-oriented investment should be allocated by means other than consumer choices, and that consumer choices themselves should be set within certain definite bounds through investment, production, pricing, and taxation policies worked out by central planning agencies.

Let us assume that at the end of another two or three decades, barring international catastrophes, the Soviet Union has a GNP at least as large as the present American GNP, and perhaps considerably larger. Unless the cost of superpower weaponry has meanwhile soared astronomically, by that time few Americans will be inclined to accuse Moscow of sacrificing the welfare of its citizens on the altar of military primacy. And even if these same decades have brought the American people both unparalleled luxury and the good sense to pass enough of it around to those who presently need it most, the difference in levels of comfort between U.S. and Soviet living standards will not in itself make one economy radically different from the other. Where will the difference lie? Will it make a difference that one economy rents its apartments and the other assigns them? Or that one produces millions of private cars for sale, and the other millions for state-run rental services?

The Soviet doctrinal statements of the Khrushchev era and afterwards do indeed promise an age of high mass consumption that will benefit a society whose main occupation is not to consume, but to develop its full human potential. The reader has been warned (in the Preface) that these chapters will look closely at the trends and policies first, and at ideology only later, in passing. This is in order that the reader not be prejudiced in his judgment, one way or the other, by seeing the ideological derivation of these policies before he has had a chance to pass judgment on them as policies. Let us simply note at this point that as public welfare expands in the Soviet Union, the nation's leaders have promised to use this welfare in a way not yet seen among the world's high-consumption industrial nations. Consumption is to be an instrument rather than an end. It is meant to help build a certain type of human being and a certain type of society; and while consumption is only one major influence among several which is to accomplish this purpose, it must perform the important function of freeing men from things rather than binding them to things.

Of the various economic devices which have been built up to spur this process, probably the most important—and certainly the most intriguing—is the intention to expand the forms of consumption which are not distributed through the market place. More and more of the individual's overall income, or overall income-plus-benefits, will come in the form of things that are shared rather than hoarded, used rather than owned. The dream of ever so many utopian communities which sprang up—many of them in North America—and perished in the last century is now meant to be realized on the scale of an entire society. The forms of distribution, sharing, and use which in Soviet ideology are the growing foundation of this new order are presently grouped under the concept of the "social wage."

THE IDEA OF THE SOCIAL WAGE

Soviet authorities have long stressed the importance of forms of income which Soviet citizens receive in addition to money earnings. Many newspaper items and public statements remind the public of the benefits which make no claim on their incomes. Foreign observers who have found Soviet wage levels low as among wages in the industrial nations generally are challenged to compute the costs to wage earners in their own countries of services which in the Soviet Union are free or heavily subsidized.

Few of the individual features of the Soviet social wage are unique to the Soviet Union or even to the communist world. Socialized medicine is not a monopoly of the communist world, nor are comprehensive pension systems, and doubtless an international survey would turn up numerous national programs for subsidizing day-care centers and summer camps for children. Free public education is either a reality or a goal for most of the nations of the world. A juxtaposition of the value of all social wage benefits with all disposable income in some countries of Western Europe and elsewhere might possibly turn up ratios of social wage to earnings greater than those of the Soviet social wage, whose value has added between 28 and 35 percent to earnings during the post-1945 period (see Table 2-1). Other types of international comparisons could be based on the proportion of national income occupied by the social wage, or on the place of the social wage in total consumption by individuals. The first was just somewhat under 20 percent during the 1960's, and rising slowly during this same decade, while the second was exactly one third in the middle of the decade.[22] Unfortunately, many items in the social wage, notably the wages and salaries of the service professions and occupations, are not reckoned into the Soviet

[22]Basov, 1967, p. 52.

national income or GNP, hence, an exact calculation is quite troublesome.

Table 2-1
EARNINGS AND "SOCIAL-WAGE" BENEFITS OF
SOVIET WORKERS AND EMPLOYEES*
(in post-1960 rubles)†

Year	(1) Average Monthly Earnings per Worker	(2) Legal Minimum Wage‡	(3) Average Monthly "Social Wage" Benefits per Worker§	(4) (3) As a Percent of (1)
1940	33.0	–	7.6	23.0
1950	63.9	22	18.5	29.0
1955	71.5	22	20.3	28.4
1960	80.1	27 to 35	27.6	34.5
1965	95.6	40 to 70	33.4	35.0
1968	112.5	60 to 70	38.5	34.2

*Does not include collective farmers.

†One post-1960 ruble = $1.11 at the official Soviet-determined exchange rate.

‡There are different minimum wage levels for different categories of workers and employees.

§Because public health benefits and—since 1965—state pensions are accorded to collective farmers, who do not fall under the category "workers and employees," the figures here are somewhat inflated.

Source: *Narodnoye khozyaistvo SSR*, 1965, p. 567; *Pravda*, January 25, 1968 and January 26, 1969. Columns (3) and (4) are computed.

Official Soviet statistics on the relationship between the social wage and average earnings are shown in Table 2-1. In order that the reader properly understand these and other earnings and income data, several warnings are in order. First, readers not familiar with the problems of comparing the value of the ruble and the dollar should realize that this official exchange rate of U.S. $1.11 to 1 ruble tells very little. Public transportation fares of 3 to 5 kopeks (there are 100 kopeks to the ruble) must be balanced against private automobiles commanding twice the price of equivalent American cars, at the official exchange rate. If the Soviet housewife pays less than half the American price for a loaf of bread, she sometimes pays a good deal over American prices for the better meats. Housing absorbs not 25 percent of the Soviet worker's income, but typically less than 10 percent; food, on the other hand, often takes as much as two thirds. The worker may save to buy a co-op apartment or to vacation in the Caucasus, but he has no need to save for his son's university education. As a rough criterion of what a Soviet income will obtain, during the 1960's earnings of 60 rubles per month appeared to be the minimum for sustaining an individual living alone in Moscow; it may have been somewhat less in other cities and towns.

A second qualification is that the Soviet income tax reduces take-home pay from the earnings shown in Table 2-1 according to the rates shown in Table 2-2. While a law of 1960 specified a stage-by-stage reduction of the income tax plus the tax on single persons and small families, with the intention of abolishing both, this process was suspended two years later. To the extent that it was carried out, it benefited the low-income categories, with the result that today no monthly income of 60 rubles or less is taxed. Note that this is a tax not on income but on earnings, and the rates apply to earnings from different sources, even if the same family or individual has earnings from different taxable sources. It is quite common, actually, for workers to supplement their income by individual jobs; a lathe operator, for example, might spend his evenings and weekends doing residential maintenance and repair work for housing administration offices or cooperative apartments. In this case he would pay according to the rates in both the first and fourth columns in Table 2-2. For regular wage and salary earnings, the maximum rate for the first 100 rubles is 8.2 percent; for that part of wage and salary earnings above 100 rubles, the maximum rate is 13 percent. Here the Soviet financial legislators were clearly taking care not to modify greatly the incentive provided by wage and salary differentials, which are discussed in detail in Chapter 5. Meanwhile, earnings from professions and trades which may be pursued independently (including, for example, private medical practice) are dealt with far less gently, with the sole exception of the earnings of creative and performing artists.

A final qualification is that computations of the average *per capita* social wage are not very meaningful as such because of the great variety of family and individual situations they embrace. Calculations of nonwage benefits per worker or employee and per family unit simply overlook the circumstance that the greater part of the social wage, as the U.S.S.R. Central Statistical Administration (CSA) defines it, goes to the nonemployed. The survey of Vasilii I. Basov, a Soviet economist who has specialized in social wage questions, concludes that 60 percent is thus used, a figure which breaks down

Table 2-2
SOVIET TAXES ON INDIVIDUAL INCOME FROM DIFFERENT SOURCES AS OF MARCH 1, 1968
(expressed as a percentage of gross monthly earnings from each source for selected average monthly earnings levels)*

	Average Monthly Earning Level in Rubles													
	60	70	80	90	100	110	120	130	150	200	250	300	400	500
Tax based on:														
Wage and salary earnings†	0.0%	4.1%	6.6%	7.7%	8.2%	8.6%	9.0%	9.3%	9.8%	10.6%	11.1%	11.4%	11.8%	12.0%
Above, plus tax on bachelors and childless couples‡	0.0	7.5	12.4	13.8	14.2	14.6	15.0	15.3	15.8	16.6	17.1	17.4	17.8	18.0
Contracts for writing, art work, and for artistic performances	6.0	6.6	7.3	7.8	8.2	8.6	9.0	9.3	9.8	10.6	11.1	11.4	11.8	12.0
Private medical practice, private teaching, and other professional services§	12.3	14.3	15.8	17.2	18.5	19.8	21.0	21.9	23.5	27.6	31.4	34.9	39.3	43.0
Earnings by individual artisans, and manual workers on individual contract‖	17.0	19.0	21.3	23.1	24.6	26.3	27.8	29.0	31.0	35.8	39.8	43.6	43.0	52.6

*Each type of income is taxed at its own rate, including cases in which a person has more than one type of earnings. Figures for the last three categories represent taxes collected from annual rather than monthly earnings, hence, the monthly earnings levels here represent averages rather than sums taxable as such. Taxes on ordinary wages and salaries are simply deducted from pay envelopes.

†For employees and workers with four or more dependents, the amount of the tax is reduced by 30 percent.

‡Applies to single males and to couples without children, from age 20 to 50 (but to 45 for women). It is added, where appropriate, to ordinary tax rates.

§Such services may include those of engineers, technicians, typists, and stenographers who are paid by individual arrangement rather than as staff employees. This rate also applies to earnings from the sale to individuals of works by artists and sculptors, whether through commission (second-hand) stores or by private transactions.

‖Also included in this category are earnings from casual work by workers and artisans, take-home work from factories, services of clergy, rental of individual houses or rooms in apartments, income from patents, sale of certain items at farmers' markets, and certain types of photographic work.

Source: *Spravochnik po nalogam i sboram s naseleniya*, 1968. Computed from rates shown on pp. 16, 37, 44, 45, and 72. U.S.S.R. income tax law of April 30, 1943, *Vedomosti SSSR* 1943, No. 17, as amended to 1968.

into 26 percent for pensions and payments, 26 percent for primary schools and other children's facilities, and 8 percent for secondary and higher education of all sorts.[23]

Nevertheless, in a society where custom, housing shortages, or other circumstances preserve three-generation family units in an urban setting, there is some point in looking at the family size averages. H. Kent Geiger, in his massive study of the Soviet family, assumed from partial data that the three-generation family is as prevalent in the city as it is in the countryside.[24] Furthermore, the family as a budgetary unit may be larger than the family as a residential unit. The 1959 census shows data not only on family unit size, but also on family members living apart from their family units who are nonetheless linked to them by a common budget. This category included over 7 percent of the nation's urban population of just under 100 million. If this figure is taken into account, then persons not connected with any family unit numbered only 6 percent. At the same time, urban family units are not large: the 1959 census showed an average family unit size of 3.5 persons; furthermore, 70 percent of all urban family units contain 4 or less members, and 90 percent contain 5 or less members.[25]

Naturally, the notion of a "common budget" is relative. A young person living apart from his family may be either the recipient of transfer payments (such as allowance money for students to supplement the state stipend, which according to the author's own observations is a common practice) or a contributor from earnings. But on the whole it is meaningful to study the social wage benefits accruing to family units as such. It is just as important to keep in mind the fact that increased housing, including more homes for the aged, will mean that more and more of the retirement-age population will be living apart from its wage-earning children.

High-level Soviet policy and program statements since the mid-1950's suggest that the social wage per worker will not only multiply in absolute value, but that in the communist future it will occupy a considerably larger proportion of the worker's total income than it does presently, something on the order of 50 percent as against one quarter during the 1960's. These pronouncements enjoy a well-

---

[23]Basov, 1967, p. 30.

[24]Geiger, 1968, p. 176.

[25]Pisarev, 1966, pp. 125-26; Tsentral'noye statisticheskoye upravleniye . . . , *Itogi vsesoyuznoi perepisi naseleniya 1959 goda; SSSR*, 1959, p. 244.

established ideological paternity in Marx's prophecy of the abolition of wage labor, which in turn is based on the Marxian doctrine of the apportionment of a society's entire output on the basis of need as the logical end result of industrial development. The current Soviet discussion of the social wage began with the surge of official enthusiasm in the late 1950's about the predicted 20-year transition from the present socialist society to the future communist society. This was the fruit of a number of statements made by Khrushchev and others before and during the 21st Party Congress in 1959. Public commentary about a decline in importance of individual earnings in overall income and benefits was promoted by Khrushchev's unequivocal statement at this gathering that the role and significance of the social wage were due to increase dramatically. One must not imagine communism, he said, simply as a state of affairs under which one earns five times the wage one was earning under socialism.[26] His further statement about meeting the needs of the "normal cultured person" as a production and distribution criterion under full communism gave impetus to studies of consumption patterns and development of exact measurement of consumption. Among the commentators who went beyond official statements in this respect was the dean of Soviet economists, Stanislav G. Strumilin (see Chapter 7), who made some prophecies about free lunches and free clothing for everyone.[27]

The predictions which were written into the 1961 Party Program did, as a matter of fact, include the famous free lunch, though served at places of employment only. (In view of the large number of Soviet families where both parents work, take the main meal of the day at their places of work, and do only minimal cooking at home, this particular benefit may loom larger in consumption than at first appears, if it is actually realized.) But no form of non-market distribution of clothing, or, for that matter of any other consumers' goods among those which money can buy, durable or nondurable, found similar favor. Khrushchev's promotion of car rental garages as a state-determined alternative to the further growth of private car ownership apparently fell by the wayside during the 1960's as a policy; while some rental services were indeed set up, Soviet press commentary during the latter half of the 1960's has supported efforts to ease the various problems and inconveniences experienced by private car owners.

---

[26] *Vneocherednoi XXI s''yezd KPSS,* 1959, Vol. 1, pp. 49-50.

[27] See his articles in *Novy mir* No. 7, 1960, and *Oktyabr'* No. 3, 1960.

Certainly there is little reason why rationing shoes and overcoats, as a substitute for money transactions, should appeal to Soviet policymakers from either a practical or psychological point of view. The Program's social wage formula for 1980 consists of the services presently embodied in the social wage, a small additional list of free public utilities and public transportation, and finally the abolition of user fees for partly subsidized services (e.g., preschool care and boarding schools). Facilities for rest and recreation—rest homes, resort housing, and the use of sports equipment—will be subsidized only partially, with the remaining cost covered by user fees.[28] At the 23rd Party Congress in 1966, Prime Minister Kosygin presented the same list of benefits together with the prediction that by 1970 the social wage would add 50 rubles' worth of benefits to the expected average monthly earnings of 115 rubles.[29] While the speculation of the late 1950's about dramatic new additions to the social wage had died out by the mid-1960's, the social wage concept itself is still vigorously publicized in newspaper items and in statistical presentations of Soviet economic life.

It should be noted in passing that at the same time as subsidies are growing in all the categories covered by the social wage, a campaign is on to remove subsidies, direct and indirect, from the retail and service establishments which still receive them. In part this is the logical consequence of the 1965 economic reforms, which among other things are an effort to relate production of consumers' goods more effectively to sales volume and demand. There also appears to be pressure from *Gosplan* on local governments to tidy up the many small service operations under their jurisdiction—repair shops, laundries, local entertainment, and the like—in an effort to stop this unnecessary "leakage" from local budgets.[30]

The social wage is both an economists' and a philosophers' concept derived from a number of separate economic policies. It has been publicized in many official statements. It has raised philosophical questions which may or may not emerge as well-defined policy issues. For example, should the proportion of nonpayment benefits to payment benefits increase? Or should nonemployment-related benefits be increased relative to employment-related benefits? So far there is no evidence that those policymakers who are

[28] *XXII S''yezd KPSS,* 1961, Vol. 3, pp. 301-2.

[29] *XXIII S''yezd KPSS,* 1966, Vol. 2, pp. 45-46.

[30] A. Zharskii, Deputy Chairman of *Gosplan,* in *Pravda,* July 1, 1968.

concerned with the entire range of social wage benefits join the philosophers in thinking about the social wage in such terms. If they now proceed to evolve policies in answer to these and similar questions, their contribution to the social policy field will be a unique one. As matters stand now, they are working with an array of separate policies none of which is unique to the communist world or to Marxist thought.

The fact that the CSA has provided a definition of the social wage is a matter of statistical convenience and publicity rather than a statement of policy. In fact, this definition has not settled the debate among Soviet economists and other commentators as to just what the social wage should include. But the areas of disagreement are not wide. The commentators and CSA do agree that the list should include income in the form of direct payments as well as income in the form of benefits and services. They also agree that benefits and services may include those for which the beneficiaries must cover a certain (even if usually small) proportion of the cost, as is the case, for example, with summer camps and day-care centers for children. Finally, there is agreement that the social wage should embrace payments and benefits from three sources: (1) the state budget, (2) the social insurance budget (derived from employer contributions), and (3) production units as such (that is, payments and benefits provided by employers in a manner other than channeling funds through the state or social insurance budgets). The last category includes state enterprises, cooperative and nongovernmental *(obshchestvennye)* enterprises and organizations, educational, medical, and other public institutions, and both state and collective farms.

The CSA includes the following items in its social wage statistics:
(A) Payments
    (1) Pensions
    (2) Support payments to unwed, widowed, and separated mothers, also to mothers with large families
    (3) Support payments for temporary loss of working capacity
    (4) Support payments during maternity leave from employment
    (5) Bonuses from employers (less taxes on these)
    (6) Paid annual leave (less taxes)
    (7) Students' stipends (to cover living and miscellaneous expenses, tuition being free)

(B) Benefits and services

(8) Free medical services (which do not cover the cost of pharmaceuticals obtained outside of health institutions)

(9) Passes to sanatoria and rest homes (to the extent not paid for by the recipients of these passes)

(10) Education and improvement of qualifications (not including living expenses for students in higher education, which are largely covered by (7) above)

(11) Housing maintenance (to the extent not covered by rent payments)[31]

The CSA's computation of totals for these payments and services is shown in Table 2-3, together with actual ruble figures for the USSR national income for a number of recent years, cited here simply in

Table 2-3
EXPENDITURES FROM ALL SOURCES FOR ITEMS IN THE
"SOCIAL WAGE," COMPARED WITH NATIONAL INCOME
(in billions of post-1960 rubles)

Year	Social Wage Expenditures	National Income
1940	4.6	n.a.
1950	13.0	n.a.
1958	23.8	127.7
1960	27.3	145.0
1965	41.5	192.6
1968	55.0	*237.

*Computed on the basis of a stated 23 percent increase in national income for the years 1966-68, using 1965 as the base year.

Source: *Narodnoye khozyaistvo SSSR,* 1963, pp. 501, 505; 1965, pp. 589, 593. *Pravda,* January 26, 1969.

order to furnish a rough notion of scale. Since the Soviet concept of national income excludes payments for services in the nonproduction sphere (e.g., the salaries of teachers and medical personnel), a considerable part of the social wage figure constitutes an *addition* to national income as defined in the Soviet Union. In 1963 the system of calculating the social wage was enlarged to include the social and cultural expenditures made by collective farms, trade unions and nongovernmental organizations, state expenditures on housing maintenance not covered by rent payments, and certain other payments

---

[31]*Narodnoye khozyaistvo SSSR v 1965 g.,* pp. 840-41.

and benefits. These additions increased the original overall social wage figure by as much as 15 percent.

While annual increases in the overall social wage figure in the 1950's and 1960's were often 8 to 10 percent, they represent a continuation, expansion, and qualitative improvement of existing programs rather than the addition of new programs to the social wage. Improvements in pension and social insurance payments account for over one third of the increase in the overall social wage figure between 1950 and 1965. The extension of the pension system to collective farmers, together with the demographic increase of the retirement-age population, is currently boosting the social security bill at a rapid rate. Expansion of health services, together with salary raises in 1964 for all public health personnel, account for over 20 percent of the total increase.[32] Primary and secondary school teachers and preschool personnel received an across-the-board 25 percent increase in the same year. The bill for paid annual leaves increases in proportion to both wage levels and the length of the annual leave period. Thus, it should be kept in mind that while some components of the considerable annual increases in the social wage represent improved benefits, other components represent the increased cost of maintaining the same benefits, plus the cost of extending them to additional segments of the population. Because the social wage embraces chiefly ongoing programs whose expansion has shown no sharp discontinuities, Soviet planners have been able to predict with good accuracy the growth of the bill for social wage benefits.

The CSA's definition of the social wage contains some items which are puzzling to foreign observers, and some even more puzzling omissions. To be sure, the social wage at present is nothing more or less than a statistical grouping of benefits made for the purpose of demonstrating what Soviet citizens receive from society above and beyond the things that their wages can purchase. Such a manner of advertising benefits can surely be recommended to governments which have thus far not taken the trouble to present them in easily understandable form. But the CSA did some picking and choosing among the many items of nonwage benefits which suggest an attempt to present a philosophy of distribution rather than a simple listing of all nonwage benefits.

The most conspicuous single omission is that of state investment in housing construction; analogous to this is this omission of

[32] Field, 1967, pp. 128-30.

construction investments in, and capital repairs to, educational, medical and cultural facilities, stores, and service facilities. Tables 2-4 and 2-5 give a general idea of the role of these investments in the overall Soviet investment picture. During the 1960's the state's investment in a single apartment has fallen in the range, roughly, of 2,000 to 8,000 rubles, the exact cost varying with apartment size (one to four rooms) and local construction costs.[33] Written off over 25 years, even without the addition of interest charges, this would add 80 to 320 rubles annually to the nonwage income of the family unit. A working couple without dependents, which lives in a state-built apartment, might actually receive most of its nonwage income, thus calculated, in the form of the 100 percent state subsidy for housing construction. To this should be added that portion of housing maintnenance (roughly 60 percent) not covered by rent payments (item 11 in the CSA's list cited above). Moreover, improvements and major repairs which come under the heading of "capital repairs" are omitted from the CSA's calculations; logically, they should be included as well. Part of the difficulty of including capital construction expenses in the social wage is that of establishing depreciation norms. In the field of housing, particularly, Soviet economic planners have seen no practical need for establishing such norms. The CSA's computation of the portion of national income consumed by individuals, shown in Table 2-6, does include depreciation on housing, according to a norm which is not explained in official statistics.[34] While there are fixed amortization periods for state loans to housing cooperatives and individual builders, these are too brief (10 to 15 years) to be used as a guideline for establishing depreciation. Another problem in adding housing construction to the social wage figures is establishing a scale of value as between old and new housing. Should the social wage which a family receives in the form of freedom of direct responsibility for housing construction costs be calculated at levels which diminish as its housing ages? Basov's book dismisses the whole question with the observation that construction investment in both housing and cultural facilities is reckoned as part of the reinvested portion of the national income as opposed to the consumed portion.[35]

The social wage does recognize some of the wages paid for services

[33]See, for example, the figures cited by Ye. Kriger and K. Svirkov in *Izvestiya*, December 25, 1963, p. 3.

[34]*Narodnoye khozyaistvo SSSR*, 1965, p. 592.

[35]Basov, 1967, p. 26.

Table 2-4
HOUSING INVESTMENT, BY CATEGORY OF INVESTOR
(billions of rubles, in 1965 prices)

Year	State Enterprises and Agencies	Individuals and Collective Farms*	Housing Cooperatives*
1950	1.3	.7	n.a.†
1960	5.5	2.7	n.a.†
1965	5.8	1.8	.5 §

*Includes mortgages from state banking institutions.

†Was probably negligible.

§Assumes that state mortgages for 1965 represented 60 percent of total investment; figure for state enterprises and agencies reduced accordingly.

Source: *Narodnoye khozyaistvo SSSR*, 1965, pp. 532-33, 790.

Table 2-5
STATE AND COOPERATIVE INVESTMENT IN
NONPRODUCTION CONSTRUCTION OTHER THAN HOUSING
(in 1965 prices, expressed in billions of post-1960 rubles)*

Year	(1) Retail Stores, Local Services and Utilities, Health Facilities	(2) (1) As a Percent of All Capital Investments	(3) Scientific, Cultural, and Educational Establishments†	(4) (3) As a Percent of All Capital Investments
1950	1.0	11.0	.3	3.4
1958	2.5	10.5	1.1	4.4
1960	3.3	10.9	1.8	5.8
1965	4.6	10.7	2.6	6.2

*Investment by collective farms not included.

†Scientific establishments include those devoted to military purposes, and to other purposes not directly related to consumption and welfare. Basov, in proposing that operating expenditures for science and culture be included in the social wage, pointed out that such a distinction ought to be made. Basov, 1967. p. 2.

Source: *Narodnoye khozyaistvo SSSR*, 1965, p. 533. Columns (2) and (4) are computed.

or labor in the "nonproductive" sphere, whose fruits are consumed directly by the populace. Services of this type are not included in Soviet computation of the GNP; they include the salaries of physicians, teachers, social service administrators, and service employees generally. This broad definition of service occupations increases still further the ratio of the social wage to the national income. The wage and salary bill for services is not given systematically in Soviet statistical collections, although some data are available. In 1959, 1961, and 1962, its inclusion in the national

Table 2-6
CONSUMPTION CATEGORIES OF THE NATIONAL INCOME,
AND WAGE AND SALARY EXPENDITURES IN PUBLIC SERVICES*
(billions of rubles)

Year	(1) National Income	(2) Portion of (1) Consumed by Individuals	(3) Portion of (2) Devoted to Operating Expenditures Not Covered in (4)	(4) Wage and Salary Expenditures*
1959	136.2	88.0	7.2	6.7
1962	164.6	104.5	9.5	7.0
1965	192.6	123.9	12.4	n.a.

*Public services, in the Soviet statistical definition, include all "nonproductive" services, which means activities not directly related to material production. This includes not only ordinary services to consumers, but education, public health and cultural activities. Nonwage and nonsalary expenditures in these fields are included in the Soviet national income and GNP figures, however. Therefore, wage and salary expenditures must be shown separately.

Source: *Narodnoye khozyaistvo SSSR,* 1962, p. 483; 1965, pp. 589, 592; Buxlyazkov, 1964, pp. 31, 37.

income would have added just under 5 percent to the total (see Table 2-6).[36]

The CSA's selection of the social wage expenditures appears to be first of all a matter of convention and convenience. Hardly any single criterion or principle sets these expenditures apart from others, except perhaps the fact that none of them consist of regular wage and salary payments. Services and money payments; distribution according to labor, age, and need; free services and partially subsidized services; benefits promoting labor productivity and benefits relating to the use of the workers' leisure time—all these principles are intermingled. Basov maintained that the fundamental principles are (1) distribution according to need, (2) free distribution, (3) promotion of satisfaction of healthy desires on a scientific basis, and (4) promotion of self-government in the realm of distribution. The social wage, he said, still "bears the stamp of its connection with the quantity and quality of labor."[37] The official Soviet statistical annual, in describing the method of computing the

[36]For the official description of the reasoning behind Soviet national income calculations, see *Narodnoye khozyaistvo SSSR,* 1965, pp. 850-51.

[37]Basov, 1967, pp. 17-19.

social wage, rather wisely confines itself to a listing of categories, omitting any definition of principles.

Column (1) of Table 2-7 gives ruble totals for major categories of social wage expenditures according to figures derived by the writer from official data, and column (2) the totals according to the percentage breakdown cited by Basov, which is doubtless more accurate. Recalculation of the social wage to include everything that might be regarded in the noncommunist world as nonwage income would add 11 percent to the CSA's total for 1965; this is shown in column (3). One might justifiably omit construction investment of many types from the social wage on the ground that it offers no measurable "flow of benefit" to the individual. But if such investments are included in the social wage, then there is no good reason for omitting investment in streets, parks, some public utilities, and various urban amenities, not to mention the construction of retail stores, whose rent payments do not cover amortization. Soviet official statistics exclude this type of investment for the same reason that housing investment is excluded: there is no measurable annual "flow of benefit" to the individual or the family unit.

It is only fair to point out that similar problems would arise in any attempt to compute the benefits which the American public receives in return for its tax dollars, nationally or within any governmental unit which levies taxes. Outside of public housing, welfare payments, and services to individuals, little that governments do at any level can be computed handily in terms of per capita benefits. From among the general services, would there be any reason for excluding police protection while including free concerts in a park? Even in the case of public housing, a subsidy-type benefit, one may ask whether the magnitude of the benefit should be calculated in terms of prevailing commercial rents, actual governmental outlays year by year, or a figure based on a given rate of depreciation.

Even a list of social wage benefits revised to conform to Western concepts is open to criticism on certain counts, from the point of view of what may be regarded as a "benefit" outside of the communist world. Public health measures, for example, include health and labor-protection measures at places of employment. Would an American worker regard free protective clothing or the free treatment of on-the-job injuries as an addition to his income? If American industry had just arrived at the point where protective clothing was being provided by employers for the first time, it would represent a perceptible addition to income; but the worker already

Table 2-7
COMPUTATIONS OF THE SOCIAL WAGE FOR 1965 BY THE
CENTRAL STATISTICAL ADMINISTRATION, BASOV AND OSBORN
(in billions of rubles)

Item	*(1)* CSA*	*(2)* Basov†	*(3)* Osborn‡	*(4)* *Figures in* *(3) Expressed* *as a Percent* *of Total*
Education and culture	15.2	12.9	19.0	39.0
Public health and physical culture	7.4	7.0	8.4	17.2
Social security and social insurance	14.1	14.3	14.1	28.9
Bonuses which are not part of the wage fund	n.a.	.7	§	§
Paid annual leave	5.6	4.4	§	§
Housing maintenance	1.5	2.3	1.5	3.1
Housing construction	§	§	5.8	11.9
Totals	43.8	41.6	48.8	100.1 ‖

*Education and culture: expenditures for science, the press, the arts, and radio broadcasting are not included, in keeping with the official social wage definition. A further 2.0 billion for capital construction in all these areas is not included, for the same reason. Public health and physical culture: omits a component for capital construction proportional to that omitted for education and culture. Housing maintenance: based on figures by Timothy Sosnovy in U.S. Congress, Joint Economic Committee, *New Directions in the Soviet Economy*, 1966, Part II-B, p. 549. Paid annual leave: total number of workers and employees during 1965 multiplied by average annual leave compensation per worker.

†Computed by multiplying the CSA's official total of 41.5 rubles (not the same as the total in column (1), which was derived from CSA figures for the individual categories) by Basov's percent breakdown.

‡Education and culture: Expenditures of 21.9 billion from all sources, minus 4.3 billion for current expenditures on science, and minus an estimated .6 billion for capital construction in the area of science; but 2.0 billion added for capital repairs to cultural and educational facilities, as proposed by Basov, 1967, p. 25. Public health and physical culture: 1.0 billion added for construction.

§ Category omitted as a basis of calculations.

‖Excess due to rounding.

Source: *Narodnoye khozyaistvo SSSR*, 1965, and Basov, 1967, p. 28, data of both computed as indicated in footnotes.

accustomed to this is hardly likely to regard it as an addition. Factory clubrooms and sports facilities are psychologically convincing as benefits, but the same can hardly be said of the provision of drinking water and efficient ventilation in the shops, which Soviet social wage figures include. Westerners may balk at the idea that official propaganda paid for from the cultural budget is a benefit, but judgments in this area are too highly subjective to permit us to omit any form of communication which we might consider propaganda. Holesovski would go as far as to exclude education because it is not in itself a consumption item, but an investment whose benefit is realized only in the future; and he would also leave out preschool institutions because they represent a service formerly performed by households, and not an addition to services provided. Criticisms of this variety, too, rest on subjective judgments of what is meant by consumption and benefits, and they overlook the additions to cash income which education and preschool care make possible.[38]

The social wage items described in Chapter 3 are not intended to be either a complete catalogue of benefits, or an exhaustive description of any particular kind of benefit. The reader may check the details for himself in the translations and descriptive accounts cited in the footnotes. What is important here is the kind of reasoning which these benefits represent. Why, to begin with, have certain benefits and services been selected for distribution in ways other than consumer choice? Why not take the funds that are earmarked for these purposes and distribute them in the form of higher earnings so that the citizen may choose more freely among his benefits? A letter to the newspaper *Sovetskaya Rossiya* asked just this question: "Instead of paying a worker 100 rubles, for example, and then giving him handouts in the form of public consumption funds, it is better to increase his wages and make him pay for day-care centers, education and so on." The letter writer reasoned that "not everyone needs day-care centers, but everyone's earnings would be increased." Another letter quoted in the same item pointed out that nothing is really "free," that the social wage is simply a system of distribution: "You write that our education is free, as is medical care, and the state pays for the day-care centers. But where does it get the money for all these benefits? Can it be that we live at the expense of the state but that the state does not exist at the expense of the workers and collective farmers?" As one would expect, *Sovetskaya Rossiya* then deluged its readers with first-hand accounts of individual and family experiences with social wage benefits, and asked its readers to imagine themselves with extra cash in hand but without the protection of state-guaranteed distribution.[39] Still one may ask whether assigning a lump of cash to the state to transform into benefits is as reasonable a procedure with regard to housing construction as it is with regard to medical services. The active promotion during the 1960's of cooperative housing,

---

[38]Holesovski, 1964, pp. 60-63.

[39]*Sovetskaya Rossiya*, September 17, 1965. This and a series of related items are translated in *CDSP* XVI:4, pp. 5-12.

where residents foot the construction bill themselves in return for better surroundings and more secure occupancy, may be an indication that Soviet planners have had some thoughts about this, too.

To what extent should state-distributed benefits be linked to employment—first of all to the fact of being employed, secondly to the earnings, seniority, occupation, and other attributes of employment? As will be evident from the discussion below, a substantial portion of the social wage *is* distributed according to various employment-related criteria. There are several kinds of links between employment and benefits: benefits can be used as an additional work incentive on the job, as an incentive to stay with one enterprise or one occupation instead of moving about in pursuit of higher earnings, as an inducement to enter the more arduous occupations (e.g., mining), or simply as an inducement (for wives, in this case) to choose employment in preference to tending their garden plots and keeping house.

The 1961 Party Program proposed the abolition of charges and fees in a manner already described. Nonetheless, the charges which exist today may be of some interest because of the way in which they are related to need and to income levels. Why have there been charges at all? Have they worked in the direction of equalizing income? If so, why not preserve and extend the progressive income tax (which is presently on the way out) and use the added receipts to subsidize services fully instead of only partially?

There is the further question of whether the social wage as a whole, or any of its major components, are in fact structured to work in the direction of equalizing overall income (earnings plus nonwage income). Since Soviet economists themselves have difficulty calculating the effects of the social wage in this regard, equalization can hardly have been a topic of policy discussion up to now. The professional discussion of this point is of some interest, however. One planning official took the average compensation of the top 10 percent and bottom 10 percent of all workers and employees, which he found to have a ratio of 5.8:1. He then added the social wage to each earnings category and recomputed the ratio, which turned out to be somewhat smaller, 4.75:1.[40]

---

[40] Buzlyakov, 1964, pp. 32-33. Unfortunately, it was not specified whether the social wages accruing to the employed persons alone were being computed, or those accruing to their family units; presumably it was the latter, since employed persons receive a rather small portion of the social wage in direct benefits to themselves.

Boris V. Rakitskii, an economist who has studied the social wage question, believes that the social wage is not and should not be an equalizer of income. He based his conclusion on two studies done in 1956-57 by the Institute of Labor, a facility run by the All-Union Council of Trade Unions. Unfortunately, the results, in addition to being somewhat dated, were ambiguous. The one result which stands out clearly is the fact that the family units in the very lowest income group in both plants received more social wage, both in absolute terms and in proportion to income, than any other income group. In the food industry plant, the lowest family income group (families receiving under 600 rubles annually) received roughly twice the social-wage benefits of any other group; in the heavy industrial plant, the same held true with the sole exception of the highest income group (over 1,560 rubles annually) whose social wage benefits were 78 percent of those of the lowest. A comparison of the overall earnings-plus-social wage scale with earnings alone shows that the social wage can in fact have a certain leveling tendency: the ratio of top-group to bottom-group family earnings in the two plants was on the order of 2:1; the addition of the social wage brought both ratios down to 1.5:1. In the case of the heavy industrial plant, if one leaves aside the 8 percent of the sample in the bottom income group (under 840 rubles, in this case), the value of the social wage did indeed increase with increasing earnings; but in the food industry plant, where earnings were lower, the increase was negligible.[41]

Naturally, one must ask just what kind of "equalization" might be used as a yardstick for measuring the effect of the social wage. Unequal needs require unequal expenditures. Moreover, the large outlay on students in higher education (4,000 to 5,000 rubles per graduate) entitles university and institute graduates to substantially higher earnings during their lifetimes than those without higher education. In the case of old-age pensions, which to a large degree are earnings oriented, the definition of equality takes into account a continuing reward for the recipient's contribution to the economy as measured by his wage or salary level at retirement.

Tables 2-8 and 2-9 summarize a 1967 survey of social wage benefits received by the employees of an Ivanovo textile mill and their families which tends to support the "equalization thesis." Both the sample and the definition of the social wage used in this survey weight the results somewhat on the side of greater equality. First of all, the family units that were surveyed are not a completely

[41]Rakitskii, 1966, p. 38 ff.

Table 2-8
SOCIAL-WAGE BENEFITS, ACCORDING TO THE BROADEST POSSIBLE
DEFINITION, RECEIVED DURING 1966 BY THE LABOR FORCE* OF THE
KONSTANTIN FLOROV MIXED-FABRIC PLANT, IN IVANOVO
(rubles)

Item	Value	Percent of Total
Pensions and paid leave of all kinds (including annual leave)	2,110,909	29.8
Medical services	880,736	12.4
Recreation and physical culture (rest homes, sanatoriums, children's camps, dietetic foods, maintenance of prophylactoria, etc.)	534,854	7.5
Adult education and part-time education (evening and correspondence institutes and technicums, schools for working youth)	224,035	3.2
Labor hygiene (special foods, protective clothing, drinking water, ventilation)	207,000	2.9
Schools and preschool facilities	1,588,450	22.4
Communal services (housing maintenance, heating, operation of service establishments)	716,000	10.1
Housing construction (new housing for 610 persons)	714,000	10.1
Construction of cultural and health facilities	114,602	1.6
Total	7,090,604	100.0

*This includes 11,200 employees *plus* their dependents. But because the members of some families are employed at other plants, the total number of dependents was regarded as "divided" proportionally as between the Florov Plant and other places of employment. Thus, the benefits received by 9,906 dependents are included in these figures.

Source: A. Gur'yanov, "Our Earnings Plus Millions," *Pravda,* August 20, 1967.

representative sample of the mill's labor force, which certainly includes single workers not attached to any family unit. Secondly, the survey's definition of the social wage included construction costs for residential, health, and cultural facilities, all of which are omitted from the definition used by the CSA. These constitute more than 11 percent of the total benefits. If this mill is at all typical of Ivanovo's sizable textile industry, the labor force is largely female. The earnings shown are, taken as an average, 17 percent below the 1965 national average for industrial earnings (957 rubles against 1131), although the actual difference is somewhat narrower because the national average is computed before deduction of taxes, the Ivanovo figure after taxes. At the same time, the percent added to earnings by the social wage at the mill is well above the 1965 national average for industrial workers, 60 percent as opposed to 43 percent,[42] a

[42]Computed from *Narodnoye khozyaistvo SSSR,* 1965, p. 566. The social-wage-to-earnings ratio for industrial workers was in turn somewhat higher than the ratio for all workers and employees, which was 35 percent in 1965.

difference only part of which can be ascribed to the inclusion of construction costs.

The 12 families whose income is compared in Table 2-9 were chosen, according to the *Pravda* article, because they are "diverse in numerical composition, in the number of employed persons, children and old people, and in the number of evening students." Social

Table 2-9
ANNUAL EARNINGS AND SOCIAL-WAGE BENEFITS OF 12
SELECTED FAMILY UNITS OF WORKERS AT THE KONSTANTIN
FLOROV MIXED-FABRIC PLANT, IN IVANOVO, DURING 1966
(rubles)

Family Unit	Number in Family Unit	Number Employed	Total Earnings, Less Taxes	Value of All Social Wage Benefits	Social Wage Benefits as a Percent of Earnings	Earnings plus Social Wage Benefits per Member
Murin	2	2	1,475	729	49	1,102
Opurin	4	2	2,148	2,018	94	1,041
Naumov	3	2	2,178	1,067	49	1,082
Presnyakov (Nina)	4	2	2,427	1,946	89	1,093
Abramov	4	3	2,493	1,733	69	1,056
Antonov	5	2	2,645	2,181	82	965
Presnyakov (Rimma) ...	5	2	2,673	4,233	158	968
Yegorov	3	2	2,768	627	23	1,132
Anisimov	4	3	2,774	1,309	47	1,021
Konovalov ...	4	2	2,972	1,053	35	1,005
Sarychev	8	5	4,488	2,786	62	909
Blinov	10	6	6,207	3,830	62	1,004

Source: A. Gur'yanov, "Our Earnings Plus Millions," *Pravda*, August 20, 1967. The definition of the social wage here is the same very broad one used in Table 2-8. The last two columns are computed.

benefits per family unit range in value from 23 to 151 percent of earnings. Unfortunately, the status of nonemployed family members is not specified; in the reckoning of nonwage income and benefits it makes a good deal of difference whether the individual who is subsidized is a kindergartener (300 rubles per year), schoolchild (90 rubles), university student (850 rubles), pensioner or invalid (650 rubles, let us say). On the other hand, total earnings plus social wage benefits *per family member*, which average 1,031 rubles, vary scarcely more than 100 rubles upward and downward from the average.

In the face of such unclear evidence for the greater equalization of family income via the social wage, it is doubtful that Soviet consumption planners would know where to begin even if there were a policy decision to press for family income equality in this fashion. At the same time, it may be argued that the social wage stands as a barrier to the inequalities of need satisfaction that would result from raising money incomes at the expense of subsidized services and nonwage payments. Circumstances of illness, number of dependents, and number of children to be educated would then serve as "de-equalizers" of consumption of food and other basic items.

Should the distribution of the social wage be carried out through enterprises and employers generally, or the level of benefits linked in any way to the success of enterprises? Rakitskii expressed the view that distributing even a part of the social wage is a function unsuited to employers because of the inequality of benefits which inevitably results.[43] One labor resources analysis of the Western Siberian Region found that the unequal distribution of a large proportion of nonwage benefits through employers was in itself a major cause of the high labor turnover which has long plagued that area (see Chapter 5). Part of the difficulty is that both the dimensions and the very availability of nonwage benefits differ greatly from enterprise to enterprise, so that a family may understandably migrate from employer to employer—and very likely also from city to city—in search of a good housing arrangement. The availability of day care may be quite important. The enterprises best able to provide child-care facilities are the heavy industries, which use an overwhelmingly male labor force. The light industries, employing a largely female labor force, are less able to provide for their employees' children.[44]

Furthermore, social wage needs differ from employer to employer. Differences between one enterprise labor force and another with respect to age, sex, educational level, and other factors result in higher and lower claims to social wage benefits per worker. Factories which employ higher than average proportions of adolescents, of workers who combine study with full-time employment, and of women in the age range of high childbearing, will have a higher level of claims to satisfy. Furthermore, a labor force which shows these statistical characteristics is likely to be found in enterprises with comparatively low productivity and low profit rates.

---

[43]*Pravda*, November 30, 1966, pp. 3-4.

[44]*Zapadno-sibirskii ekonomicheskii raion,* p. 187.

Rakitskii is among those Soviet economists who propose that enterprises be required to reimburse the state annually for the quality of education given by the state to their respective labor forces, and he points out the favorable influence on distributing the social wage which an extension of this principle would bring. Let the enterprise, he says, reimburse the state each year not only for part of its labor force's education, but also for the working capacities of its labor force generally, taking age, sex, and other productivity determinants into account. The enterprise administration would then be motivated not only to make full use of the qualifications of skilled workers, thus maximizing their potential earnings, but also to employ and improve the qualifications of those portions of the labor force (e.g., adolescents) which many enterprises try to avoid employing.[45]

Should emphasis be placed on the distribution of social wage benefits in forms other than money payments? The ratio of money benefits to benefits in kind within the social wage is significant because a number of Soviet commentators view it, among other things, as a harbinger of the communist form of distribution and the elimination of the cash nexus between consumers and goods. Within the CSA's definition, benefits in kind only slightly exceeded cash benefits during the first half of the 1960's; in 1950 they comprised 58 percent of the whole, and 65 percent in 1940.[46] The change can be explained not by any cutback in allocations to education and public health, but rather by the increasing wage levels of the 1950's (which increased the bonus and annual leave components) and even more by the new social security benefits established in 1956.

It is doubtful whether the ratio of cash to noncash benefits is in itself the object of current policy discussions. Soviet economic planners would achieve little by reflecting on whether there should be more cash benefits or more noncash benefits in the overall social wage for a given planning period. Three of the social wage's four largest components—education, social security, and extra wage money compensation by employers—serve three different clienteles, while only health services and housing maintenance subsidies serve all three simultaneously. Inputs in each of these areas are presumably determined by the needs in each area as policymakers see them, also by priorities of emphasis as among areas. A priority for increasing pension payments will increase the cash component of the social

[45]*Pravda,* November 30, 1966, pp. 3-4.

[46]Basov, 1967, p. 32.

wage; a priority for raising doctors' and teachers' salaries will increase the noncash component.

Should social wage benefits be related to employment status and earnings, or should they be distributed without regard to employment? Ideological pronouncements going all the way back to Marx's *Communist Manifesto* of 1848 indicate that work contributions will ultimately be separated from rewards. Just which benefits should be called work-related and which should not is a matter of opinion. Some are related to earnings levels (pensions), others to the fact of employment (social insurance, or eligibility to use a plant's child-care facilities). The awarding of stipends for living expenses in higher education is related to family income in that a small proportion of students is not eligible because their family income is over the norm. Rakitskii estimated the work-related portion of the social wage to be around 70 percent of the total in the mid-1960's, while Basov calculated about 45 percent for the same period.[47] Interestingly, Basov's system of reckoning shows the work-related portion to have *increased* to its present level from 28 percent in 1940 and 35 percent in 1950.

Answers to all of these questions are yet to come. It may very well be that the political leadership and economic policymakers will try not to confront such issues directly, but rather to expand and improve existing forms of nonwage distribution. The post-Khrushchev administration, at least, does not thus far seem inclined to embark on qualitatively new programs in the field of distribution. It may, on the other hand, gradually open up channels for local experimentation in distribution, whether at the level of the republic, of local governments, or of enterprises. As concerns enterprise-distributed benefits, it may turn out that further moves toward enterprise autonomy will accentuate the difference in benefit levels. At some point Moscow may have to face a moment of truth on this score. Cutting back the authority of large enterprises and their trade unions to distribute vast benefits would be a most unpopular move with many high economic officials. The point is whether equality of benefits refers to a minimum or to a reduction in disparity of benefits. In any case, it is not likely that during the balance of the present century the Soviet Union will furnish a clear-cut, unambiguous definition of the difference between socialism's formula "to each according to his work" and future communism's formula "to each according to his need."

---

[47]*Pravda*, November 30, 1966, p. 4; Basov, 1967, p. 33.

.3. *Public Expenditures and Private Choices*

For many Americans the kinds of choice which carry the most value, for better or for worse, are the choices made by spending one's income. For some, spending income and multiplying income are desired activities in their own right; a government which reduces these activities is reducing freedom, in their eyes. Also, many Americans still have deep-seated feelings against the very scale of national programs, and against the central setting of standards as such. All these feelings have served to divert our attention from questions of purpose in governmental expenditures, and from the content or impact of the choices which governments are able to open up.

Therefore, we as Americans must be particularly careful to look at the content of the choices which are offered to Soviet citizens through the state budget and certain other organized channels. Was Khrushchev's program for building boarding schools a restriction of the choices of parents? Certainly his original proposal for total conversion to boarding schools would have been. A program scaled down so as to make boarding schools generally available but not compulsory would have been a different matter entirely. What actually emerged (see below) was neither of these things. But not only did much Western public commentary fail to make these distinctions, it also failed to note that in measuring restriction versus expansion of choice one is often dealing with incommensurables, in this case the choice by parents among types of education versus the choice by mothers to pursue the more demanding careers.

54

Consider similarly the manner in which the Soviet Union restricts and manipulates consumer choices through very high sales ("turnover") taxes. Among the services which this taxation makes possible are child care and maternity benefits, and these in turn provide more labor for a labor-hungry economy by motivating mothers to earn a much-needed second income for their families. Or, what about the way in which Soviet higher education maintains a fairly rigid cut-off point for the number of people who may enter higher education, and determines centrally the number of degrees to be granted in each specialty? A great deal of frustration and disappointment attend the whole process of admission to the nation's universities and institutes, and not infrequently students enter specialities for which they have no inclination simply because these offer open places. But the same Soviet students whose educational choices are channelled and limited this way, and whose first three years of work will be in a job to which they are assigned, honestly wonder what becomes of American students for whom these choices are not organized in this way. We Americans, for our part, can reply only that the particular risks of our educational and job choices are part of our nation's cultural concept of desirable choices and freedom from restriction of choice.

Americans will find it much less difficult to appreciate the Soviet approach to transfer payments—social security, social insurance, and grants-in-aid. It might be argued, in fact, that Soviet transfer payments are more closely linked to the labor reward system than are such payments in the United States. The Soviet Union never attempted any kind of experiments with a flat benefit system, save for payments to unwed mothers and to the mothers of large families. In the United States, the extent of transfer payments not related to earnings has been determined largely by the extent of the adult population which is unemployed or chronically underemployed, and whose employment status therefore provides no basis for earnings-related benefits.

However one may judge the extent and quality of the choices open to Soviet and U.S. citizens in matters of education and security, one difference stands out clearly: Resource allocation choices in these areas are largely the prerogative of the state in the Soviet Union, with some exceptions which will be noted. In the United States a larger proportion of these choices, however measured, are still made by individuals managing their own or their families' budgets. The sacrifice of immediate family consumption in favor of expanded educational choices for the children, which plays an enormous role in American family budgetary choices, is ordinarily a peripheral item in the Soviet family budget. It is true, though, that Soviet parents often do sacrifice some things during their children's university years in order to supplement the higher education stipend, which is still rather low for many students. Also, it is not uncommon for Soviet parents to bear the cost of a year of tutoring and private study for secondary school graduates who fail to gain admission to higher education on the first try.

The fact that such consumption choices have been lifted from the shoulders of the Soviet family is justified in three ways by Soviet policymakers. First, it guarantees the kind of labor force needed to strengthen the nation's productive capacity, and frees workers and professional people alike from cares that would divert attention and energy from their work. Every policy choice discussed in this study may be regarded as determined by the labor force requirements that are worked out in *Gosplan*, the State Planning Committee. Secondly, Soviet leaders contend that they are equalizing the ability of citizens to make the important choices in their lives. Finally, the leadership interprets these very same policies as a means of freeing the individual and the family for self-realization outside of work. A further purpose which foreign commentators of past decades sometimes imputed to Soviet policymakers, the breakup or weakening of family ties, can no longer be supported. Admittedly, the accusations about a Soviet attack on the family as such did have some evidence to feed on in the 1920's, notably the ultraliberal divorce laws of that period and statements by some radical Communist public figures.

The state's policy of expanding and improving the training of the Soviet labor force is evident even from an elementary description of the way in which the Soviet citizen's choices in education and welfare are organized. It is a more complicated task to identify the promotion of equal choices as a policy guideline. Finally, any evaluation of the stated Soviet policy of promoting individual self-realization outside of work must rest to some extent on subjective judgments.

PRESCHOOL INSTITUTIONS

Many visitors to the Soviet Union, including the writer, have been impressed with the extent and quality of preschool facilities. While commentary by Soviet educators stresses the purpose of child development as a reason for the major expansion of these facilities, the 1961 Party Program and other official commentary places the first emphasis on freeing women for productive labor, and removing the last remaining causes of female inequality.[1]

Female participation in the Soviet labor force is already very high. After the male labor deficit occasioned by World War II had abated somewhat during the immediate postwar years, the proportion of women among all workers and employees (i.e., all labor except that of collective farmers) settled at a level of 47 percent during the 1950's, then rose to 50 percent in the mid-1960's.[2] It is difficult to estimate the expansion of the female labor force which the completion of the preschool network would make possible, a system providing for all preschool children. As of the 1959 census, about 69 percent of the female population in the 16–59 age bracket was employed, including collective farm employment.[3] The proportion of mothers prevented from taking employment by the absence of preschool facilities (and by the absence of extended-day programs in primary schools) is available only in scattered local surveys. A Novosibirsk survey of the mid-1960's, for example, turned up the following proportion of women in the childbearing age range (16 to 44) unable to take employment, classified by educational level: over 3 percent of those with higher and specialized secondary education, and over 15 percent of those with a completed secondary education.[4] Since existing preschool facilities are without exception filled to capacity and frequently have waiting lists, the nonparticipation of mothers in the labor force can hardly be explained to any degree by reluctance to place their children in state-run nurseries and kindergartens. Enrollment tripled during the 1960's, and the demand is apparently as strong as ever (See Table 3-1). There is no indication that enrollment is intended to be anything but voluntary, now or in the future.

As of 1965, some 67,000 permanently functioning nurseries and kindergartens looked after 6.2 million children in the 1-to-6 age range, of whom 5 million (over 80 percent, that is) resided in cities and towns. Probably one child out of two in the urban population was enrolled that year, in some cities as much as 70 percent of the

---

[1] *XXII S"yezd KPSS*, 1961, Vol. III, pp. 300-301.

[2] *Vestnik statistiki*, No. 1, 1968, pp. 86-87.

[3] Dodge, 1966, p. 32.

[4] Musatov, 1967, pp. 110-11.

Table 3-1
ENROLLMENT IN PERMANENTLY FUNCTIONING PRESCHOOL
FACILITIES—NURSERIES AND KINDERGARTENS
(in millions)

Year	Total Enrollment	Enrollment in Urban Areas Only
1945	1.5	1.1
1950	1.2	1.0
1955	1.7	1.4
1960	3.1	2.6
1965	6.2	5.0
1968	9.0	n.a.

Sources: *Narodnoye khozyaistvo SSSR*, 1961, pp. 686–87; 1965, pp. 686–87; *Pravda*, October 11, 1967, and January 26, 1969.

preschoolers. The urban nurseries and kindergartens averaged 108 children and 14 staff members each as of 1965, for American standards a very good ratio.[5] The vigor of the present drive for more preschool care may be seen in the fact that enrollment three years later (in 1968) was 9.0 million, plus another 4.5 million in seasonal facilities, which serve mainly the children of farm mothers during the planting and harvest seasons. All told, about 45 percent of the nation's approximately 30 million preschool children were enrolled during 1968.[6]

Operating costs paid from the state budget amounted to 1.8 billion rubles in 1965, or 290 rubles annually per child; the balance, to make up a total per-child outlay of between 300 and 400 rubles, came from parents' fees plus contributions from employers and trade unions. The state has been covering about 80 percent of the costs of all preschool institutions in recent years.[7] Table 3-2 shows that per capita costs for preschool institutions are roughly four times the costs for children in ordinary primary and secondary schools, and one third to one half the costs for students in higher education. The fact that Soviet children begin first grade at age seven rather than at age six, as in the United States, means an additional outlay for preschool facilities.

Fees paid by parents may cover one tenth to two thirds of the

[5]*Narodnoye khozyaistvo SSSR*, 1965, pp. 687-87; *Narodnoye obrazovaniye* No. 7 (July, 1968), p. 15.

[6]*Ekonomicheskaya gazeta*, No. 2 (January, 1969), p. 15.

[7]Kharchev, 1964, p. 275.

Table 3-2
PER CAPITA ANNUAL EXPENDITURES ON PERSONS ATTENDING
EDUCATIONAL AND PRESCHOOL INSTITUTIONS
(in rubles)

Institution	Normal Range of Per Capita Annual Expenditures
Preschool facilities	300-400*
Regular primary and secondary day schools	80-90
Schools with extended-day programs	150
Boarding schools	500-650†
Specialized secondary schools	450-500‡
Institutions of higher education	820-850‡

*Includes payments by parents.

†Buzlyakov gave the figure of 900 rubles, which seems high. All other figures which the writer has been given are in the range indicated here. Noah, 1966, p. 108, calculated an average of 645 rubles as of 1959-60.

‡Includes payment of stipends to students which cover at least minimal expenses for board and room. Stipends account for about one quarter to one third of the total outlay. DeWitt, 1961, p. 69.

Source: N. Buzlyakov, chief specialist of the U.S.S.R. State Scientific-Economic Council, in *Izvestiya,* June 2, 1962; these figures antedate the teacher salary reform of 1964, which raised salaries in primary and secondary education by roughly 25 percent. Salaries account for nearly three quarters of the total outlay in regular schools.

total cost for their children, according to regulations of the Ministry of Higher Education. Statistics from the 1950's show the proportion of these payments to per-child cost to have risen from about 18 percent in 1951 to a little under 24 percent in 1957. In the 1960's most parents were covering between 10 and 30 percent of the cost of 300 to 400 rubles per child, although in a few cases they were paying more than half. A factory-operated nursery and kindergarten which the writer visited in Oryol in 1969 covered about 18 percent of its annual 89,000-ruble budget from fees.[8]

A comprehensive scale of payments established in 1948 is still in force, though applied with considerable local variations. One of the surprising things about it is that the variation of payments with earnings levels is regressive if one accepts a fixed percent of income as a norm. For a 9-to-10-hour daily stay per child in an ordinary

[8]One economist calculated the average payment per child in nurseries at an annual 58 rubles. The full table of fees is in Dodge, 1966, pp. 81 and 86. See also: DeWitt, 1961, p. 64; Kapustin, 1962, p. 85; N. Buzlyakov in *Izvestiya*, June 2, 1962; *Sovetskaya Rossiya*, July 21, 1964.

nursery with no special facilities, fees vary from 3 to 8 rubles monthly as parental income varies from under 40 to over 120 rubles. From a payment equalling 10 percent of earnings at an earnings level of 40 rubles (now below the minimum wage of 60 rubles), the proportion of wages taken by the payments descends irregularly to 6.5 percent at the 100-to-120-ruble level, then to 5.3 percent at 150 rubles and to 4 percent at 200 rubles. The entire scale of payments increases for prolonged or 24-hour care, the top payments being for nurseries located in their own special buildings. The kindergarten payments scale is analogous, though it is higher by 1 to 5 rubles. But this scale, too, displays the feature already noted: the higher the parents' earnings, the smaller the proportion of earnings they contribute. From the 120-ruble earnings level upward, the ruble payment does not increase at all.

However, reductions of 25 to 50 percent are provided for families in the lower income brackets which maintain more than one child in preschool institutions. The 50 percent reduction applies not only to families with four or more children, but also to children of war widows, and to children of single mothers under the 60-ruble income level. Money paid out in fees is not altogether lost to the family budget, either. There is one less mouth to feed for at least one meal of the day, and sometimes for all meals. Also, to the extent their finances permit, preschool institutions provide the clothing which the children wear during the hours they spend away from home.

Why is there any contributory arrangement at all for preschool institutions? The 1961 Party Program calls for the abolition of such fees by the 1980's. But as of 1965 this would have cost the state roughly 600 million rubles for that year, well under 1 percent of the state budget, and not much over .25 percent of the official national income figure—and the latter ratio would be even smaller if services, including preschool care, were included in the Soviet definition of national income. To some extent, these payments represent a redistribution of income as among the families which make use of preschool facilities. The top payments for every scale (applied to families with monthly incomes over 120 rubles) typically are related to the lowest payments by a ratio of 2.6:1; and if the special reductions are taken into account, the ratio is around 5:1. To some extent the payments represent a tax on the two-income family, which can more easily afford it. Though preschool facilities are in short supply in many localities, probably the payments scales do little to reduce demand for them.

The alternative to user fees would probably be, at present as during the last four decades, a small increase in the turnover tax, whose incidence is regressive. In 1965 this would have meant to 1.5 percent addition to revenue from the turnover tax. Such a change would be hardly noticeable in itself. If, on the other hand, it were added to the taxes which would be required by sudden abolition of *all* the present user fees scheduled for eventual reduction or abolition under the Party Program, the effect on retail prices would be quite noticeable. People anywhere will part with small fees in return for important services from which they immediately benefit, and even—as with the New York Port Authority's bridge and tunnel tolls—with substantial fees which go to pay for more than the immediate service provided. Doubtless, it has been the psychological impact of increased retail prices which Soviet planners have sought to avoid in prolonging the collection of most such fees.

While the fee scale is designed not to work hardship on low-income families, neither does it appear designed to make the affluent two-income families contribute very heavily to the maintenance of preschool institutions. Certainly it is not intended to work substantially in the direction of equalizing family incomes. The fact that the fees are simply waived or else subsidized from local trade union budgets in a large number of hardship cases means that a more radical scale of equalization of burdens may be applied in practice through local initiative.

Another important feature of preschool care finance, which is shared to some extent by school finance, is the fact that the presence or absence of good physical facilities—or of any facilities at all, sometimes—depends on the size and prosperity of enterprises. The bulk of nurseries and kindergartens, according to the writer's impression, are located at enterprises and run for the benefit of their employees. Because some employers can afford more of these important fringe benefits than others, the pattern of their distribution is quite uneven. State budgetary funds for these institutions have been far too limited up to now to compensate for this unevenness.

One alternative policy would be to apply to preschool institutions the same kind of financial boost from the incomes of affluent Soviet citizens that state housing has received from housing cooperatives. Purchases of co-op apartments have served among other things, to free additional funds for building more state housing, whose construction is covered entirely from the state budget. The co-ops, which became a large-scale phenomenon only in the 1960's, are financed entirely by their members in both construction and maintenance, though with the help of state loans for construction. An analogous policy was proposed for preschool facilities by the director of a metallurgical plant in Kazakhstan who wrote in 1968 that he considered the shortage of preschool facilities unjustified and unnecessary as long as there were parents with very high earnings who nevertheless paid only 12.50 rubles monthly per child:

We have quite a few working people who are very well off materially and would readily agree to assume the major expenses for their children's support in nurseries or kindergartens. So why not take advantage of this source of finance? Why not create a broad network of economically accountable kindergartens and nurseries to supplement the ordinary ones, just as there are, say, economically accountable polyclinics? Such an arrangement has long been necessary.[9]

Aside from the cooperative housing program, programs for distributing benefits by tapping the resources of the affluent are presently limited to affluent enterprises. In the 1950's and 1960's, roughly one fifth of the expenditures on education, culture and scientific research taken together have been covered each year from sources other than the state budget, which means that enterprise profits—and to a much lesser extent collective farm profits—have been used for this purpose. For 1965, for example, 4.4 billion of the 21.9 billion rubles that were spent for these purposes came from nonbudgetary sources.[10] There are unfortunately no data on how this sum was distributed to supplement the 1.8 billion devoted to preschool facilities, the 6.2 billion spent on primary and secondary schools, the 1.6 billion for higher education, the .9 billion for vocational schools, or related items.

FINANCING THE SCHOOL SYSTEM

The "patronage" (*shefstvo*) of industries over schools and culture is strongly encouraged in the Soviet press, and labor-hungry industries are anxious to advertise these as among their most important fringe benefits. In this way the resources which the Soviet Union has bestowed generously upon favored sectors of the economy are reflected in the distribution of the social wage, except for those parts of the social wage which come in the form of money payments

---

[9] *Literaturnaya gazeta*, May 8, 1968, p. 2. Trans. in *CDSP* XX:20, p. 3.
[10] *Narodnoye khozyaistvo SSSR*, 1965, pp. 781, 783.

whose level is set in national legislation (e.g., pensions). While no Soviet child is denied the opportunity of being educated in primary and secondary schools (at least through the eighth grade, at present), the quality of the school he attends, the teacher-pupil ratio, the adequacy of the physical facilities, and the "extras" which can make so much difference in education, may depend on whether there is a large, profitable industry in the vicinity.

While it is doubtful that inequalities in Soviet school financing, either in capital investment or operating budgets, are as great as inequalities in the United States under any type of measurement, systematic regional and local data for the Soviet Union are not available. At a time when Americans are waking up to the financial disparities not only as between Mississippi and New York, but as among schools within the same school systems, it would be interesting to know how rigorously and in what manner the Soviet school system is seeking to realize its professed principle of equal educational opportunity.[11] Probably the most important disparities among Soviet schools would be those between urban and rural schools, although the small size of many rural schools means abnormally high per capita expenditures which in themselves do not indicate a correspondingly high quality of education.

At the same time, all Soviet education is organized according to central standards, the more so that there is now (since 1968) a U.S.S.R. Ministry for Public Education to coordinate the programs of the 15 public education ministries of the 15 union republics. No matter what resources it is willing to inject into local schools, an industry is not permitted to use these resources for educational purposes outside the framework of the regulations.[12] The same principle applies to housing: No matter how much an enterprise finds it is able to invest in housing for its labor force, it may not exceed the governmental housing space norms in assigning apartments. Hence much of the inequality of standards which is occasioned by the presence or absence of profitable industries may be described as the difference between segments of the economy which have attained the national norms and other segments which have not.

A feature of the 1958 educational reforms which attracted much attention outside the Soviet Union was Khrushchev's adovcacy of a

---

[11] See the disparities between the predominantly black and predominantly white schools in the Boston school system as described in Jonathan Kozol, *Death At An Early Age* (New York: Bantam Books, 1967) pp.54-55.

[12] Data on "patronage" financing of education is also scarce, unfortunately. See Noah, 1966, pp. 63-73 for the extent of what is known.

massive conversion of primary and secondary education to boarding schools, the first of which had already been in operation as of 1956.[13] Today these include not only boarding schools in the usual sense of self-contained institutions (*shkoly-internaty*), but also boarding facilities serving regular day schools (*internaty pri skholakh*), which are used especially as a means of consolidating rural school districts where daily transport to school is a problem. A companion program, initiated in 1959, was the "extended day," a system of formal after-school supervision and programs for grades one to eight. It lengthens the school day to a total of 9 to 12 hours and provides all meals as well.[14]

The proposal for massive conversion of the school system to a boarding school system raised the double question of quality and equality. Up to the latter 1950's, existing boarding schools had favored children from "problem situations" in their admissions. These included primarily orphans and half-orphans, plus others from family situations which made institutional care of some kind advisable. Mikhail A. Prokof'yev, who was then First Deputy Minister of Higher Education, told the writer in 1959 that there were long waiting lists for places in most boarding schools. The 1956 resolution calling for expansion of boarding schools stressed boarding *facilities* first of all, dormitories which can accommodate children attending nearby schools which are also attended by children who live with their parents. It did, however, also call for the design of new types of school complexes especially designed as boarding schools, which would also promote the goal—and this was two years before Khrushchev began pressing his major educational reforms—of "uniting instruction with productive labor by students, and connecting schools with the real world."[15] But priority in admission, as long as room in boarding facilities remained scarce, was to be given to the problem-situation children. The point here was not only to provide an institutional home for those children who have no satisfactory home, but to remove some of them from negative influences which hinder their performance in school. The Russian Republic's Minister of Public Education reported in 1968 that the continued shortage of boarding schools and school-related boarding facilities is directly responsible for the failure of many students to finish their secondary education.[16]

---

[13] *KPSS o rabote sovetov*, 1959, pp. 465-67, 576.

[14] *Spravochnik partiinogo rabotnika, vyp.* 3 (Moscow: Politizdat, 1961), pp. 435-36.

[15] *KPSS o rabote sovetov*, 1959, p. 465.

[16] *Narodnoye obrazovaniye*, No. 8 (August, 1968), p. 9.

However, a further Party and State resolution issued in the wake of the 1958 reform law shifted the emphasis to quality education in the boarding schools. No longer should their primary function be that of accommodating children in need of institutional living facilities. Instead, boarding schools should now be regarded as "the most successful form of bringing up and educating children under circumstances of building communist society." Existing children's homes, the resolution continued, should be converted into full-scale boarding schools; these were institutions which already served as "boarding facilities serving regular day schools."[17]

There is every indication that the policy goal of providing boarding schools for all or most pupils was dropped only a few years after it was announced. The 1961 Party Program made but slight mention of boarding schools. In two places it noted that the use of boarding schools, as of preschool facilities also, is to remain completely voluntary.[18] Boris E. Svetlichnyi, an architect and high urban planning official whose views on social planning are reviewed at length in Chapter 6, wrote that if boarding schools are available only for some children and not most or all, they will create an educationally privileged class of children. Therefore, admission to boarding schools should serve the children from problem situations for whom they were first intended in the mid-1950's. In 1968 Mikhail A. Prokof'yev, the newly appointed U.S.S.R. Minister of Public Education, affirmed this admissions policy.[19]

A look at the educational operating costs shown in Table 3-2 will show the wisdom of the cutback decision, which was made at a time (the early 1960's) when the expansion of Soviet domestic social and cultural programs was restricted noticeably because of the increased international tensions of that period. By 1961 construction outlays for boarding schools were absorbing one third of all budgetary funds designated for school construction, while at the same time regular schools held classes in two and sometimes three shifts for want of space.[20]

The consequence of these problems with boarding school expansion has been that the extended-day programs have been pushed much more rapidly than construction of new boarding

[17]*Spravochnik partiinogo rabotnika, vyp.* 3 (Moscow: Politizdat, 1961), pp. 460-62.

[18]*XXIII S"yezd KPSS*, 1961, Vol. III, pp. 302,321.

[19]Svetlichnyi, 1964, p. 168; *Izvestiya*, July 3, 1968, *KPSS o rabote sovetov*, 1959, pp. 456-57.

[20]Kaser, 1968, pp. 94-95; I. Metter, "They Left School," *Literaturnaya gazeta*, January 13, 1962.

schools, while the goals of the latter have been cut back drastically. Enrollment in all boarding schools rose from 56,000 in 1956 to 700,000 in 1961 and 1.3 million in the fall of 1968. But the target set for 1965 had been 2.5 million, and, meanwhile, enrollment in the extended-day programs had risen to 3.9 million (in the spring of 1968).[21] The extended-day programs share with the broader boarding school policy the concept of providing a greater degree of "upbringing" (*vospitaniye*) under institutional auspices. But from the point of view of family convenience, the extended-day program is an aid to working parents, who thus have time to work a full day and call for their children at the schools either before or after the evening meal. It is probably this function which has spurred the comparatively rapid expansion of these programs.

One motive which still serves to promote the boarding school program was that of school consolidation in rural areas. In 1968 Prokof'yev termed a third of the nation's regular schools too small, and called for a further push for dormitories attached to regular schools, so as to permit school enlargement.[22] One of the difficulties with school consolidation, as anyone familiar with the Soviet country side can testify, is the lack of secondary all-weather roads which could be used by school buses. While one of the goals of rural planning is the progressive consolidation of villages and population centers, Prokof'yev pointed out that this would come about too slowly to justify letting school consolidation depend upon the pace of demographic reorganization. Meanwhile, the small rural schools are not only inferior in quality, but are consumers of some of the highest per-pupil expenditures in the educational system because of their very smallness. One rural school principal in the Ukraine wrote of the reluctance of parents to let their children live in boarding schools away from home, even though the distance be only five miles.[23]

The schedule of fees for boarding schools in the Russian Republic, which was set in 1956, differs somewhat from the fee scale for preschool institutions in two respects: the proportion of the monthly fee for one pupil to the parents' monthly income remains roughly constant from the lowest income to the highest, varying only between one quarter and one fifth of income; and parents having an

---

[21]*Izvestiya*, July 3, 1968; *Ekonomicheskaya gazeta*, No. 5 (January, 1969).

[22]Report to the National Teachers' Conference, summarized in *Izvestiya*, July 3, 1968.

[23]Adamskii, "Large Cares of the Small School," *Izvestiya*, October 19, 1968.

income of slightly over 100 rubles bear more than half the total per-pupil outlay. For example, a family income of 40 to 50 rubles entails a monthly fee of 10 rubles; an 80 to 90 ruble income entails a fee of 22.50 rubles; a 120 to 140 ruble income, 37 rubles; over 200 rubles of income, 56 rubles. Families with three or more children enjoy reductions of 10 to 50 percent, depending on income and number of children. Scattered reports indicate that the application of this scale has been quite flexible. For a certain proportion of families the fee is simply waived, and others pay at rates well below those of the scale, so that the proportion of money from fees in the total outlay may actually be quite small.[24]

The Soviet experience with tuition fees in higher and upper secondary education during the years 1940-56 is something of a puzzle both as to the policy motives which prompted introduction of fees, and as to the effect of the fees. The small size of the fees in proportion to average earnings in the economy, the exceptions granted for hardship cases, the payment of fees in some cases by trade unions and local governments, and the granting of stipends (for living expenses) large enough to permit tuition to be paid out of them, all argue against two theses: the Soviet explanation that the fees were a revenue measure, and the view of some foreign observers that this was a deliberate reinforcement of economic inequality. The tuition charged for grades eight to ten in secondary school was set at 15 to 20 rubles per year, at a time when average annual earnings were 400 rubles (all expressed in post-1960 ruble figures). Tuition in higher education was set at 30 to 50 rubles per year. These stipends were granted on the basis of academic performance rather than financial need. But at the same time, the universities and institutes were reluctant to withdraw stipends once granted, regardless of the students' academic performance. Hence, even the motive of promoting academic excellence—if this was a policy motive—failed in its application. The only remaining explanation is that fees were established at a level just somewhat more than nominal in order to foster greater respect among students for the opportunity they enjoyed to proceed beyond the eighth grade into the upper realms of education and career opportunity.[25] Interestingly, the one recent public proposal that tuition be reestablished in higher education

_____

[24]Dodge, 1966, p. 88; Noah, 1966, pp. 108-9.

[25]This is the interpretation given by DeWitt, 1961, pp. 64-66, from which the figures cited are likewise drawn.

employed this same motive. Vladimir D'yagilev, a writer who has specialized in works about the medical profession, wrote in *Oktyabr'* (normally one of the more conservative journals) that introducing tuition in medical schools would discourage applicants for whom medicine would simply be a road to a higher education and a better position in life. This would serve, said D'yagilev, to weed out many of those who, like a certain proportion of present-day Soviet doctors, are indifferent to their patients and sacrifice professional responsibilities to their personal convenience.[26]

PENSIONS AND PAYMENTS: EQUALIZER OR INCENTIVE?

The meeting's chairman read a letter as follows: "While people are working . . . let each person receive according to his labor, but when they are pensioned they should all be paid equally: The state receives the same benefits from all old people." . . . M.P. Dmitriyev, a mechanic in the technical department, did not agree. He said: "I have worked in production for 27 years and have given much of my energy to the plant. The time will come when I am pensioned. And what then? Will I be equated with loafers? I do not agree. Through his work a person creates wealth for society. And society should pay him depending on his labor contribution! If you have done more on the job, you get more when you are pensioned. The same principle is applied with perfect justice in giving vacation and sick pay. In our plant, conscientious regular workers are the first to get apartments and passes to resorts."—From a meeting at a Novosibirsk radio parts plants on the subject of welfare and benefits.[27]

It is very doubtful that retirement benefits in excess of the Federal minimum wage would be considered appropriate in a flat-benefit system so that quite obviously a flat-benefit approach would make the system considerably less adequate for the average worker. A flat-benefit system almost by definition becomes a system geared solely to the lowest pay. A system financed entirely by general revenue can hardly justify giving larger benefits to the typical worker than it does to the lowest paid worker, but under a contributory system the higher contributions of the average and above average worker are the means by which he helps buy protection for himself and his family. Looked at as a tax, these contributions are a very special kind of tax—what is sometimes called a user's tax—with those who pay receiving the benefits and with those who pay more receiving more . . . It is interesting to note also that those few countries that had only flat-benefit social security systems—like the United Kingdom and Canada—on the basis of experience have now moved, or are moving, to a

[26]Summarized in the *New York Times*, September 8, 1968, P. 40.

[27]*Sovetskaya Rossiya*, July 21, 1964.

wage-related approach.—Anthony J. Celebrezze, then (1965) Secretary of Health, Education and Welfare, in a letter replying to an editorial in the *Washington Post*.[28]

There seems to be little disagreement between U.S. and Soviet policymakers that social security in the form of money income, at least, should be geared to the recipient's work record. In both countries, earnings levels and length of employment are used as criteria for fixing benefit levels. The main difference is that in the Soviet Union, nothing is deducted directly from the worker's paycheck to help finance his future security. Enterprises contribute a portion of their profits which is set as a proportion of their total payrolls. While part of this contribution is paid out by the same enterprise in sickness, injury, maternity, and other benefits to its working force, most of the remainder helps finance fringe benefits, largely through the channel of the local trade union at the enterprise. Roughly three quarters of all transfer payments are covered directly from the state budget.[29] But at the same time, the Soviet Union has been in a position to put into action a principle which former H.E.W. Secretary Celebrezze indicated Congress would not accept: benefit levels graduated on the basis of employment record and earnings levels, which are financed mainly from the general state budget.

A description of some of the principal features of the major income maintenance programs will clarify their relation to the nation's labor reward system. Those in search of a comprehensive and detailed account of these programs are referred to several items in the Bibliography: Bernice Madison's *Social Welfare in the Soviet Union* (1968), *A Report on Social Security Programs in the Soviet Union* (1960), and the articles by Kuypers (1958) and Naleszkiewicz (1964).

Old-Age Pensions. The pension reforms of 1956 constituted one of the Khrushchev administration's first presents to the Soviet consumer. The long-overdue reform of old-age pensions, particularly, displayed features that have characterized the Soviet approach to welfare and consumption from 1956 right up to the present. The

---

[28]*Washington Post*, July 3, 1965, p. A7. The editorial appeared in the issue of June 24, 1965; it argued that the contributory method of financing social security bears too heavily on low-paid workers.

[29]The U.S. social security team that visited the U.S.S.R. in 1958 found contributions ranging from 4.4 to 9.0 percent of payroll, with an average of 6.3 percent. Contribution rates vary from year to year and from enterprise to enterprise, and published data on them are scarce. *A Report on Social Security Programs in the Soviet Union*, 1960, Ch. 13.

"floor" was raised to 30 rubles monthly and the "ceiling" fixed at 120 rubles; but the differentials injected between these lower and upper limits both refined and reinforced the idea of linking pension rewards to earnings differentials. While the very largest pensions were cut back considerably, the better paid workers, technicians, engineers, and administrators were still favored somewhat in the pension-earnings relationship over those whose earnings were below—or at least not far above—the national average. While the former 50 percent pension-to-wage relationship, with no ceiling, for workers in certain favored industries was now limited by a 120-ruble ceiling, still the 50 percent ratio remained after 1956 all the way up to an earnings level of 240 rubles, which was over three times the average earnings of the mid-1950's.[30]

Under the pre-1956 pension legislation, the flat rate of 50 percent of earnings for most ordinary pensions applied only to the first 30 rubles of wages or salary. As wage levels rose during the inflationary 1930's and thereafter, the maximum pension of 15 rubles, a bare sustenance-level sum to begin with, turned into a uniform payment level for most pensioners which scarcely could support a pensioner who had no other resources. What made existence possible for most pensioners was the extended family, the mixing of generations in the same housing units. The elderly played—and to a great extent still continue to play—an important role in household tasks, which includes care for children, long hours of shopping and preparing meals, and tending garden plots where these are available.

The Soviet social security system has not been so all-embracing as to do away with the Soviet citizens' legal obligation to support needy family members and relatives. The new family legislation of 1968 reaffirmed, in fact, the long-existing provisions that minors, invalids, and others in need of aid be supported by their near relations to the extent necessary. Orphans must be supported by their grandparents or elder siblings; needy adults incapable of working receive support from their parents, children, stepchildren, and grandchildren. Support payments in all these cases may be exacted by civil suit if necessary, and are set at levels proportional to the supporter's income.[31] The military draft laws similarly recognize relations of

---

[30]Law on State Pensions, adopted by the USSR Supreme Soviet, July 14, 1956. Text, with 1959 amendments, in *Pensionnoye obespecheniye v SSSR*, 1960, pp. 7-22.

[31]The older legislation is in *SU RSFSR* 1926, No. 82, Art. 612, pars. 42-56. This was replaced by *Vedomosti SSSR* 1968, No. 27, Art. 241, pars. 18-23.

material dependence and make generous provision for them. Under the 1967 law, specifically, a young man aged 18 to 26 may be deferred if he is the only able-bodied family member available to support his retired or invalided parents and siblings, his two or more children, his invalid wife, his able-bodied wife if she has two or more children under eight, and his siblings under 16 years of age, in the event no institutional care is available for them. If this dependence continues until the young man reaches his 27th birthday, he is put on the list of reserves and exempted from active military service.[32]

The housing construction upsurge which began in the latter 1950's will increasingly have the effect of enabling a certain proportion of the elderly to live apart from their families. This in turn will require not only increased pension levels for the elderly, but more and better organized services and day-care programs for growing families. Part of the increases in social wage benefits, therefore, must go for services which were already being provided by households. City planners are aware that one of the functions of the microdistrict (see Chapters 6 and 7) is to provide shopping services in a form that will greatly simplify running a household for families in which both parents work and there is no household help.

Under the pre-1956 pension system, when many or most pensioners were receiving their 15 rubles, there was no effective ceiling at all on pensions for workers retired from high-priority industries, such as the coal, metal, and chemical industries. Because of the great wage differentials promoted during the first two five-year plans (1929-37) and the post-World-War-II reconstruction period, the flat 50 percent rate for pensions not subject to the ceiling provision meant pension levels as high as 300 rubles for some. Although this result probably had not been intended by those who drafted the older pension legislation, by the 1950's there had emerged an egalitarian pension rate for the many and a highly advantageous flat 50 percent scale for the few in favored industries and occupations. The enormous advantage enjoyed by workers in these industries consisted largely in their enjoying relative security against inflation. Far from being a product of the inflationary 1930's, this dual system was formally and generally established only in 1947. Prime Minister Bulganin, in introducing the 1956 pension reforms, made quite a point of these and other disparities: Some of the highest pensions, he said, were being received by persons still

---

[32] *Vedomosti SSSR* 1967, No. 42.

employed, the high pensions were going to all employees of given sectors rather than just to those working at arduous jobs, and so forth.[33] Today, following the raising of the minimum wage to 60 rubles (as of 1967), the actual ratio of the highest to lowest pensions is approximately 3:1 instead of 30:1. The system of preferential pension levels for the favored *industries* was replaced by preferential levels for difficult or hazardous *occupations*.

Lower-range pensions were improved not only by the introduction of the 30-ruble floor, but by a 100 percent pension-to-earnings ratio up to a level of 55 rubles for those with a long employment record or with dependents. Also, pension rates were now to be based on earnings rather than on basic wage rates. In 1956 wages constituted 45 to 65 percent of earnings, so that the difference in pension awards for a given wage level was considerable. The policy of the past dozen years, though, has been to increase the proportion of basic wage rates to roughly three quarters of total earnings from a given industrial job.[34] This is dealt with further in Chapter 5.

The fact that the pension ceiling was reduced in 1956 at the same time the "floor" was raised may have been determined primarily by budgetary considerations. If the primary need was raising the 15-ruble "floor," one obvious way of financing the rise was to take it out of the top-level pensions. The cost of pensions, furthermore, had been mounting rapidly since the 1930's: While the average wage had risen by 116 percent between 1940 and 1955, the outlay for social security had multiplied more than nine times.[35] War-related pensions accounted for much of the increase, naturally. But even after the 1956 law had added 50 percent to the annual pension outlay, the pension bill, mainly because of the rising average wage, continued tó rise at a rate considerably greater than the rise in the number of pensioners. During the period 1958-64 (that is, after the 1956 provisions were in full effect, but before the extension of pension benefits to collective farmers) the number of pensioners of all kinds rose by 29 percent, while the pension outlay rose by 48 percent.[36]

The ratio of benefits to earnings is of some interest. This ratio

[33]*Pravda*, July 12, 1956, pp. 2-3. Trans. in *CDSP* VIII:28, pp. 4 ff. See also the statement by RSFSR Minister of Public Health Komarov, cited in Kuypers, 1958, p. 53.

[34]Batkayev and Markov, 1964, p. 39.

[35]*Narodonoye khozyaistvo SSSR*, 1965, p. 567; 1958, p. 906; statement by Bulganin reported in *Pravda*, July 12, 1956.

[36]*Narodnoye khozyaistvo SSSR*, 1964, pp. 602, 772.

descends from 100 percent at the lowest wage level to 50 percent for those earning 100 or more rubles per month. While a scale of this type embodies the same principle as the graduated income tax, in which the better paid sacrifice a larger proportion of their income, the graduation feature stops abruptly at an earnings level of 110 rubles, beyond which the ratio remains fixed at 50 percent of earnings up to the maximum pension level of 120 rubles. This has the somewhat peculiar result, as Table 3-3 shows, that pensions for earnings above the 110-ruble point rise faster in relation to earnings than do pensions below that point. A wage earner who has put forth the effort to raise his earnings from the 30-ruble level to the 110-ruble level just before retirement has, in effect, brought his potential pension payments from 30 rubles up to an actual 55 rubles. At the same time a worker or professional person who finds himself at the above-average level of 110 rubles, and similarly increases his monthly earnings by 80 rubles through better work performance and

Table 3-3
SELECTED MONTHLY PAYMENTS OF OLD-AGE PENSIONS UNDER
THE 1956 LAW ON STATE PENSIONS
(in post-1960 rubles)

Monthly Earnings Used as the Basis for Pension Awards*	Pensions for Workers in Nonhazardous Occupations		Pensions for Workers in Hazardous Occupations (e.g., mining, high-temperature work)	
	Maximum†	*Minimum*	*Maximum†*	*Minimum*
30	30.00	30.00	30.00	30.00
40	40.00	35.00	40.00	36.00
60	56.25	45.00	60.00	48.00
80	65.00	52.00	70.00	56.00
100	68.75	55.00	75.00	60.00
120	75.00	60.00	83.50	66.00
160	100.00	80.00	110.00	88.00
200	120.00	100.00	120.00	110.00
240	120.00	120.00	120.00	120.00
300	120.00	120.00	120.00	120.00

*Earnings include all regular income from the pension applicant's regular job, but not earnings for overtime work or from second jobs. The applicant may, at his discretion, use as his earnings basis either (1) average earnings for the last 12 months preceding retirement, or (2) average earnings for any five year period during the 10 years preceding retirement.

†The maximum pension for any earnings level except the lowest levels represents an addition to the pension award of up to 25 percent of the basic payment. Included in this can be 10 percent for a 30-year or 35-year work record overall (for women and men, respectively) or for 15 years of unbroken employment, also an additional 15 percent for pensioners supporting two or more dependents.

Source: *Vedomosti SSSR* 1956, No. 15.

further training, has improved his potential pension level from 55 rubles to an actual 95 rubles, a difference of 40 rubles as opposed to 25. With the minimum wage at 60 rubles since January 1968 and average earnings at 112 rubles, it is appropriate to compare the result of a 60-to-110 earnings increase with that of a 110-to-160 increase: the first adds 10 rubles to the pension, while the second adds 25. The difference in the two results, in each case, reflects the difference between the principles which are embodied in the two halves of the pension scale: the graduated decrease in the pension-to-earnings ratio in the lower half, and the fixed ratio of 50 percent in the upper half.

The latest minimum wage law in effect wiped out those portions of the pension scale based on 100, 85, and 75 percent of earnings, leaving the portions based on ratios of 65, 55, and 50 percent only. The separate scale for hazardous occupations (mining, high-temperature work, and others) displays the same features. On both scales, pension supplements accentuate these differences somewhat since they are based on fixed percentages of the pension rather than earnings. Presumably the bulk of the pensions which have been awarded during the post-1956 period have fallen in the graduated-decrease portion of the scale, based on earnings of between 60 and 110 rubles; for during this period average earnings have risen from about 75 rubles in 1956-57 to 103 rubles in 1967 (see Table 2-1).[37]

The employment requirement for old-age pensions is important, and there is a 10 percent pension supplement for working 10 additional years beyond the minimum. For men the minimum period is 25 years, for women 20 years. Another way of obtaining the 10 percent supplement is to have accumulated 15 years of seniority at the same place of employment, a provision included in the 1956 law at the last moment. The age requirement is lower than that of the U.S. Social Security System: age 60 for men, age 55 for women. For workers in hazardous occupations, all these requirements are more liberal: retirement is at ages 50 and 45, and the employment record 20 and 15 years, for men and women, respectively. All pensions embody a need component, too: nonworking pensioners receive an additional 10 percent if they must support a dependent, and 15 percent for two or more dependents.

The trend in employers' policies in the United States is not only to

---

[37]*Narodnoye khozyaistvo SSSR*, 1965, p. 567; the 1956-57 estimate is derived from the figures for 1955 and 1958.

motivate employees to retire at a given age, but to enforce retirement at that point, or after an interval of a few years. In the Soviet Union, the problem of policymakers has been to make indefinite continuation of employment attractive without at the same time disadvantaging those who choose to retire at retirement age. It is not surprising that a labor-hungry economy seeks to encourage its retirement-age population to stay on the job for a period of time, or to take over the service jobs which are chronically underfilled. While both Soviet and foreign commentators have pointed out the problems being caused by an increase in the proportion of the retirement-age to working-age population, this increase is not apt to be dramatic. This can be seen in the estimates in Table 3-4. They assume the largest conceivable decline in the fertility level during the 1960's, and project its consequence for the population of 1980. On the other hand, a larger proportion of the working-age population will be in the schools and universities. The large excess of females over males in the retirement-age population, according to these same projections, will persist: In 1980, 71 percent will be female, as compared with 74 percent in 1960.

Table 3-4
TWENTY-YEAR PROJECTION OF THE GROWTH OF THE
WORKING-AGE AND RETIREMENT-AGE POPULATION OF
THE U.S.S.R., 1960-80

	1960	*1980*
Total population	212,200,000	259,000,000
Retirement-age population (males 60 and over, females 55 and over)	26,200,000	41,100,000
Working-age population (males 16 to 59, females 16 to 54)	119,100,000	156,400,000
Percent of total population of retirement age	12.4	15.9
Retirement-age population as a percent of working-age population	22.0	26.3

Source: James W. Brackett, "Demographic Trends and Population Policy in the Soviet Union," in U.S. Congress, Joint Economic Committee, *Dimensions of Soviet Economic Power*, 1962, pp. 564-69. Brackett's Model 3 and Assumption D are shown here, which assume the greatest foreseeable decline in fertility rates for the period indicated, as among a total of four fertility variants.

Under the pre-1956 legislation, old-age pensions were paid regardless of the work status or earnings of pensioners. Considering the low level of most old-age pensions, they scarcely motivated the retirement-age population to leave the labor force. Increased pension levels might provide such a motive; hence it was necessary to find some way of combining pensions and earnings so as to make continued employment attractive. The 1956 law offered a somewhat crude solution to this problem by simply retaining the maximum 15-ruble pension for persons earning up to 100 rubles monthly, and barring the payment of pensions to anyone earning over that limit. However, those receiving preferential rates for arduous or hazardous occupations were granted 50 percent of their pensions regardless of their earnings. The active concern of Soviet policymakers with keeping pensioners on the job is the fact that the 1956 law as enacted included something which the bill did not: provision for calculating the pension on the basis of earnings at the time of the the pension award, rather than at the legal retirement age.[38]

The labor needs of the 1960's apparently caused Soviet policymakers to take a second look at the employment potential of pensioners. The result was a 1964 amendment which granted a flat 50 percent of pension to employees of pension age in a large number of industries and callings, 75 percent for those returning to work in the Urals, Siberia, and the Far East, and full pensions to those still capable of working in the arduous and hazardous occupations. This was intended to add 1 million pensioners to the labor force, according to a social security official.[39]

Years-of-Service Pensions. Another motive offered for continuity of employment is the years-of-service pension. This dates back to the 1920's, and like other pension systems was badly in need of adjustment and simplification by the 1950's. A single law of 1959 reorganized years-of-service pensions for two professions which had long been low paid, but were soon (1964) to receive 25 percent raises: public education and medicine. Both are female-dominated professions numerically, and women may be more inclined than men to leave them after 15 or 20 years in order to take less demanding work, to tend their children's families, or for other reasons. As of 1965, 69 percent of the nation's schoolteachers and 74 percent of its doctors were women; together they included some 10.8 million persons. Other years-of-service pensions apply to pilots and other

---

[38] Arts. 15 and 54 of the law.

[39] *Pravda*, March 6, 1964; *CDSP* XVI:10, p. 29.

flight personnel in civil aviation, to certain agricultural specialists, and to certain categories of performing artists.[40]

All these pensions have common features: They range from 30 to 120 rubles, as do the standard old-age pensions; their level is 40 to 50 percent of salary (not of earnings); they are granted after a given number of years in service *in the profession*, regardless of the age of the recipient or of interruptions in service, or of employment status after the pension award; except in the case of performing artists, they are paid *in addition to* earnings; they are not taxed; and if the recipient remains in his or her profession, the pension increases in proportion to salary. Flight personnel, and a number of agricultural specialists who actually reside in the countryside, all receive the 50 percent rate, the rest 40. Actual residence in the countryside also makes the difference between a 25-year qualifying period for doctors and the 30-year period for those who have practiced in urban areas.

As numerous Soviet newspaper articles testify, rural areas and small towns are particularly unattractive places of employment for people with a professional education, and this is probably more true of the Soviet countryside than of rural areas in most of the rest of the industrial world. Formerly, Soviet doctors residing in rural areas were given the 50 percent rate in addition to the shortened service period, but this was reduced to 40 percent in the 1959 law.[41] One compensation for living in rural areas and small towns is the availability and size of garden plots, which even today are an important supplement to the income and/or diet of those who work them. It is for this reason that old-age pensions are reduced by 15 percent in the case of "persons connected with agriculture." Until the introduction (in 1965) of pensions for collective farmers, this category referred to the agricultural specialists, tractor drivers, and the like, who are treated as state employees even though they may work and live on collective farms.

With the sole exception of test pilots, no recipient of a years-of-service pension who continues to work may draw a pension which puts his total (salary plus pension) income above 200 rubles. Thus, the maximum advantage accrues to a teacher, doctor whose salary is in the 140-150 range, and to a pilot or veterinary specialist

---

[40]*SP SSSR* 1958, No. 14, Art. 11; 1960, No. 1, Art. 2 and No. 3, Art. 16. *Narodnoye khozyaistvo SSSR* 1965, pp. 559, 683, and 745. *Trudovoye pravo*, 1963, pp. 309-10.

[41]*SZ SSSR* 1929, No. 63, Art. 582.

earning in the 130-140 range. Airplane pilots earn well above this level, and they enjoy an addition of 3 percent of salary for every year worked beyond the qualifying period of 25 years, up to a pension level totalling 75 percent of current salary. The recipient may continue to draw his pension indefinitely, regardless how much longer he continues to work in his profession. But upon retirement, those receiving the 40 percent rate switch over to the standard old-age pension, provided they have reached retirement age. An amendment inserted just before the enactment of the 1956 law provided that pensions in such cases should be calculated on the basis of earnings *plus* the years-of-service pension.

Few will disagree that Soviet doctors and other medical personnel were long underpaid by comparison with other professions requiring equivalent training, and as demanding in terms of responsibility and sacrifice. The pay of beginning physicians was set in 1955 at 72.50 to 77 rubles per month (average earnings in that year being 71.50 for all workers and employees in the national economy); in 1964 it was raised to 90 to 105 rubles per month, with average nationwide earnings at 90.10 rubles. At the end of 30 years of service (or 25 years in rural localities), a physician can be earning 195 to 200 rubles monthly; during 1955-64 he received 108 to 110 rubles for the same length of service. Nurses now receive 60 to 110 rubles, and nonprofessional personnel 45 to 50 rubles.[42]

The salaries of teachers in primary and secondary schools have a considerably smaller range than the salaries of doctors, and their average earnings (as distinguished from basic salary) may actually have fallen behind the average for all workers and employees during the 1960's. Harold J. Noah of Columbia University Teachers College estimated that average monthly earnings for teachers fell between 78 and 83 rubles during the period 1955-60, during which time the national earnings average rose from 71.50 to 80.10 rubles. His complete table of pre-1964 basic salaries, based on 1948 regulations for the Russian Republic which are still in effect, shows monthly salaries ranging from 46.80 to 84.15 rubles for those actually engaged in teaching. The rates varied with years of service, type of school, training, and subjects taught (academic or nonacademic). To the basic salary are added allowances for extra duties, and for teaching in special schools (schools for the deaf or blind, for example). Rural teachers have salaries roughly 10 percent below those of their urban

---

[42]Field, 1967, pp. 128-31.

counterparts, although benefits and compensating factors actually bring their overall per capita compensation somewhat above the corresponding urban compensation.[43]

In 1964 the entire salary schedule was raised by about 25 percent, and some categories of lower paid teachers received up to 40 percent more salary. It was at this point that the years-of-service pension was terminated for teachers not already receiving it. Very likely this change was based on the fact that the supply of teachers had increased by the 1960's and consequently no added incentives were necessary in order to retain middle-aged teachers for another 5, 10, or 15 years of service. While the salary raise as a whole probably required several times the annual outlay for years-of-service pensions for teachers up to 1964, the "spreading out" of this pension money helped make the teaching profession more attractive as a whole. In fact, it put both average salary and average earnings ahead of the national wage-and-salary average, at least for the moment. The new pay scale eliminated both the urban-rural differential in salary levels, and also the differential for grades, which had meant salaries nearly 25 percent higher for teachers of grades 8-10 than for teachers of grades 1-4. Basic salary now begins at 80 rubles per month, rises to 100 rubles at the end of 10 year's service, and to 137 rubles after 25 years. The substantial increase after 25 years may be seen as the reincarnation of the years-of-service pension. Additional payments for guidance work and grading papers adds 6 to 16 percent to the basic salary.[44]

Doctors were treated similarly. The pre-1964 beginning basic salary was 72.50 rubles monthly in cities, the salary after 10 years 95 rubles, and after 30 years 108 rubles. These levels were now raised to 90, 110, and 165 rubles, respectively. Service in the countryside was rewarded with extra pay after the reform as before, but at an increased premium of roughly 15 percent instead of the former 3 or 4 percent. Country physicians, accordingly, now begin at 105 rubles and are raised to 125 rubles after 10 years and 170 rubles after 25 years. Specialists receive premiums which place their salaries well above these levels, and other medical personnel were given analogous raises.[45]

Will there ever be an economy which offers its maximum rewards

---

[43]Noah, 1966, pp. 178, 181-90, 236-37.

[44]See Khrushchev's address introducing these reforms in *Izvestiya*, July 15, 1964. Trans. in *CDSP* XVI:29, pp. 14-15.

[45]*Ibid.*, pp. 15-16.

to people who are in mid-career, who are in the process of raising their families, equipping their homes, and engaged in the many expensive activities which are common to this period of life? The Soviet Union, from an administrative point of view, has the practical means for organizing its reward system this way if its policymakers wish. But, instead, as the writer heard one of his colleagues say of many occupations in America, "You get paid extra just for getting old." So it is in the Soviet Union also. To this it may be replied that some very important costs which are borne by American families are largely covered by state subsidies in the Soviet Union: most educational and child-care expenses, housing, and some outlays for recreation. But feeding and clothing one's offspring still take a substantial portion of the Soviet family budget, and the sacrifices which parents make to supplement their sons' and daughters' university stipends are familiar to the writer from contact with Soviet students. These circumstances argue at least for a uniformity of salaries as between the age spans of 25-45 and 45-60; instead, Soviet policymakers have chosen a familiar pattern of increasing rewards for length of service, as the very name of the "years-of-service pension" implies.

The years-of-service pension and its substitute in the form of periodic salary raises appears to be an inducement to professional people and specialists in the "difficult professions" to devote their entire active careers to their specialty. Naturally, one wonders why there should have been concern that a doctor or airplane pilot voluntarily abandon his career at age 40 or 45. Few are likely to do so: As of 1960, 80 percent of the recipients of years-of-service pensions were still working in their professions.[46] The concern with these two occupations seems to be rather that their practitioners not direct their careers toward duties which are more "comfortable" but for which there is less demand. In the case of doctors, this means first of all medical research or administrative posts; in the case of pilots, it probably means well-paying ground jobs. In the 1959 law on years-of-service pensions, medical *research* posts were conspicuously absent from the long list of medical occupations for which these pensions may be awarded. For medical personnel of lower rank as well as for public school teachers and the personnel of preschool institutions, the attraction of a 40 percent to 50 percent annual "bonus" from one's early 50's to retirement, whether in the form of

[46] Acharkan, 1960, p. 6.

a pension or an automatic salary increase, may be decisive in preventing the departure of many of them for better paying industrial jobs during their 30's and 40's. The case of performing artists is different again, since middle age itself is an occupational hazard for many of them and some kind of support is necessary for those who are obliged at this point to move to other occupations. A 1958 decree specifically ruled out the payment of a years-of-service pension to performing artists who continued to work as performing artists. It is meant specifically for those who change occupations, or who spend a period of time developing a new occupation.

The plethora of decrees and directives dealing with benefits for agricultural specialists working in rural areas (that is, not those who staff offices and research laboratories in or near urban areas) speaks eloquently of the difficulty of inducing specialists who have been trained in urban areas to devote their lives and careers to the countryside. The first years of collectivization (1929-31) saw enactment of a large group of these decrees, and the difficulties of reorganizing the collective farms following World War II produced more decrees in the late 1940's and early 1950's. Medical and veterinary personnel down to the rank of nurse and veterinary *fel'dsher* (a medical rank representing a level of training somewhere between doctor and nurse) were given years-of-service pensions in 1929, and agronomists in 1930, all of them to the extent of 50 percent of salary at the end of 25 years of service in rural areas. Legislation of the 1950's then assured years-of-service pension rights to rural workers in a long list of specialties, including service as collective farm chairman in the qualifying period.[47] In short, rewards came early to all those who possessed the talent, initiative, and luck to leave the collective farms and gain a specialty before returning to the countryside; those who stayed on the collective farms waited for 35 years after the beginning of collectivization drive to gain the right to a pension.

Pension Elites. Is there a pension elite in the Soviet Union? Do Party secretaries, members of the Central Committee, and members of the Council of Ministers have to content themselves with the 120-ruble maximum? Most of them do not. What they do receive, under the 1956 legislation, is up to 200 rubles monthly together with a number of fringe benefits: 50 percent rebates on rent and utilities,

---

[47]Partial tests of all these decrees are in *Pensionnoye obespechniye v SSSR*, 1960, pp. 165-86.

housing space above the established norms, free or subsidized pharmaceuticals and prosthetic devices, and a miscellany of further items. There are annual bonuses of up to two months' salary for those who have been Party members for over 30 years. All these amenities are granted as "personal pensions" to "persons who have rendered exceptional service to the Soviet state in the areas of revolutionary, governmental, social, and economic activity, and persons who have rendered exceptional service in the fields of culture, science, and technology."[48]

Two other categories of persons are given exceptional treatment: officers of the armed services, and academic and research personnel. The former include not only career officers, but career non-commissioned officers as well, together with officers of the militia (ordinary police) and the state security forces (KGB). Article 52 of the 1956 pension law set all these apart for special legislation at the discretion of the USSR Council of Ministers, which responded six months later with a decree on the subject.[49] The officers' pension is granted on a years-of-service basis, although officers have the option of receiving standard old-age pensions instead on reaching the age of 60. The years-of-service pension is calculated on a *rising* percent-of-salary scale. It begins at 50 percent of salary after 25 years of service, and increases 3 percent for every additional year served, up to a maximum of 75 percent; thus, 34 years of service will assure the maximum pension. Group I disability pensions for service-related injuries are a flat 75 percent of salary regardless of length of service; nonservice-related injuries entail a 60 percent pension level which rises to 70 percent after 10 years of service. While no recent comprehensive data on officers' salaries are available, one set of data for the early 1950's shows the following army salaries (given here in current rubles), whose level is determined by both rank and command: a lieutenant commanding a platoon, 120 rubles monthly; a major commanding a battalion, 220 rubles; a colonel commanding a regiment, 310 rubles; a lieutenant general commanding a division, 500 rubles. To these are added supplements for length of service, which rise to a maximum of 20 percent after 20 years' service; officers who have graduated from a military academy receive an additional 10 percent.[50] If the salaries of the 1960's are comparable

[48]USSR Statute on Personal Pensions, November 14, 1956, *SP SSSR* 1957, No. 2, Art. 8. Text in *Pensionnoye obespecheniye v SSSR* (1960), pp. 196-207.

[49]*SP SSSR* 1957, No. 3, Art. 23. This is summarized in *Sovetskoye pensionnoye obespecheniye*, 1966, Ch. 15.

[50]Martens, 1956, pp. 26-27.

to these, the 50-to-75 percent ratio of pensions to salary allows the upper echelons well over the 200-ruble ceiling set for personal pensions.

University and academic personnel are entitled to a flat 40 percent of salary on reaching retirement. These include not only university teachers and administrators, but members and corresponding members of the various learned academies, research workers who have teaching functions, and professional educational research workers. In the 1959 census the total in all these categories was 316,000, over two thirds of them university teachers.[51] Teachers in higher education are very well paid indeed, and the same can probably be said of the others covered by this special pension, which rests on a decree of 1949.[52] Salaries of the assistant professors (*dotsenty*) whom the writer met at Moscow University began at 180 rubles and rose to over 250 rubles. Those of professors could run as high as 500 or 600 rubles, although the rank of professor is proportionally less widespread among Soviet university faculty than it is in the United States. In any case, the high salary level was probably what occasioned the choice of a 40 percent pension as against 50 percent for the top bracket of regular old-age pensions. There are ceilings, however: 240 rubles for members of the learned academies, 160 rubles for professors and holders of the doctor's degree, and 80 rubles for the lower academic ranks.

Executive salaries of unspecified size—"personal salaries" for outstanding performance (*personal'nyi oklad*)—have long been available through special funds placed at the disposal of employers. These are paid as supplements to regular salary, and are probably available to some but not all branches of the economy. In 1958 these were limited to 350 rubles per month, although the level of personal salaries awarded up to that time was not affected.[53] These generous supplements may or may not be identical with the so-called "Party envelopes" given to some high officials every month together with their salaries. The personal salaries are terminated with the termination of employment in any given post, but whether the Party itself makes any special awards to its more distinguished pensioners is not known. On the other hand, both the Khrushchev and Brezhnev administrations have made an effort to limit excesses of privilege

---

[51] Tsentral'noye statisticheskoye upravleniye . . . *Itogi vsesoiuznoi perepisi naseleniya 1959 goda; SSSR*, 1962, p. 165. *Pravda*, October 21, 1968, p. 3.

[52] Summarized in *Sovetskoye pensionnoye obespecheniye*, 1966, Ch. 14.

[53] *Trudovoye pravo*, 1963, pp. 285-86.

generally, so it would be no surprise if the Party envelope has been reduced in size by this time, or eliminated for many Party members who formerly received it. However, no official information is available on this whole subject, which the writer and others have learned about only from conversations with Soviet citizens. The eminent Soviet physicist Andrei D. Sakharov in his 1968 essay on social and world problems, published only outside the Soviet Union, mentioned both the sealed pay envelopes and the concealed distribution of consumer goods as having been characteristic elite privileges of the Stalin period.[54]

Disability Compensation. Wide differentials are understandable as a basis for reckoning pension levels for old-age and years-of-service pensions. But it is puzzling to find that Soviet disability compensation discriminates sharply as between work-related and nonwork-related disability. Furthermore, compensation for nonwork -related disability is limited in that awards can be made only to those who have worked a certain length of time by a given age. Under the 1956 pension reforms, a man in the 26-to-31 age bracket must have worked five years, for example, and a woman three; a man 51 to 56 must have worked 16 years, a woman 13. Those with less than the required employment history receive pensions reduced proportionally.

The differences in compensation which result from this distinction are low, however. Compare, for example, the pensions for work-related and nonwork-related disabilities received by Group I pensioners, those adjudged the most seriously disabled in the opinion of a Committee of Medical and Labor Experts. Those injured at work in underground mining, high-temperature work, and the other "arduous and hazardous" occupations receive 100 percent of the first 60 rubles of their earnings, and 20 percent of the balance. For nonwork-related disability, a worker in a nonhazardous occupation receives 85 percent of the first 50 rubles and 10 percent of the remainder. All other scales fall in between these norms. Legislation of 1965 established a "floor" of 50 rubles for the lowest rates.[55]

For all disability pensions, supplements of up to 30 percent of the base pension figure are available; part of these depend on the pensioner's having worked 10 or 15 years without interruption prior to his disablement, the remainder upon his need to support

[54]*New York Times*, July 22, 1968, p. 16.
[55]*Vedomosti SSSR* 1965, No. 1, Art. 5.

nonworking dependents. In spite of the emphasis on differentials, the highest base rate for any given salary level is roughly 50 percent more than the lowest, and the proportionate difference between the two base rates rises only very slowly with a rising salary level (see Table 3-5). The difference between the pension based on the minimum wage and the pension based on relatively high earnings is similarly small. As between the minimum wage level of 60 rubles and the 150-ruble level, for example, the pension increases by less than 35 percent on the most advantageous scale, and by less than 20 percent on the least advantageous scale. Thus, both kinds of differentials were drawn within limits considerably narrower than those for old-age pensions.

Table 3-5
SELECTED MONTHLY PAYMENTS OF DISABILITY PENSIONS
FOR GROUP I INVALIDS (THE MOST SERIOUSLY DISABLED),
NOT INCLUDING SUPPLEMENTS, UNDER THE 1956 PENSION LAW
(rubles)

Monthly Earnings Preceding Disablement*	Nonemployment-related Disability		Employment-related Disability	
	Nonhazardous Occupations	Hazardous Occupations	Nonhazardous Occupations	Hazardous Occupations†
60	43.50‡	51.00	50.60	60.00
100	47.50‡	59.00	55.00	68.00
150	52.50	69.00	60.00	78.00

Calculated in the same manner described in Table 3-3, footnote.

†An exception is made for disability due to work-related respiratory diseases, for which the Group I invalid receives a pension equal to his entire former earnings, up to a maximum of 120 rubles.

‡A 1964 law set a minimum pension of 50 rubles for all Group I pensioners. *Vedomosti SSSR* 1965, No. 1.

Source: *Vedomosti SSSR* 1956, No. 15.

The pension scales for invalids in Group II and Group III, the partially disabled, are entirely analogous to Group I pensions except that the increments of 10, 15, and 20 percent of earnings above a given minimum begin at somewhat lower points. Group I and II pensioners have an absolute incentive to work to the extent their disabilities permit, since their full pensions are paid regardless of earnings. Group III pensioners, the least handicapped, have an incentive to work up to the point where earnings and pension together equal former earnings. Beyond this point there is a certain "disincentive range" in which increases in earnings are offset by corresponding decreases in pension payments. But when the pensioner is earning enough to bring his pension payments down to 50 percent of their original level, the payments remain at that level regardless how much more he earns.

Pensions for noncareer service in the armed forces below the rank of commissioned officer (draftees, for the most part) are covered by the 1956 law, too, and are paid according to the same norms as those just described. They preserve the distinction between hazardous and non hazardous occupations pursued before induction, but naturally substitute service-related for employment-related disability. For servicemen who enter the service with no previous employment record, the 1956 law set minima of 30 and 38 rubles (the latter for service-related disabilities); then the 1964 amendment raised both of these to the new 50-ruble minimum. Survivors' insurance for the families of both workers and servicemen was in most cases set at the same levels as Group I disability pensions.

Employee Work Records and Further Benefits. Most of the many payments and benefits which are distributed by local trade union organizations, or whose distribution is watched over by the unions, are likewise linked to labor performance in one fashion or another. Sickness benefits, sanatorium passes, maternity benefits, special diets, retraining expenses, and funeral allowances are the ones common to all enterprises. Like the disability pensions, these too fall under the concept of social insurance (*sotsial'noye strakhovaniye*) as distinguished from pensions, and they are administered by the trade unions rather than by the state. Local union organizations also have at their disposal a variety of further benefits, whose extent varies greatly from enterprise to enterprise and depends first of all on the size and production record of the enterprise. Beginning in 1969, *all* benefits except pensions were entrusted to the administration of the trade unions, regardless of their source of financing.[56] Trade union subsidies for preschool and educational fees are widespread, and the union is the most important single agency in determining the order of distribution of state and enterprise-built housing as apartments become available. The reader may consult Emily Clark Brown's *Soviet Trade Unions and Labor Relations* (1966) for a well-documented account of the union's role in performing all these functions.

Where these benefits are linked to work performance, in most

---

[56]*Izvestiya*, April 27, 1968.

cases it is length of employment rather than earnings level which forms the link. Particularly important is seniority at one enterprise, "seniority" here meaning length of service regardless of sequence of hiring. Benefits for temporary loss of working capacity (sickness or injury) come in the form of full wages where the illness is employment-related, regardless of length of employment. For other illnesses, however, the newcomer receives only half of his wages during the first three years of employment, and is entitled to the maximum of 100 percent only after eight years of uninterrupted employment at the same enterprise.[57] Benefits for workers who are not trade-union members are considerably lower, but union dues are nominal and everyone belongs. Naturally, there are numerous reasons for interrupting employment which are recognized by the unions as not entailing a reduction of benefits. However, workers who were fired from their former jobs for violations of labor discipline or of the law must first work six months before they are eligible for benefits in the case of nonemployment-related illness.

There is no Soviet unemployment insurance, save for a payment covering relocation expenses for those leaving jobs in hardship areas. At present the average loss of working time of those changing jobs, as an average for the entire nation, is 23 to 25 days.[58] The legal penalties for job leaving which were abolished in 1956 after some years of nonenforcement were replaced by a job-leaving "disincentive." This was ineligibility for benefits for temporary loss of working capacity during a period of six months, following a voluntary change of employment. Within less than a year, however, the ineligibility period was abolished as concerned work-related disability, and in 1960 the ineligibility period was abolished altogether, provided the worker had found new employment within a month after leaving his previous job.[59] Job leaving and job changing for a variety of reasons which the law recognizes as valid does not entail any loss of benefits regardless of the interval between one job and the next: for educational reasons and military service, for prolonged disability, because of labor force reductions and authorized transfers of workers, because one's spouse is moving in connection with a job change, and so forth. Nevertheless, voluntary

---

[57] *Gosudarstvennoye sotsial'noye strakhovaniye*, 1963, pp. 42-77; *Izvestiya*, July 21, 1968, p. 2. Until 1968, the maximum was 90 percent after 12 years.

[58] *Izvestiya*, October 18, 1968.

[59] *Vedomosti SSSR* 1956, No. 10; 1960, No. 18.

job changing does still mean not just loss of enterprise seniority, but also a break in the worker's period of uninterrupted service for the purpose of calculating benefit *levels*. It has the same consequence for pension supplements which are awarded for uninterrupted service. The principle applied here appears to be that job changing itself, it it means simply leaving one job in order to look for a better one, should mean a definite reduction in benefit levels, but not deprivation of minimum security. At the same time, recent criminal legislation protected the worker's uninterrupted work record in the event of conviction for disorderly conduct and all the other minor offenses which fall under the category of "hooliganism." Since the workers cannot be fired for such convictions either, their seniority is protected as well.[60] Here the concern of the legislators appeared to be that loss of these additional work incentives might simply be an inducement to switch jobs or to remain unemployed for a time. Both courses of action would take the wayward worker away from the watchful support of his co-workers, the "collective" whose social pressure may help keep him from further mischief.

The generous maternity leave period of 14 weeks was the fruit of a wartime (1944) law which sought both to maintain a female labor force as large as possible, and to make up for the catastrophic decline in births occasioned by the war.[61] Such benefits are the logical instrument of a government which is both moderately pronatalist in outlook, and in critical need of human resources with which to meet its ambitious production targets. While the right to full wages during the 14 weeks carries the qualification of three years of employment (or two years of uninterrupted employment), those women without even a full year's employment receive two thirds of wages, and certain allowances are made for women under 18. The one-time payment of 30 rubles for layettes and food carries only a three-month employment requirement.

Seniority at one enterprise is of primary importance in the distribution of the many benefits which are managed at the discretion of local trade unions: housing assignments, sanatorium passes, vacation resort passes, passes to children's camps, assignment of garden plots, educational subsidies (boarding school fees, increased university stipends), the use of preschool facilities, and a variety of other fringe benefits. While the central trade union

[60]Decree of July 8, 1944. *Vedomosti SSSR* 1966, No. 30.

[61]Law of July 8, 1944. *Vedomosti SSSR* 1944, No. 37.

organization in Moscow regulates the distribution of these benefits through an unending stream of directives to its branches, in the last analysis it is the local trade union committee at a given enterprise which decides who will get what. However, the central organization has acted to reinforce the extra incentives and benefits enjoyed by workers in the high-priority, high-pay industries. In the distribution of sanatorium passes, for example, mining enterprises have the first priority, followed by the metallurgical and machine-building industries.[62]

A primary objective of seniority-related benefits is that of reducing excessive labor turnover, a problem discussed at length in Chapter 5. However, the vast majority of those who flit from job to job are under 30, and many young people place no immediate value on the things that seniority may get them. If being able to move out of a workers' dormitory into an apartment means a wait of two or three years, let us say, a young worker is probably better advised to go from job to job until he finds one whose waiting lists are shorter. It remains to be seen whether the Soviet industrial establishment will hit on the solution which American industry discovered long ago: Issue easy consumer credit and mortgages with low down payments both as an inducement to stay on the job, and even more as an inducement for workers to take a job in the area in order to qualify. While one might imagine this device to be furthest from the thoughts of Soviet economic policymakers, consumer credit and loans to the buyers of cooperative apartments have been expanding rapidly. Already one serious proposal for linking credit to stability of the borrower's employment record has appeared in the Soviet press (see the discussion of labor turnover in Chapter 5).

DISPOSABLE INCOME AND CONSUMER CHOICE

What would be the consequence of delivering a much larger share of the national income to the public in the form of earnings, pensions, and other payments, and letting a larger portion of social wage benefits be met through consumer choices? So far, cooperative housing is the one major embodiment of this principle.

The cooperative housing program was first of all an effort to direct the choices of those with savings and/or comfortable incomes. Instead of letting this money exercise an inflationary pressure on

[62]*Literaturnaya gazeta*, May 8, 1968, p. 10.

disposable consumer goods, Moscow's idea in reviving the cooperative apartment movement in the 1960's was to harness these funds to supplement an existing governmental program. Motivating the affluent to invest their funds in return for a gain in comfort was apparently far preferable to reducing inflationary pressures via the route of taxation, confiscation, or obligatory purchases of state bonds. Khrushchev was not loathe to state this reasoning publicly: "Thought should be given," he said in 1958, "to enlisting the funds of those segments of the population that have savings and need better housing."[63]

Would there be any comparable advantage in financing state-owned housing entirely or largely from rent payments, presumably controlled? What if the money spent through the state budget for housing construction and partial maintenance were paid instead to the labor force in the form of higher wages? It could also be returned to them indirectly in the form of a reduced turnover tax and cheaper consumers' goods. This would, at first glance, extend the realm of choice of families and individuals by enabling them to decide what proportion of their budgets to spend on housing. There may indeed be a good argument for this today, but the primary advantage would be sound maintenance practices rather than a better system of investment choices. The point is not so much who actually funnels the money to state construction enterprises which build housing, but who decides how much money is to be allocated and where. To permit consumers to decide the annual level of housing construction starts would be to limit the other investment choices of the state. The Soviet regime decided against this in the late 1920's and subsequently; and in view of the international crisis and war which followed, it is hardly the place of foreign critics to fault this choice. Americans should be mindful of the way in which the interest rate decisions of the Federal Reserve Board, whose actions are not subject to any kind of direct control from the White House or Congress, affect the volume of housing purchases and housing construction starts. In the Soviet Union, the supply of housing grew slowly as cities grew rapidly in population; and little was devoted to maintenance—for, as a prominent Soviet city planner told the writer, "We just didn't repair our housing, period." To have let rents seek their own level would have meant a fearful inflation in housing costs to families and individuals. To have provided materials and services

---

[63]*Pravda*, March 15, 1958.

to anyone who had money to invest in a private house would have meant diverting resources from the industrialization and rearmament drive. After World War II, some of these possible courses of action were in fact undertaken: In 1948 the building of private housing was encouraged by safeguarding the ownership through law,[64] and ten years later investment in cooperative apartments was revived by offering state loans and the services of construction organizations and local governments. To offer such a choice became possible only to the extent that resources were made available. Where part of these resources have been accumulated in the form of private savings, the area of choice could be increased further. The time may be approaching when housing specialists in *Gosplan* and elsewhere must ask themselves whether, within the limits of the materials and manpower available for housing, the Soviet state's paying out a flat 130 rubles per square meter and half the annual maintenance costs is really the most efficient way to house the nation.

Could the same reasoning be applied to medical services? There is a good deal more individual payment for medical care in the Soviet Union than one might expect. Some polyclinics do in fact have a scale of fees, and the indications are that these are enjoying increased popularity because one may choose one's own doctor. These are termed "economic-accountability" clinics, a term usually applied to any organization whose income makes it self-sustaining, whether or not this is literally the case with these clinics.[65] Medicines for use outside of hospitals and clinics must be purchased, although the cost of these is generally not high.

Some Soviet doctors accept private patients in return for privately set fees. While Soviet health authorities certainly do not encourage this, and may attempt to discourage it to the extent it detracts from physicians' staff duties, it is quite legal. Here, too, the choice of physician and the assurance of personal attention are the attractions. Solzhenitsyn argued in his novel *The Cancer Ward* (which has not been published in the Soviet Union, of course) that the fee system was one way of restoring the kind of doctor-patient relationship which in a sense is an important part of what any doctor should offer. Statistics on the extent of fee payments for medical services are not available, and it remains to be seen whether this is a growing

---

[64] *Vedomosti SSSR*, 1948, No. 36.

[65] A. Luk and V. Tardov, "The Patient and His Relatives," *Literaturnaya gazeta*, December 8, 1966.

trend or not. Unlike the area of citizen-financed housing, the area of private fee-covered medical care has received no official encouragement.

There is an important difference between private payments in these two areas, though. Cooperative and individual housing construction channel funds back into the nation's housing construction budget by removing the need for state subsidization from a portion of total construction. But as to fee-covered medical care, it is difficult to imagine that a more extensive use of fees would greatly increase the funds available for free medical care. Fees paid by individual arrangements with doctors go into individual incomes rather than being returned to state agencies. An expanding network of fee-supported clinics would in some measure reduce the pressure on state-supported medical services. But the lower ratio of patients and patient visits per doctor which the fee system encourages might mean diverting medical personnel from the state-supported sector, with a consequent deterioration of care.

The same considerations that apply to state-supported health services apply also to education. The Soviet assumption is that education is not to be treated as a commodity: fees charged at any level would fall unequally on different families, and the educational income needs of families would "hump" at certain times in a manner familiar in the United States. More important, even the highest tolerable fees would not cover more than a portion of the total educational outlay, especially in higher education. The American experience offers clear testimony: during the first half of the 1960's, student fees accounted for about one fifth of the educational and general income of all American institutions of higher learning; and this proportion does not take into account the receipt of endowment funds and grants for plant expansion.[66]

A somewhat different set of considerations applies to the services for which fees are still required in the Soviet Union: preschool facilities and boarding schools. The whole economic purpose of having comprehensive preschool facilities (as contrasted with their educational or psychological value) is that they free the beneficiary, the mother, to earn a wage. In some cases (which include friends of the writer at Moscow University) they free the mother to get a higher education and the good salary which it makes possible later on.

---

[66]*Statistical Abstract of the United States*, 88th Edition (Washington, D.C: U.S. Government Printing Office, 1967), p. 133.

Working mothers thus pay a small "tax" on the second paycheck which they bring home, but the "tax" may be justified if it makes possible the more rapid expansion of day-care facilities than the state budget alone permits. Not always, of course, is the working mother's income a second one for the family. The difference in standard of living between a one-income and a two-income family is one which will remain as long as work incentives themselves remain.

Boarding school fees, were they collected strictly according to the norms described earlier in this chapter, would take a much bigger bite out of the second income than does day care. But these fees are apparently modified downward or else waived in so many cases that this early scale may have little meaning today. In the writer's opinion, two factors inhibit the enforcement of fee collections: one is the often rather casual attitude toward collections on the part of local and institutional officials, and the other is the fact that where income from fees is small in proportion to total outlay, administrators are inclined to make many adjustments.

Soviet policymakers and economic planners can now look back on a dozen years or more of good increases in overall consumption during which the entire population, including the collective farmers and the lowest categories of pensioners, have been brought within the compass of at least minimum social wage benefits, uneven though the provision of some benefits may be from place to place. The completion of this "platform" of distribution in the latter 1960's has raised the question of what should be built upon it. If the platform is left as it is, it is possible that the gap in distribution will increase as between those who must rely on the platform and those for whom it is an adjunct to a prosperity which their labor has earned. That is, it would more and more slip into the role of "welfare" in the sense of minimum adequate distribution of the essentials for low-income groups. The increasing number of Soviet citizens who can build up savings would purchase cooperative housing in order to be freed from reliance on somewhat inferior state housing; they would purchase private medical services in order to insure greater care; they would take more expensive vacations than what trade union vacation subsidies represent. The things which they would continue to consume on an equal footing with the rest of the population would be of two types: those which cannot be improved by an outlay of personal funds, such as tuition in higher education, and those whose consumption is limited by law, of which the only important example is housing space (though not housing quality). In all other areas of consumption, the distinction between adequacy and abundance would persist and increase. Does the old Marxist watchword "to each according to his needs," the principle of communist society of the future, refer simply to a comfortable universal minimum? Or does it include all the greater material rewards which become the "needs" of those whose high incomes permit them to pursue these rewards?

.4. *Equality of Educational Choice*

Khrushchev, in pressing his 1958 campaign for educational reforms, displayed very deep concern with the low social standing of manual labor and with what he considered the needless pressure on young people to get into higher education at all costs. Secondary school graduates who go to work after graduation do this unwillingly, he said: "They look upon this as though it were an insult to them." Part of the blame for their attitude rests with their parents, who warn their children that the punishment for doing badly in school is a life of manual labor. Another substantial part of the blame is shared by the schools, said Khrushchev, which prepare their students for higher education and for nothing else. In so doing, the schools are neglecting their task of preparing students either educationally or psychologically for the world of work; the 10-year school is "divorced from the real world." Finally, in spite of all that the Soviet regime had done to open the road to higher education to the children of ordinary working people, the nation's universities and institutes still contained a far higher proportion of children of professional and white-collar people than Khrushchev was willing to call normal. Of the students in Moscow's university and institutes, he said, no more than 30 or 40 percent were the children of working-class parents. No longer were many applicants to higher education coming from the evening schools, where formerly many ordinary workers had completed secondary school and qualified themselves for further education. The regular 10-year schools were not only supplying more than enough applicants; they were also turning out hundreds of thousands of graduates every year who could not possibly be accommodated either in higher education or in the technicums (see Table 4-1). In 1957 alone, more than 800,000

Table 4-1
SECONDARY SCHOOL GRADUATIONS AND ADMISSIONS TO
HIGHER EDUCATION AND THE TECHNICUMS
(in thousands)

	Secondary School Graduations			*Admissions to Higher Education*		*Admissions to Technicums**	
Year	*General Schools*	*Part-time Schools and Others*	*Total*	*Daytime Divisions*	*Part-time and Correspondence Divisions*	*Daytime Divisions*	*Part-time and Correspondence Divisions*
1950 ...	220	22	242	228	121	350	77
1955 ...			1,246	257	204	424	164
1958 ...			1,573	216	240	364	250
1960 ...			1,000†	258	335	415	354
1965 ...	900	450	1,350	378	475	582	518
1967 ...	1,700	700	2,400	416	484	716	523

*A substantial proportion of those admitted each year have come directly from 8th grade rather than from among those who have completed secondary education. No breakdown according to level of admission is available.

†This sharp decline in graduations is the consequence of the wartime decline in births.

Source: *Narodnoye khozyaistvo SSSR* 1958, p. 835; 1961, p. 694; 1965, p. 695; Goodman and Feshbach, p. 20; U.S. Congress, Joint Economic Committee, *Soviet Economic Performance 1966-67*, pp. 83, 86.

secondary school graduates found no place in either system; during the period 1954-57 a total of 2.5 million graduates had found themselves in the same position. Often enough, Khrushchev emphasized, the decisions as to which graduates entered higher education and which did not were made not by examination scores, but by pressure from influential parents. Though Khrushchev might well have added the further criticism that the economy was in great need of skilled workers and technicians, whose ranks could be multiplied by diverting more students into the vocational schools and technicums, he chose instead to concentrate on the question of career values as such.[1]

The "extra 800,000"—those who in the summer of 1957 found no further education open to them except the vocational schools—had already created a problem *within* the 10-year schools. Up to the early 1950's, every graduate could nourish some real hope of getting into a university or institute, even if this took several years of trying. Now this hope no longer existed for many. Wrote one Leningrad school teacher at the end of the 1957-58 school year:

As recently as two or three years ago hardly any graduates even wanted to hear about a plant or factory. A person who did not gain entrance to an institute felt he had experienced a real tragedy. There were young women and even young men who lived off their parents for years and tried year after year to get into a higher educational institution, without success. I work in a school and can firmly state that the number of people who feel this way has greatly decreased. Young people have become accustomed to the idea that after they finish school they will work, and the majority of them are not afraid of work. But a new and very dangerous tendency has cropped up, which reduces to approximately the following reasoning: Since we are not going to an institute, but to a factory, there is no reason to exert ourselves; we can study any old way, just so we get a diploma . . .

Ask any teacher and he will tell you bitterly that graduating classes in recent years have been poorer than those in previous years and that many young people do little reading and are insufficiently interested in study.[2]

As the ratio of applicants to places in higher education increased, so did the devices used by parents to get their children in through influence. Here the intelligentsia possessed an enormous advantage, for it was they who had the connections and the knowledge to. do this. "In some cases." said Khrushchev to the Komsomol Congress in April 1958, "the higher educational institution accepts not the candidate who is well qualified but the one with an influential papa or mama who can help in getting son or daughter into the higher educational institution. Such a situation contradicts the very essence

---

[1] These points and the proposals cited below are a summary of two major statements by Khrushchev: his speech to the 13th Komsomol Congress, *Pravda*, April 19, 1958, and his memorandum as approved by the Party Presidium (Politburo), *Pravda*, September 21, 1958. Trans. in *CDSP* X:17, pp. 17-19, 35 (condensed), and X:38, pp. 3-8. The *CDSP* translations are used for the quotations given here.

[2] N. Dolina, "Concerning the Future of Our Schools," *Izvestiya*, June 7, 1958. Trans. from *CDSP* X:23, pp. 22-23.

of our socialist system, since often it is not the most deserving who gain admission but those who have an inside track to the people in charge of determining who is to be accepted at the higher educational institutions and who is not. This is a shameful phenomenon."[3]

The solution which Khrushchev first promoted in April 1958 would have meant a radical change in the prestigious "academic track." This was—and still is today—the track which leads directly through 10 years of full-time schooling to higher education (see Diagram 1). From the point of view of the students and their parents, this track leads preferably to the *daytime* divisions of higher education, rather than to the evening or correspondence divisions. The advantageous position of this track would have been greatly modified under Khrushchev's original proposal. From eighth grade on, everyone without exception would go to work, and those with the ambition to continue their education would attend evening schools. The earlier system of evening schools, the *rabfak* or "workers' faculties," had diminished greatly in size and importance after World War II; now it was to be revived as the "Schools of Working and Rural Youth." Even this new system would not concentrate primarily on academic preparation for higher education, since of course the universities and institutes could not accommodate all their graduates. Instead, they would mingle general education with technical and vocational training. Those of their graduates who then applied for higher education would be judged not only on the basis of their entrance examinations. The Komsomol, the trade unions, and co-workers at the factories and farms where they had been employed for two years or more would be asked to submit their evaluations. Thus, the universities and institutes, instead of being a haven for good performers in academic subjects regardless of their social attitudes or capacity for work, would be reserved for students who combined scholarship with a dedication to labor. Each would have learned a trade, practiced it, and learned something of the technology of production as well.

The responsibility for working at a regular manual occupation would not stop even with admission to higher education and the technicums, according to Khrushchev's original proposal. During their first year or two of study, students would continue to work full time; later they would be released for two or three days of the week;

[3]*Pravda*, April 19, 1958. Trans. from *CDSP* X:17, p. 17.

Diagram 1
SEQUENCE OF SOVIET EDUCATION AND VOCATIONAL TRAINING,
IN SIMPLIFIED FORM, SHOWING THE OPTIONS OPEN AT THE
EIGHTH-GRADE AND 10TH-GRADE CHOICE-POINTS; SYSTEM OF THE
LATTER 1960's.

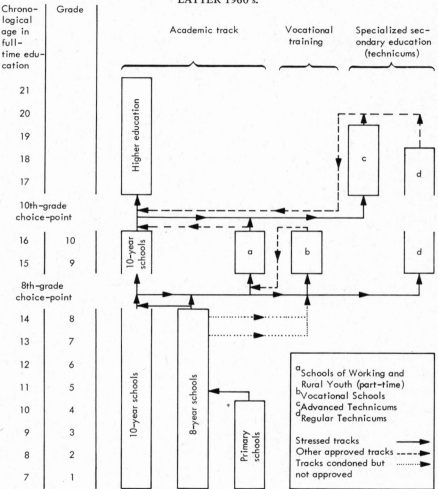

and in the final year or two of study, they could at last devote full time to classes and examinations. This, according to Khrushchev, would produce specialists who were not afraid of work and would become productive right away after graduation. It would also eliminate the great distinction in both quality and prestige between the daytime divisions of higher education on the one hand, and the evening and correspondence divisions on the other.

Khrushchev had both early Soviet educational experience and the views of Karl Marx on his side in proposing this drastic change. The Marxian view of man in the future communist society includes labor as a "prime necessity of life" rather than as just a means to existence. A harmonious society would be one in which everyone participated in producing the abundance which in turn would make communism possible. No human being could be truly human who did not participate in labor, including physical labor; and ultimately, the difference between manual and mental labor would cease to exist anyway as tasks became more complex. In *Das Kapital* Marx called for "an education that will, in the case of every child over a given age, combine productive labor with instruction and gymnastics, not only as one of the methods of adding to the efficiency of production, but as the only method of producing fully developed human beings."[4] Soviet education in the 1920's had seen widespread experiments in learning by doing and learning by observing the Soviet economy in action; but these experimental features, which in many ways followed the views of the American educator John Dewey (1859-1952), were cut short by the abrupt policy shift to a standard academic curriculum in the 1930's. The combination of general education, vocational training, and production experience was actually achieved in the communes for rehabilitating wayward youth which were begun in the latter 1920's by Anton S. Makarenko (1888-1939). His concept and his voluminous writings on the subject continued to enjoy high official and public esteem in spite of the Stalin-era policy of holding regular secondary education within a conventional academic format.

By the time the new law on education was passed in December 1958,[5] Khrushchev had been obliged to accept some very substantial modifications to the proposals he had made to the XIII Komsomol Congress the preceding April. He did, to be sure, succeed in raising the level of compulsory education to eight years from seven, and the

[4] Karl Marx, *Capital*, Vol. 1 (Moscow: Foreign Languages Publishing House, 1961), pp. 482-83. See also Friedrich Engels, *Herr Eugen Dühring's Revolution in Science* (New York: International Publishers, 1939), pp. 347-51.

[5] *Vedomosti SSSR* 1959, No. 1. The CPSU Central Committee's resolution of November 12, 1958, justifying and explaining this law, is carried in *KPSS o rabote sovetov*, 1959, pp. 564-94.

number of years in secondary education from 10 to 11. The latter change was made in order to permit the intermingling of general education with the learning of a trade and the pursuit of "polytechnical" knowledge, *i.e.,* learning the fundamentals of technology and production. The regular schools were all redesignated "Secondary, General-Education, Labor, and Polytechnical Schools," a designation which they still carry in spite of the subsequent abandonment of many features of the 1958 reform. But already by September 1958 Khrushchev had conceded that some secondary schools would offer grades 9-11 on a full-time basis; and to this extent, some of the existing 10-year schools would be retained simply by enabling them to add an 11th year. The curricula for grades 9-11 which were drawn up in 1959 and subsequently hardly met Khrushchev's criteria of combining education with production experience. By and large, they still represented the "general acquaintance of the students with various types of work done by adults," itself no novelty in Soviet education, which Khrushchev's September memorandum had criticised as inadequate.[6] For the most part, the existing 10-year schools were simply adapted to the 11-year format. The total of hours of instruction in standard academic subjects was not reduced, either, but was simply stretched out over the three years. The schools for gifted children likewise were retained, a concession already made by Khrushchev in his September memorandum.

Secondary evening schools were now revived and rapidly expanded under their new designation of "Schools for Working and Rural Youth." The November 1958 Central Committee resolution had declared these to be part of the "basic track," the track which would receive primary emphasis. Students finishing the eight-year schools would *first* acquire a manual skill on the job, preferably with the help of evening vocational training, and *only then* complete their secondary education. The other two tracks were to be completion of grades 9-11 on a full-time basis, and entry into a four-year technicum, whose completion also counted as the completion of secondary education.[7] But the distinction between full-time and part-time education remained, as did the vast difference in quality

---

[6] For a detailed analysis of curriculum changes during this period see Dewitt, 1961, pp. 103-12.

[7] *KPSS o rabote sovetov*, 1959, p. 574.

between the two. The 10-year schools remained, albeit in their new 11-year form, with a curriculum placing additional stress on labor experience and knowledge of technology. Their teaching and administrative staffs remained too, the same personnel which according to Khrushchev regarded their task as one of preparing students for higher education.

In Khrushchev's original proposal, every student who completed secondary school would already have at least two years of work experience behind him. Consequently, the much-discussed, much-readjusted, two-year work experience requirement was not part of his original (April 1958) proposals concerning admission to higher education. As a matter of fact, the preference in admissions for those with work experience was already part of the Ministry of Higher Education's regulations at that point.[8] Khrushchev proposed simply that evaluations of the applicant's work record be made part of the criteria for admission. But the decision to retain full-time secondary education posed a different problem: Would those who completed all 11 years on a full-time basis be expected to complete two years of work before they could be considered by the universities and institutes? After all, these would probably include the best academic performers, among them the nation's future physicists, mathematicians, and other much-needed specialists. Would two years of production work benefit either the students' subsequent performance, the factories and farms where they would work, the public's and the Party's feelings about equal opportunity, or their own social attitudes, to the extent that a break in their formal full-time education was worthwhile?

The law of December 1958 made some concessions in the matter of higher education admissions, too. It did not make two years of production experience mandatory, but simply recommended that preference be given to those with work experience, and specified no length of time. While it also incorporated the idea of recommendations from one's place of employment as a criterion for admission, it said nothing about the weight to be assigned to them, or the manner in which they were to be evaluated.[9] Actually, the work-requirement provision was already being used by some Soviet

---

[8] *Izvestiya*, June 2, 1957 . Trans. in *CDSP* IX:22, p. 16.
[9] Article 28 of the law, *Vedomosti SSSR* 1959, No. 1.

universities and institutes, and from 1955 on the admissions regulations of the Ministry of Higher Education had given some preference to applicants with work experience or with a record of military service. The system of recommendations, for its part, had been extensively used before the mid-1930's.[10] What happened as the reform law went into effect was that the Ministry of Higher Education decided to admit at least 20 percent of all matriculants directly from secondary school, primarily those entering in mathematics and the exact sciences. In practice, much was left to the discretion of individual institutions, which in effect grouped their applicants into those with and without work experience, then decided on admissions for each group separately.[11]

As regards Khrushchev's idea that the first one or two years of higher education be pursued on a part-time basis, together with a regular production job, the reform law left to individual institutions the particular form of combining work and study. Here, too, those in mathematics and the exact sciences were specifically exempt from the work requirement. Those in the social sciences, humanities, and law were required by the Central Committee resolution, but not by the law, to combine work and study in a manner to be determined by their institutions.[12] The law did not, however, eradicate the distinction between the daytime divisions of higher education and the evening and correspondence divisions. Here, too, the difference in educational quality and opportunity which Khrushchev had sought to abolish was preserved with only certain modifications. Even the modifications were not so firmly fixed in law that they bound the policies and preferences of the Ministry of Higher Education.

In 1965, a bare seven years later, the Ministry of Higher Education found part-time higher education to be substantially inferior to full-time education, and it pressed for a proportionate increase in the latter. In the evening and correspondence institutions of the Russian Republic, according to an official Ministry statement, "may be observed low rates of attainment and a large number of failures; admission is carried on without any competition in fact; and a

---

[10]Dewitt, 1961, pp. 246-50?; *Vestnik vysshei shkoly,* No. 8 (August, 1957), pp. 3-10.

[11]The admissions rules for 1959-60 are carried in Dewitt, 1961, pp. 629-34.

[12]Arts. 30 and 35 of the law. *KPSS o rabote sovetov,* 1959, p. 589.

considerable number of students are taking subjects which do not correspond to the specialties in which they are working."[13] The next year a Party resolution affirmed these findings, suggested that there is a greater investment per student in part-time education, and authorized the Ministry henceforth to stress development of full-time education. The same applied to the technicums, which are also under the Ministry's jurisdiction (technically it is the "Ministry for Higher and Specialized Secondary Education").[14] Combining work and studies, whether or not it was found to be producing the desired attitudes among students, was definitely found to be producing inferior education.

As regards the secondary schools, the first legislative step toward reversing Khrushchev's reforms came even before the ebullient First Secretary was deposed; this was the reduction of secondary education to its original 10-year period, a move which was carried out between 1964 and 1966.[15] The inevitable consequence was abandonment of the idea that each graduate of the full-time secondary schools have learned a manual skill by the time he graduated. A law of 1966 formally removed the vocational training requirement, while leaving such training as a matter of local option "where the right circumstances are present." This still left the regular schools with the obligatory triple function of providing (1) general education, (2) polytechnic education, and (3) something which may be translated literally as "labor upbringing" *(trudovoye vospitaniye)*, the inculcation of positive attitudes toward labor.[16]

One may not justifiably conclude that the Marxian concept of education had been a failure, for the evidence suggests that few Soviet schools were in a position to give it a full trial. Their greatest single obstacle had been the difficulty of organizing effective vocational training, although there was the further problem of trying to interest university-bound students in making use of what training the schools could offer. Simply locating or organizing facilities was quite a problem in itself. At best, only a narrow range of specialties

[13] *Vestnik vysshei shkoly*, No. 9 (September, 1965), pp. 82-83.

[14] *Vestnik vysshei shkoly*, No. 9 (September, 1966), pp. 3-6. The law concerning the technicums is in *Vedomosti SSSR* 1967, No. 32.

[15] CPSU Central Committee resolution of August 10, 1964. *Spravochnik partiinogo rabotnika, vyp.*6 (Moscow: Politizdat, 1966), pp. 357-58. A year later, an exception was made for the three Baltic republics, which chose to retain the 11-year system. *Vedomosti SSSR* 1965, No. 32.

[16] Decree of March 14, 1966, *Vedomosti SSSR* 1966, No. 12.

could be offered within each school. What of the future electronics technician whose school offers instruction only in tractor driving and maintenance? Also, trades could not be effectively learned in the number of hours allotted to them, in view of the increasingly specialized knowledge demanded by most. The administrative problem of linking training to local job markets proved to be particularly knotty.[17] But in the writer's opinion, the real problem of this central feature of the 1958 reforms was the motivational one. Students and teachers alike in the 9th through 11th grades were justified in asking just what relation either vocational or polytechnical education, in the form in which they were offered, bore to their careers and aspirations. Did they meet the needs even of those students who were content to learn a manual trade?

The 1966 curriculum readjustment reduced the time occupied by actual instruction in labor skills from 18 percent to 7 percent of total instructional time for all 10 years of school. According to the Russian Republic's model curriculum of 1966, teaching related to labor skills and observation of production processes occupied two hours per week in each of the 10 grades, out of a total weekly instructional time of 24 hours (in grades 1-4) and 30 hours (in grades 6-10). U.S.S.R. Minister of Public Education Prokof'yev reported in 1968 that the regular schools' role in vocational and technical education would henceforth be a quite limited one. More stress, he said, will be placed on *observation* of technical applications of principles learned in the standard curriculum. While general education will still be directed toward preparation for manual skills, as a rule vocational specialties will be acquired after completion of either an 8-year school or a 10-year school rather than before.[18]

There are some countertrends as well. Some secondary schools have recently received large-scale investments in vocational training facilities in an effort to give their students real training in production. When the Party announced the sweeping modification of polytechnical education in 1966, it encouraged those schools which had already found or built "production bases" to keep them and improve them. In Moscow, for example, about one quarter of the secondary schools have established technical training either in

---

[17]*Komsomol'skaya pravda*, February 21, 1964; Medved'yev, 1962; article by L. N. Kogan in Osipov, 1966, p. 203.

[18]Prokof'yev, 1967, p. 91; *Izvestiya*, July 3, 1968; *Vestnik vysshei shkoly*, No. 9 (September, 1966), pp. 7-8.

cooperation with regular enterprises, or in special "production-training combines." The Latvian school system has been developing a production training approach all its own. From time to time the press and specialized journals have carried accounts of experiments in given cities which bring secondary students into local factories in a relationship which is determined by the individual schools and factories involved.[19]

Clearly new emphasis has been placed on increasing the number of secondary school graduates rather than trying to divert a certain proportion to strictly vocational training after the 8th grade. While figures on the proportion of eighth-graders who go directly on to ninth grade do not indicate how many ultimately graduate, still they suggest a dramatic rise in the number of graduates. From 58 percent in 1965 it rose to nearly 68 percent in 1967. Prokof'yev foresees a 75 percent level as a goal for the near future.[20] If one considers also the recent efforts of the vocational school system to combine vocational training with the completion of secondary education (as compared with the 1958 reforms' stress on *postponement* of the latter, and the priority for vocational training alone) it is no surprise that the proportion of secondary school completions is increasing rapidly.[21] It is likewise no surprise that the phenomenon of frustrated secondary school graduates continues as a social problem, the same problem which Khrushchev had attempted to confront squarely in 1958. Are the secondary schools still turning out graduates who are highly motivated to continue in the universities and institutes (those who have any real chance of being admitted, anyway) but who are poorly motivated to do anything else?

A look at Table 4-1 above will show that the pressure for admission to higher education is likely to remain high. Of the 2.4 million secondary school graduates of 1967, less than half could have been admitted to the *daytime* divisions of both higher and specialized secondary institutions, even if they were all qualified. In 1950 the ratio of all higher education admissions to secondary school

[19] N. Aleksandrov, Deputy Minister of Public Education for the Russian Republic, in *Pravda*, January 6, 1969. *Shkola i proizvodstvo*, No. 5 (May, 1966), pp. 11-14; No. 1 (January, 1968), pp. 30-32; No. 7 (July, 1968), pp. 3-12.

[20] Goodman and Feshbach, 1967, p. 5; *Izvestiya*, July 3, 1968; Prokof'yev, 1967, p. 87.

[21] In 1968-69 only 150 vocational schools were offering the final years of secondary school along with vocational training, and early in 1969 a national conference of vocational training personnel was held in Riga to debate the expansion of this system. "A Skill Plus a Secondary School Diploma," *Izvestiya*, February 28, 1969.

graduations was roughly 1.6:1, that is, there were far more places than graduates; in 1958 it was 1:3.6, in 1960 a much lower 1:1.7, due to the wartime birth deficit, and in 1967 and 1968 it was back up to 1:2.7. The corresponding ratios for admission to the *daytime* divisions of higher education were 1:1 in 1950, 1:7 in 1958, 1:4 in 1960, and 1:6 in 1967.[22]

The Party chief of Irkutsk Province furnished an interesting case history of the drive to get into higher education at all costs. In the summer of 1967, he wrote, 13,000 of the students who had graduated that June from the secondary schools of Irkutsk Province did not, for whatever reason, enter higher or specialized secondary education. He did not give the total number of graduates, but if one assumes that Irkutsk is typical of the nation in its ratio of graduates to population, this would have been between 15 and 20 percent of the graduating class. Of these, 3,000 did not seek employment, but rather stayed home at the insistence of their parents in order to prepare for the entrance examinations which would enable them to get into higher education. The other 10,000 went to work, mainly in the Province's industries. The better part of those who did so, in the opinion of this official, regarded their employment as a temporary thing; consequently, they made no serious effort to improve their job qualifications. Both production industries and construction projects sponsor on-the-job training programs (*uchebnye kombinaty*) which include both formal course work and supervisory instruction for young workers both individually and in brigades. Such programs, the official believed, are a stopgap measure at best, and do not succeed in instilling either fundamental knowledge or good working habits. Furthermore, few of the young people of this age (18 or so) stay more than three years at any given place of employment. Of the 270,000 young workers who in the period 1961-68 have been in such training programs anywhere in the province, only 30,000 were still on the jobs for which they had been trained at the end of this period. The Party official disagreed with those who defend such improvised training as being adapted to situations in which high labor turnover is likely to occur anyway. While the training programs themselves cost rather little, there is a much larger cost in terms of delay in production schedules, and in damage to equipment and output, that

---

[22]U.S. Congress, Joint Economic Committee, *Soviet Economic Performance: 1966-67*, pp. 83, 86; ratios computed. *Ekonomicheskaya gazeta*, No. 5 (January, 1969), p. 7.

comes from using inadequately trained and poorly motivated young workers.[23]

There is irresponsibility on the part of employers too, however. Many enterprises contribute to the problem of drifting youth by refusing employment to young people of this type, especially the adolescents. It is true that some enterprises have devoted particular care to their adolescent workers above and beyond what is required by law (see the system of "counselors" described in Chapter 5). But many other enterprises still see mainly a liability and an expense in hiring them.

GUIDANCE FOR FUTURE WORKERS

Vocational Guidance: Good, Bad, and Nonexistent. In the early 1960's, the economist Vladimir N. Shubkin led a group of social scientists at Novosibirsk University in the career aspiration survey of secondary school students in that area whose results are described later in this chapter. Among other things, the survey dealt directly with the matter of environmental influences on career aspirations, including the influence of parental occupations and background. It was prompted by concern with the persistent problems of young people in finding careers, and with the lack of connection in so many instances between the motivations that schools foster and the jobs available to graduates. Among other things, it sought a definite answer to Siberia's problem of high labor turnover. In evaluating the survey's results, Shubkin argued strongly for improvements in formal vocational counseling:

In the mid-1930's work on vocational guidance and vocational counseling was to all intents and purposes halted in our country. In criticizing the pedologists, the baby was thrown out with the bath water. In our view this was a mistake. It is precisely a socialist society that offers the opportunity and feels the necessity for systematic scientific study of the preferences, abilities and interests of school-children. Without this we cannot make full use of each individual's abilities and talents. This work should help boys and girls to find their calling, to choose occupations that are necessary to society, and that will provide them with satisfaction.[24]

---

[23] Pavel B. Katsuba in *Izvestiya*, April 16, 1968.

[24] Shubkin, 1965, p. 62. Trans. from *CDSP* XVII:30, p. 5. "What Can Be Done About the Question 'What Shall I Become?'" *Literaturnaya gazeta*, March 19, 1969.

If there is such a thing as a truly professional career guidance counselor in the Soviet school system, the writer has not yet discovered any. What formal guidance is available may be found in school-sponsored extracurricular interest groups, and in special after-school programs to which people of different vocations and students from various branches of higher education are invited to speak.[25] Shubkin proposed in 1968 that the post of guidance counselor be established, "a specialist with a higher degree in education, a good knowledge of developmental psychology, medicine, techniques of discovering individual capacities, the requirements of various professions, and labor force needs." He would integrate the work of teachers and interest groups, and develop contacts with parents and employers. Up to now many schools have failed to take into consideration either individual aptitudes or local employment opportunities. Consequently, they give little support to graduates who go to work directly from secondary school.[26] In 1969 a Deputy Minister of Education for the Russian Republic described a poll of a sample of upperclass students in various areas of the Republic which, in his view, showed that career guidance does not take sufficient account of actual job opportunities in definite areas. Many schools provide only university-oriented career guidance, and deliberately•avoid encouraging those graduates who want to find jobs in industry.[27] Another frequent problem is that there is no easy source from which teachers and parents in many areas can get information about the local employment picture.[28] During the 1960's there was considerable public debate on the fundamental question of whether or not there is any purpose to establishing a long-term vocational inclination in a teenager of 15 or 16, an age at which many of them might be better advised to postpone such a choice and continue their general education.[29]

The one kind of uniform pressure which is widely used in the regular secondary schools is the drive to get large numbers of graduates into higher education. Table 4-1 and the data given below

---

[25]*Shkola i proizvodstvo*, No. 2 (February, 1968), pp. 7-9.

[26]Shubkin is quoted and paraphrased by T. Kozhevnikova, "A Bird in the Hand," *Pravda*, August 1, 1968.

[27]N. Akeksandrov in *Pravda*, January 6, 1969.

[28]Kozhevnikova, *op. cit.*

[29]Part of this debate is translated in *CDSP XV:20, pp. 14-16.*

show that much of this effort is misplaced in view of the strict numerical limitations on admissions to higher education for any given year. The tendency among school administrators to measure their success by the proportion of graduates which goes on to the universities is familiar enough in American high schools as well. Another feature familiar to Americans is the special-track or quality schools which are part of the school systems of the larger Soviet cities. Competition for entrance to these schools is keen, and virtually all of their graduates enter higher education directly afterwards. The picture gained by the writer from Soviet students, educators, and educational journals is that somewhat too much motivation is provided for university entrance, far too little for making vocational choices which do not involve higher education, and not nearly enough for those who have already left school and are making their way in the world of work.[30]

Those Who Leave School. Data on school leaving show that this is a substantial but not catastrophic problem, furthermore that it is probably diminishing. School success rates—the percent of each class which finishes 8th grade or 10th grade in the regular schools—appear to have been improving markedly during the 1960's. Success rate statistics, unfortunately, are not presented in systematic form in the annual Soviet statistical abstract, or in any other publication that the writer has so far discovered. Furthermore, it is difficult to derive them from the data which the abstract does furnish on the number of students at various grade levels in different types of schools.

Khrushchev reported in 1958 that in recent years, about 80 percent of those entering school finished seventh grade, which at that time was the limit of compulsory education. This figure included those who finished after repeating one or more grades.[31] The success rate for the compulsory level of schooling during the 1960's has been closer to 90 than to 80 percent, in this case reckoned on the basis of eighth grade completions, the level which became compulsory starting in 1959. The class which entered first grade in 1959, the year of the transition to obligatory eight-year education, ended its eight years of school in 1967 with an 88 percent success rate. Of those who finished, about 80 percent continued in either ninth grade or a technicum; an unspecified part of the remaining 20 percent entered

---

[30] See the situation described by Russian Republic Minister of Public Education Danilov, *Narodnoye obrazovaniye,* No. 8, 1968, p. 10.

[31] *Pravda,* April 19, 1958.

the vocational schools. The class which finished eighth grade in 1968, according to the writer's calculations, displayed a virtually identical success rate. Each of these classes, therefore, produced about a half million school leavers.[32] Regional variations in success rates are suggested by provincial and city data, generally from those areas which have an above average rate. Thus, in Voronezh Province the eighth-grade success rate for 1968 was 93 percent, with 71 percent of the eighth-grade graduates continuing secondary education.[33] Data on continuance of education from eighth grade to either ninth grade or the technicums shows that the proportion continuing its secondary education without interruption has been rising dramatically. From what was probably under 70 percent in the early 1960's, it rose to the 80 percent level already mentioned, and the Russian Republic Minister of Education expressed his hope that within his enormous Republic it would be up to 88 percent in 1970. The median years of school completed by the population over 16 years old was 5.9 in 1960, 6.6 in 1965, and, according to one detailed American analysis, will reach 8.4 in 1985; and these averages would be substantially higher if they included only the working-age population, or the population under 50.[34] Here, too, there are wide regional variations. In the Mordvin Autonomous Republic, which apparently has a very good educational system, over 99 percent continued their secondary education immediately after finishing eighth grade in 1967. For the Chuvash Autonomous Republic the proportion was 97 percent, for Rostov Province 93 percent, and in Moscow and the larger cities of the European U.S.S.R. the proportion has been consistently above 90 percent during the 1960's.[35] In rural Volynya Province only 18 percent went on to ninth grade in the regular schools, and an unspecified proportion to the technicums, while in industrial Donetsk Province 60 percent went to ninth grade, and again an unspecified proportion to the technicums.[36]

Success rates for the 10th grade are of course lower, but they

[32] *Narodnoye obrazovaniye*, No. 5, 1968, p. 18; No. 7, 1968, p. 14; No. 8, 1968, p. 8. *Izvestiya,* January 25, 1968 and January 26, 1969. *Narodnoye khozyaistvo SSSR,* 1965, p. 678.

[33] *Narodnoye obrazovaniye*, No. 8, 1968, p. 9.

[34] *Izvestiya,* July 3, 1968; U.S. Congress, Joint Economic Committee, *Soviet Economic Performance: 1966-67,* 1968, pp. 79-81, 88.

[35] *Narodnoye obrazovaniye* No. 8, 1968, p. 8.

[36] *Narodnoye obrazovaniye* No. 7, 1968, p. 14; No. 9, 1968, p. 8.

appear to have been improving rapidly during the 1960's. While exact calculations are hampered here also by lack of statistics on entering classes taken by themselves, the probable 1.8 million students who finished an uninterrupted, full-time regular secondary education in 1968 represented a success rate of about 40 percent. Data from the Novosibirsk study of career plans (described below) show that the 10th-grade graduating class of 1958 contained only 13 percent of the entering class, while the 10th-grade class of 1963-64 (there were 11 grades at this point) had retained about 20 percent of its original number.[37] The *overall* success ratio, which includes those who finish their secondary education later on in night school, in the technicums, or otherwise, may have been on the order of 60 percent. Of the 3.1 million who completed secondary education in 1967, for example, some 700,000 graduated in night school or in other special programs and a further 685,000 graduated from the technicums. Of these approximately 1.4 million graduates outside the regular full-time school system, nearly all had taken more than 10 years to finish their secondary education. For want of data on the distribution of these graduates by entering class, it is impossible to work them into the overall success ratios for separate classes.[38]

Another dimension of the school-leaving situation is furnished by figures on the number of adolescents aged 15 through 17 in the labor force (not including the labor force of collective farms), those who otherwise would be students in grades 8 through 10 of the daytime schools, or in the technicums. In 1961, the most recent year for which data are available, these amounted to 527,000, or .8 percent of the labor force, a sharp drop from 819,000 just three years earlier, the latter figure probably having been typical of the level of the 1950's.[39] Part of these were continuing their secondary education in evening and correspondence divisions of the general secondary schools and the technicums. An additional number was getting industrial training in the evening divisions of vocational schools.

A Leningrad Party official described the situation of the 3,000

---

[37]*Pravda*, January 26, 1969; *Narodnoye khozyaistvo SSSR*, 1965, p. 678; Shubkin, 1965, pp. 62 ff.

[38]Data given in U.S. Congress, Joint Economic Committee, *Soviet Economic Performance: 1966-67*, pp. 83, 86.

[39]Tsentral'noye statisticheskoye upravleniye . . . , *Zhenshchiny i deti v SSSR*, 1963, p. 164; *Narodnoye khozyaistvo SSSR* 1961, p. 567; 1965, p. 558.

school dropouts in that city as of 1965, meaning in this case those who had left school before completing eighth grade. This represented less than 1 percent of the total number of school-age children, he wrote, but nevertheless it was a number substantial enough to arouse his concern. A survey showed that a large number of the dropouts' parents showed a careless or negative attitude toward education. Often parents would take their children out of school and permit them to get jobs simply because they were doing poorly in school. The enterprises which hired them could not train them for ordinary workers' skills because of their deficiencies in mathematics and the basic sciences; consequently, they were given auxiliary and maintenance jobs. The need of enterprises for unskilled labor is, of course, dropping sharply. For example, the Leningrad Metalworks in 1958 employed 110 workers with only primary education, but as of 1965 there were only two. While it was still possible for the dropouts to finish eighth grade or complete their secondary education in evening and alternate-shift schools, many simply lost any remaining urge to study, and dropped out of these schools as well. The official supported present methods of motivating children to stay in school while at the same time urging their intensification: special teachers' training for dealing with difficult cases; a "big brother" program sponsored by enterprises and the Komsomol; and work by voluntary school-assistance committees, which are the equivalent of the Parent-Teacher or Home and School Associations in the United States, but operate within the framework of places of employment.[40]

The public discussion of the school-leaving problem has focused exclusively on readjusting incentives, positive and negative; there has been scarcely any mention of applying compulsion to either children or parents. Although many of the school leavers drop their studies without asking permission of the school authorities, no formal action appears to be required of the authorities in these cases. The writer has neither read nor heard of any suggestion that administrative penalties and procedures would be of any use here. On the other hand, there have been some proposals to reduce the attractiveness of work for school leavers. Those who leave before finishing eighth

---

[40]Yu. Lavrikov, Secretary of the Leningrad City Party Committee, in *Pravda*, June 17, 1965, p. 2.

grade receive the same wage as any other worker; consequently, some commentators have proposed that their wage incentive be reduced.[41] The teen-ager is accepted into industrial instruction courses and into some vocational schools with no questions asked, in spite of the fact that the latter are not authorized to accept students who have not finished eighth grade. Employers often do not take a worker's level of formal education into account in making promotions and granting pay raises. The needs of the Soviet Union's labor-hungry economy and the success of some teen-agers, at least, in getting well-paying initial jobs make them a positive rather than a negative example for others still in school who may be tempted to leave.

Commentators on this problem recognize that the temptation of a pay envelope is not the only motive for dropping out. The schools themselves share the blame in several ways. Poor organization of education and inadequate investment in facilities in some places create an environment in which 15-year-olds see no point in continuing. Even completion of secondary education would not enable the graduates of some local systems to compete effectively with other graduates for admission to higher education. There are schools which attempt to get rid of their poor students rather than devote the extra attention necessary to retain them. Insufficient attention to career motivations programs in the school system, and lack of support from the parents of dropouts and potential dropouts, are also mentioned frequently. To American teachers and school administrators, this catalogue of reasons should be depressingly familiar. An additional reason for school leaving which perhaps occupies a more important place in Soviet education than in American schools is the rigor with which academic performance is used as the criterion of promotion from grade to grade. Such is the writer's impression, in any case, from conversations and published commentary.[42]

Goals and Problems of Part-Time Education. If the motivations to finish eighth grade are so weak for many students by comparison with the attraction of leaving and getting a job, the motivations offered a teen-age worker to combine work and further education are likewise criticized as insufficient. Both the Schools of Working and

---

[41]B. Viktorov, "A Teen-Ager Quits School," *Pravda,* February 2, 1967; K. Kentskii, "Adult Schools Await Aid," *Pravda*, July 19, 1968.

[42]*Pravda*, November 30, 1962; February 6, 1963. Trans. in *CDSP* XIV:49, p. 21, and XV:6, pp. 37-38. B. Viktorov, *op.cit.*

Rural Youth (evening secondary schools) and the evening divisions of the technicums offer the possibility of completing secondary education. The former offer the standard academic curriculum, the latter various technical curriculums more advanced than those of the vocational schools. The Schools of Working and Rural Youth, successors to the "workers' schools" (*rabfak*) of the 1920's and 1930's, offer anyone who has completed the eighth grade the opportunity of completing a regular secondary education in the evening, or at hours accommodating work shifts. After the near-demise of these schools during the World War II period, they were revived and upgraded in the 1950's; their evening and correspondence enrollment in 1967-68 was some 4.5 million, nearly 10 percent of the total enrollment in all primary and secondary education. The present policy objective is to improve their curriculum to the point where it is the full equivalent of grades 9-10 in the regular schools. Under the 1958 educational reforms, students in the part-time schools were given a somewhat reduced work week plus special leave benefits for taking examinations. Under legislation of the mid-1950's, workers under 18 are restricted to a six-hour working day and are assured a whole calendar month of annual leave. In 1967, all the part-time secondary schools (evening, alternate-shift, seasonal, and correspondence schools) graduated 700,000 students, as compared with 1.7 million graduating from the regular full-time secondary schools.[43]

While the evening schools' quantitative contribution to secondary education is substantial, still such education is by all accounts as difficult a road for teen-agers and somewhat older workers as is part-time education anywhere. Attendance rates are well below those of the regular daytime schools, and the quality of instruction is a problem. The weariness and boredom of the students take their toll. The students are generally those who have done poorly in the regular schools. According to the director of one evening school, they include a high proportion of the "difficult" adolescents whose parents have put them to work for want of a better way of dealing with them. Another factor affecting their quality is that employers have no particular motivation to accommodate worker-students in this category because they consider that they derive little or no

---

[43]*Izvestiya*, July 3, 1968; DeWitt, 1961, pp. 90-97; U.S. Congress, Joint Economic Committee, *Soviet Economic Performance, 1966-67*, p. 86.

immediate benefit from the schools' largely academic curriculum. The students themselves are likely to be motivated to end their careers as workers as soon as they can qualify for a technicum or institute.

Evening schools at the secondary level are particularly dependent on the resources and attention devoted to them by the enterprises in which their students work. The most important services rendered by enterprises are those of providing space, publicizing the schools' offerings, seeing to it that the young workers attending school are put on shifts which do not interfere with their studies, and assuring them time off for examinations and other school-related activities. In some cases, it is the practice to give worker-students inducements to study, such as priority in the distribution of resort passes. Whether industries actually provide these things depends on the extent of their resources, the inclinations of their directors, and the degree to which trade unions are willing to press for secondary education for young workers. The evening schools generally have a higher rate of school leaving and of nonpromotion from grade to grade than do the full-time secondary schools. Teachers are sometimes motivated to assign grades leniently—to give passing "3's" instead of failing "2's", mainly—since their jobs depend on the number of students they teach.[44]

VOCATIONAL TRAINING: DEAD END OR DOORWAY?

The vocational schools (*professional'no-tekhnicheskiye uchilishcha*) are administered separately from the Soviet Union's regular primary and secondary education system. They are the successors to the former Labor Reserve Schools, and they have offered a one-to-three-year program which now is being extended to a two-to-four-year format. Their new curriculum will include a certain amount of general secondary education. Entrants are expected to have completed eighth grade in the regular schools, but many who have dropped out of lower grades are in fact accepted. The vocational system has been expanding rapidly in the 1950's and 1960's. Admissions nearly doubled between 1958 and 1968, rising from

•[44] K. Kentskii, "Adult Schools Await Aid," *Pravda*, July 19, 1968; B. Viktorov, *op. cit.*; Kh. Tammiste, "Why Desks Are Unoccupied in the Evening Schools," *Pravda*, January 28, 1969; *Sem'ya i shkola*, No. 8, 1966, pp. 8-10; Dewitt, 1961, pp. 95-96; L. Tairov, "Not Good Deeds, But a Duty," *Pravda*, October 21, 1968.

691,000 to 1,325,000. The figures seem to indicate that over 90 percent of the trainees ultimately graduates; in any case, graduations during this same decade have been nearly equal to admissions in any given year.[45] Over 80 percent of the trainees admitted have been male, and well over half are from rural areas. The need for semiskilled labor with formal training is very great, and it has been so for many years. While the head of the nation's vocational training system estimated in 1968 that two thirds of all industrial workers ought properly to have completed a vocational course, as opposed to on-the-job training, clearly only a small proportion of the present industrial labor force has come out of the vocational schools. Enrollment has been lagging behind manpower needs in spite of its rapid increase. The drafting of teen-agers into vocational schools under the old Labor Reserve system, instituted in 1940 to supplement the "labor freeze" of that year, was abolished in 1955.[46]

There are a number of reasons for this lag. First of all, investment in vocational schools has been inadequate. At the end of 1968, a planning official reported that the program for building up the vocational school system was far behind. Only half of the funds allocated for building new schools were being spent, and even less in some republics. Existing schools were characterized as having outmoded curricula and materials.[47]

Another problem, much harder to solve through national policy channels, is the poor public image of vocational training. The Party chief of Irkutsk Province quoted above described the vocational schools' general lack of popularity, even among parents who themselves are industrial workers of long experience. Their enrollment level has been static in the province for years, and even this level is hard to maintain. For the most part, the students who attend vocational schools in Irkutsk are orphans or half-orphans, plus those whom the regular schools got rid of somehow. The vocational system gives competent training, he wrote, and of those graduates who have gone to work in the province's industries, nearly all have become skilled, dedicated workers. But their annual contribution to

---

[45] *Narodnoye khozyaistvo*, 1962, pp. 474-76; 1964, pp. 568, 570; 1965, pp. 583-85; *Pravda*, July 24, 1968, p. 3.

[46] Decree of March 18, 1955. *Sbornik zakonov SSSR 1938-67* (Moscow: Izvestiya, 1968), Vol. 2, p. 179.

[47] Report by P. A. Rozenko, chairman of the Planning and Budgetary Commission of the Soviet of the Union (of the USSR Supreme Soviet), *Izvestiya*, December 12, 1968.

the industries' annual labor recruitment needs is quite small: 10 percent in production industries, and a mere 3 to 4 percent in construction. Industrial enterprises themselves tend to neglect the vocational schools. While the Irkutsk Machine-Building plant renders various kinds of support to nine general education schools under the arrangement known as "patronage" (*shefstvo*), it has no similar arrangements with any vocational schools, even though the latter are the source of its best qualified ordinary workers of the near future. But how, he asked, can this meager flow of trained labor be increased?

The whole problem, the official continued, is that attendance at vocational schools does not count as completion of a student's secondary education. The vocational schools do not confer the secondary education diploma (*attestat*) on their graduates, nor are graduates otherwise entitled to apply to the universities if they later wish to do so. The vocational schools are a dead end; the vocational student knows that he is closing the door on further education unless he wishes to sacrifice yet another two years after completion of vocational education. Completion of secondary education in night schools is not only difficult, but unsatisfactory because the evening schools themselves are inadequate. Therefore, it is no surprise that students who have finished eighth grade often prefer to get a temporary job simply in order to avoid losing these years in their education.[48] In 1968, one out of every four trainees in urban vocational schools was simultaneously enrolled in the evening divisions of secondary school, so as not to abandon the possibility of advancing beyond the kind of jobs to which vocational education alone would restrict them.[49]

The attitudes of teachers and administrators in the regular schools has definitely not favored vocational education as a valid choice for any but the academically very weak students. Gennadi V. Osipov, head of the Soviet Sociological Association, said in 1969 that the school system is not motivating enough young people to go to work in industry upon completion of their secondary education: "One-sidedness in the development of our educational system has created a situation in which a considerable proportion of young

---

[48]Pavel B. Katsuba, Secretary of the Irkutsk Province Party Committee, in *Izvestiya*, April 16, 1968.

[49]*Pravda*, July 24, 1968.

people who graduate from secondary school are not oriented toward working in the sphere of produ؟tion. As a result there is emerging a labor shortage in plants and factoͰies." Those who do enter industry often do not find jobs corresponding to their educational attainment. The result is a "noncorrespondence between the potential of a worker and his actual working conditions, which after a certain time impels him to change jobs."[50]

Parental attitudes generally reinforce the attitudes of school personnel, and this is reflected in the Novosibirsk study (see below). This is the subject of frequent comment in the press. A provincial Party official stated that on the basis of his research, "very few families of professional and white-collar workers, especially in the cities, see their children's future in workers' occupations."[51] The social pressure which this has exerted on the young people themselves is understandable, particularly in the large cities, which produce the highest share of 10th-grade graduates and university entrants per class. A Leningrad schoolteacher wrote of the social gulf which she had observed between those who finish secondary school and those who leave school for work:

Only a few years ago there was a great gulf between the 10th-grade students and young workers. This gulf was so deep that young people's newspapers sometimes had to answer such questions from readers as: "Can a schoolgirl have a boyfriend who is a worker?" or, "I have a job and study at night, while a friend of mine is a full-time student and does not work. He is condemned for having me as a friend. Is this right?" etc. This petty, overbearing, and contemptuous attitude toward labor and working people among our youth is rarely encountered now. It is on the way out . . .[52]

In view of all these circumstances, it is not surprising that the educational level, aptitude, and motivation of vocational school trainees have been well below the level of their peers in the regular schools and technicums. This is both a cause and result of the circumstance that in spite of the obligatory eighth-grade education required by the 1958 reforms, the vocational schools during the 1960's apparently made a practice of accepting substantial numbers

[50]*Pravda*, January 11, 1969.

[51]P. Yermishin, "Through the Prism of the Average Grade," *Pravda*, December 26, 1968.

[52]N. Dolina, "Seventeen-Year-Olds," *Pravda*, January 10, 1962. Trans. from *CDSP* XIV:2, p. 9.

of dropouts from the regular schools. The Leningrad Party official quoted earlier stated that the Russian Republic's vocational education administrators encourage their schools to enroll dropouts in view of their chronic shortage of applicants. While the regulations permit this to be done in exceptional cases, the vocational schools in Leningrad city enrolled over 1,500 dropouts in the fall of 1964, and a total of 3,500 in Leningrad Province. The official proposed that either this practice be stopped, or else that the vocational schools be equipped to complete the applicants' regular eighth-grade education wherever necessary.[53]

Substituting vocational school for the completion of secondary school is not necessarily a step toward occupational commitment for a teen-ager. The experience of Soviet factories with vocational graduates is that the motivation of many of them is still unstable. Many of them are chronic job changers, and are the type who get into trouble with the law. While there is a law obligating the vocational graduates to complete a three-year work assignment following graduation, just as university graduates are required to do, enterprises hardly ever report the many violators to the authorities, or even try to oblige those who leave to reimburse them for enterprise-provided travel expenses to the place of assignment.[54]

Beginning with the 1967-68 school year, steps were taken to correct the "dead-end" aspect of vocational education. Alexander A. Bulgakov, national head of the vocational school system, reported in the summer of 1968 that vocational education would be combined with completion of secondary education in the new four-year and three-year vocational courses, and in certain two-year vocational schools as well. Furthermore, students who graduate with distinction from vocational schools will be accepted into the daytime divisions of technicums and higher educational institutions regardless of production experience. They may also matriculate in the evening and correspondence divisions without meeting competitive entrance requirements. Bulgakov expressed the hope that these arrangements would both swell the ranks of qualified technicum applicants, and increase the number of working-class youth entering higher education.[55]   Prokof'yev indicated that at the very minimum,

---

[53]Yu. Lavrikov, Secretary of the Leningrad City Party Committee, in *Pravda*, June 17, 1965, p. 2.

[54]M. Garin *et al.*, "The Teen-Age Worker," *Izvestiya*, October 11, 1968.

[55]A. Bulgakov (Chairman, State Committee of the USSR Council of Ministers for Vocational-Technical Education), in *Pravda*, July 24, 1968, p. 3.

vocational school students would carry on simultaneously with their general education to the extent of one or two evening classes. This would improve their chances of completing 10th grade in night school not too long after finishing their vocational training.[56] Naturally, this means that some of those who were diverted into vocational training after eighth grade may return to an academic track that may lead them away from the trade they have learned. But removal of the "dead-end" stigma could make up for this loss many times over by swelling the ranks of entrants into the vocational system.

The current reform of the vocational schools appears to stem from the realization that a particular ladder of advancement is not likely to see heavy use if it ends abruptly after a few rungs, and if it is difficult for those who have completed these few rungs to get back onto one of the ladders which continues toward the top. What motivation does an eighth-grade graduate have for learning a trade, full time or in evening courses, when many employers are willing to hire, train, and promote him without formal training? Only an immediate possibility of advancement into the "ETP" category will serve to motivate most young workers: the letters stand for the engineering and technical personnel who are distinguished from the workers by their salaried status and—in theory, at least—by their professional education.[57]

Technicums and the Middle-Level Specialists. For an eighth-grade graduate, an alternative somewhat more attractive than vocational education is the system of specialized secondary schools, also called technicums. These have no exact counterparts in the United States, since the type of training they offer is done in this country largely in the form of training within industries, whether on the job or apart from it. The Soviet economy has been in acute need of trained "middle-level" or semiprofessional personnel having skills somewhere between those of a skilled worker and an engineer; however, a certain proportion of technicum graduates fills positions for ordinary skilled workers. But the technicums, which accept both 10th-grade and 8th-grade graduates, are not really intended to form part of the ladder to a higher education. On the contrary, the policy of the 1960's has been to increase the ratio of technicians to engineers in industry, and of semi-professionals to higher education graduates generally. The goal set in 1963 by the Party for the end of the 1960's

---

[56]Prokof'yev, 1967, p. 87

[57]See DeWitt, 1961, p. 496 ff. for a detailed characterization of ETP personnel.

was that of furnishing the nation's economy annually with three or four graduates of specialized secondary schools for every graduate in higher education.[58] This goal is still far from realization. In June 1967 the higher educational institutions graduated 432,000 students, as opposed to 685,000 graduating from the specialized secondary schools, evening and correspondence divisions included. In enrollment, the specialized secondary schools have trailed slightly behind higher education enrollment for the past decade. During the 1967-68 school year, the universities and institutes had on their rolls 4.3 million students, the specialized secondary schools 4.2 million. Meanwhile, the ratio of technicum graduates to higher education graduates employed in the economy had increased from 5:4 in 1950 to a somewhat higher 3:2 in 1965.[59]

This relative lag in the growth of semiprofessional education is puzzling at first glance. It appears to offer those who complete only eighth grade the opportunity to realize two important goals in a four-to-four-and-a-half-year course: the completion of secondary education, and a good opportunity to become part of the upper echelon of industrial workers, albeit in nonengineering posts. For 10th-grade graduates, who can finish in two to two and a half years, opportunity is naturally less attractive than that of higher education, but still considerably better than having no further formal education. While part of the problem may be that semiprofessional education is not as favored as higher education in the state budget, this still does not explain the number of student places in some technicum specialties which go begging each year. The poor quality of some technicums is another part of the answer, but again only part. The belief that semiprofessional education is of far less value than higher education is promoted by industries themselves, which call for engineers to fill positions for which technicians should be fully competent. Intentionally or unintentionally, industries are promoting the view that whoever does not become an engineer is a failure. At the same time many engineers are underused, or used on tasks not requiring an engineer's training.[60]

---

[58]*Byulleten' Ministerstva vysshego i srednego spetsial'nogo obrazovaniya SSSR,* No. 8 (August, 1963), pp. 4-13.

[59]*Narodnoye khozyaistvo SSSR* 1965, p. 573; U.S. Congress, Joint Economic Committee, *Soviet Economic Performance, 1966-67,* p. 83, Table 2.

[60]DeWitt, 1961, pp. 182-85. Anatolii Agranovskii, "Against Waste of Education," *Izvestiya,* May 3, 1963; trans. in *CDSP* XV:19, pp. 5-6. "More Technicians for the National Economy," *Pravda,* December 22, 1962; trans. in *CDSP* XIV:51, p. 37. I. Shakhov and I. Vlasenko, "An Engineer Is Not a Clerk," *Pravda,* August 9, 1965.

What Was Wrong with the Work Experience Requirement? We have already seen that as the 1958 reforms were applied in practice, the policy of the Ministry of Higher Education was to see to it that 80 percent of each entering class had a work record of at least two years. The practical justifications for this requirement had been these: It would teach respect for labor on the part of those who would occupy more elevated roles; it would assure a more serious purpose on the part of the matriculants, and render them less likely to regard themselves as a privileged stratum; it would enable others to observe the applicant's work habits and outlook; and finally, it would help the applicant himself choose a firm and realistic career orientation. All in all, the work-experience requirement would serve as a healthy "filter" to eliminate applicants whose motives for wanting a higher education may be unsound, and to reduce the number of those who feel frustrated because of their unrealistic expectations of getting into universities and institutes. Khrushchev backed this reform strongly, and it corresponded to his belief that every Soviet citizen should come to his profession with an appreciation of production work, lest he consider himself part of some kind of privileged stratum. The aim was laudable, but the means chosen to realize it proved detrimental to higher education.

The heart of this attempted admissions reform lay in the type of credentials to be presented by each applicant. In the entrance examination scores, additional weight was to be given to answers in the specific course of studies sought by the applicant, which presumably would be related to his work experience. Weight was to be given also to recommendations by trade unions or other organizations at the applicant's place of work, which would stress his work attitudes and his dedication to the higher education specialty sought. Exceptions to the work-experience qualification were to be made only for students applying for high-priority specialties, particularly physics and higher mathematics.

The policy of reserving 20 percent of all places in each daytime institution for applicants coming directly from secondary school was maintained until 1965. Since there are no published data on the characteristics of entering classes, it is impossible to say to what extent this norm was actually observed. It was at least modified to the extent of permitting the 20 percent to include students in specialties other than mathematics and physics.[61] In 1965 the

---

[61] *Izvestiya*, March 13, 1963.

Ministry of Higher Education formally dropped the 20 percent rule. Henceforth, each institution could admit applicants in proportion to the number of applications in each category: secondary school graduates, and those with production experience or military service. This still permitted the universities and institutes to hold two separate entrance competitions, and to set lower admissions standards for those with work experience or military service. Deputy Minister Prokof'yev stated firmly that greater demands would now be made of them as regards their entrance examinations. The preference for those who distinguish themselves in secondary school (recipients of gold or silver medals, or of a citation for distinction) remained, of course. This preference had been somewhat restricted but by no means abolished under the various annual admissions rules during the years 1958-64. At present, students with any of these distinctions are exempted from all but one entrance examination, namely, the one in their proposed area of study, provided they earn a top mark in this one examination.[62]

The admissions regulations left somewhat vague the criteria by which institutions were to set admissions quotas, but present indications are that they enjoy a fair amount of flexibility. The L'vov Polytechnical Institute and several other institutions have recently been experimenting with a three-part quota system which assures access to the children of workers, farmers, and intelligentsia in equal proportions.[63]

The trade-union and Komsomol character references have gone by the board too: Minister of Higher Education Vyacheslav P. Yelyutin has made it clear that the sole qualification for admission is the applicant's level of formal knowledge. The long-standing ban (from 1936) on any kind of testing but academic subject-matter tests has thus far made it impossible to include aptitude or achievement tests as admissions criteria. However, the introduction of both of these was under serious study at the end of the 1960's.[64]

The preference for applicants with a work record is still applied in admissions to the evening and correspondence divisions of higher

---

[62] *Pravda*, March 20, 1965; interview with Deputy Minister of Higher Education M.A. Prokof'yev, *Vestnik vysshei shkoly*, No. 4 (April, 1965), pp. 16-17.

[63] Anatolii Agranovskii, "Before the Start," *Izvestiya*, November 14, 1968.

[64] V. P. Bespalko, "What Do You Know? What Are Your Aptitudes?" *Literaturnaya gazeta*, January 29, 1969. Trans. in *CDSP* XXI:5, pp. 7-9, 12.

education, to the extent that applicants are sponsored by their employers to study the specialty in which they have work experience. Today the bulk of those who matriculate in the evening and correspondence divisions have work experience, and part of these are technicum graduates as well.[65] The writer has discovered no comprehensive data on the proportion of those matriculating in the daytime divisions, with their far stiffer entrance requirements, directly from the regular secondary schools.

Military Service and Higher Education. One of the great advantages enjoyed by those who are admitted to full-time higher education is deferment from military service for the duration of their studies, and in some cases exemption from service. Those who are called up for service after they have earned a degree serve only one year instead of two. The older (1939) law on military service had said nothing about either deferments or exemptions in such cases, but a little-known decree of 1943 specifically granted exemptions (not just deferments) for students in a number of technological specialties.[66] In most other fields, deferments were granted as a matter of course. In a large proportion of cases—just how large is not certain—such deferments actually became exemptions.

The 1958 reforms complicated the situation of secondary school graduates in two ways: Addition of the 11th year to secondary education meant that graduation age (typically at 18) coincided with the age of liability to military service (18-26); and the work experience requirement for admission to the universities and institutes meant that except for those entering the critical specialties (e.g., mathematics and physics), which carried no such requirement, the 18-year-old automatically became subject to the draft at the time he began his employment. These problems were resolved by the abolition of the 11th year in 1966 and by the new military service law passed in 1967.

The new law granted deferments to all students in full-time higher education without exception, but not to those in the evening and correspondence divisions. There appears to have been some debate on the deferrability of part-time students, since a 1965 law had specifically deferred them as well. As for students in critical

---

[65] *Vestnik vysshei shkoly,* No. 11 (November, 1967), p. 8. "Everything Starts with Matriculation." *Pravda,* December 25, 1968.

[66] *SZ SSSR* 1943, No. 12. See also DeWitt, 1961, pp. 52-57.

specialties, the law was silent, and according to the writer's impressions during his 1963-64 and 1969 visits in the Soviet Union, these are granted exemptions in the vast majority of cases. While the liability to military service is universal, actual inductions depend on manpower requirements; hence, Soviet draft boards do have leeway within which to exempt, in actual fact, certain types of students. One route of virtual exemption for students in some (though far from all) universities and institutes is the Soviet equivalent of R.O.T.C., the military training program (*voyennaya podgotovka*), which occupies a fairly small place in a normal university curriculum and places those who complete it in the reserves.[67]

Some technicum students received exemptions prior to the 1967 law, but this was not a general rule. The 1967 provisions now specify deferments up to age 20 only for all technicum students, including those in evening and correspondence study, who enter the technicums without having completed their secondary education. However, those technicum students who enter reserve officer training are deferred as long as this training continues. Those who do succeed in finishing the technicum before they are called up are still liable to a two-year period of service, twice that of the higher education graduates.

Should Everyone Get a Chance in the Universities? In the United States, the expansion of state universities and community colleges to meet demand serves as a "safety valve" for the growing pressure for admission to higher education. The evening and correspondence divisions of Soviet higher education serve the same purpose, as do the technicums to a lesser extent. Part of the safety-valve character of American state universities and colleges is that many of them are organized to conduct their final selection process by accepting academic risks who then eliminate themselves during their freshman and sophomore years. Leningrad State University and an institute in Gor'kii did in fact experiment with "candidate students," students of promise who were admitted even though their performance on the entrance examinations would not ordinarily have gained them admission. However, two faculty members at Leningrad State University were highly critical of Leningrad's experience with this, and urged that the whole idea be dropped. On the other hand, most

---

[67]Law on Universal Liability to Military Service, October 12, 1967, *Vedomosti SSSR* 1967, No. 42; amendments to the 1939 law in *Vedomosti SSSR* 1965, No. 13; DeWitt, 1961, pp. 53-57.

of their arguments had to do with lack of facilities and funds, not with the unworkability of the "candidate student" notion in itself.[68]

Enrollment in the evening and correspondence divisions of higher education has been growing at a much faster rate than enrollment in daytime studies, in spite of the higher attrition rate in the former. Between September 1958 and September 1966 they more than doubled both their admissions and their enrollment; enrollment for 1966-67 was 2.4 million.[69] Thus, the path to a higher education is by no means closed to those who are not admitted to the daytime divisions, which are both more prestigious and of better quality. But the part-time path to a higher education is a more difficult one than that of full-time education, which may affect the labor performance and the work attitudes of the Soviet young people who embark on it. The correspondence schools are the lowest in quality and pose the most problems for students.[70]

Whether or not the doors of Soviet universities are to be opened wide to all who would like to take their chances in higher education, Soviet educational authorities have pretty definitely rejected the idea that standards should be lowered in any way for the disadvantaged and the underprepared. If the drive for equality of educational opportunity is to continue, Soviet educational authorities believe that it must take two forms: equalization of the quality of primary and secondary education, particularly as between the cities and the small towns and villages; and special programs for launching the graduates of inadequate schools into higher education on an equal footing with other students. Minister of Higher Education Vyacheslav P. Yelyutin has stated in recent years that still not enough is being done to get the children of workers and collective farmers into the universities.[71]

Yet things are already being done to reach the educationally disadvantaged. The 1970's, in fact, may see a mushrooming of all kinds of "crash programs" to motivate and prepare young people from the villages and small towns. In 1967-68 Leningrad University pioneered in developing contacts to this end with rural and small-town schools in six neighboring provinces. Candidates from

---

[68] Anatolii Agranovskii in *Izvestiya*, December 25, 1965 (eve. ed.), and February 27, 1966; *Vestnik vysshei shkoly* No. 6 (June, 1966), pp. 53-54.

[69] U.S. Congress, Joint Economic Committee, *Soviet Economic Performance: 1966-67*, p. 83.

[70] See the account by the RSFSR Minister of Higher Education in *Izvestiya*, January 6, 1962.

[71] *Vestnik vysshei shkoly*, No. 4 (April, 1966), p. 11.

rural areas were given preference in selection of a group which was brought to Leningrad for a month's tutoring in July, in preparation for the entrance examinations in August. Moscow University offers a month-long summer preparatory session before the August examinations for a fee of 15 rubles, and there are preparatory courses by correspondence as well.[72] In 1963 some Moscow University faculty members and graduate students volunteered their time and services to form a Correspondence School of Mathematics, which later gained official status and received state support. It does not accept applicants from Moscow. Two thirds of the 8,500 students enrolled as of 1968 lived in the countryside, and most of the remainder in small towns. Every year several hundred of its graduates gain admission to Moscow University.[73] Evening preparatory courses for the university entrance examinations are widely used, but here the old problem of combining a full-time job with preparation for a demanding intellectual hurdle becomes especially acute. In 1968 the Chelyabinsk Polytechnical Institute made an agreement with a number of enterprises in that area to organize a one-year *rabfak* (workers' school) designed specifically to prepare them for the Institute's entrance examinations. The school is financed by the enterprises even though its students pursue their year's studies on a full-time basis; they receive a stipend and dormitory housing on an equal footing with students already in higher education.[74]

The human effect of the mixture of inducements, opportunities, and limitations described in this chapter was the main focus of Shubkin's 1963-64 study of 9,000 secondary school graduates in Novosibirsk, referred to above. The discrepancies between aspirations and their fulfillment, so vividly shown in Tables 4-2 and 4-3, could probably be found in any country of the world with an advanced educational system and high occupational mobility.

After nearly a decade of such experiments, the Ministry of Higher Education in 1969 put into effect a nation-wide preparatory program for the educationally disadvantaged. The Party resolution which set down policy guidelines for this returned to Khrushchev's policy of stressing work experience as one type of admissions credential. By

---

[72] *Pravda,* May 28, 1969; A. Yemel'yanov, "The Road from the Village to Higher Education," *Pravda*, November 11, 1968.

[73] Anatolii Agranovskii, "Before the Start," *Izvestiya*, November 14, 1968.

[74] V. Guzhavin (Pro-Rector for Evening and Correspondence Study of the Chelyabinsk Polytechnical Institute), "School for Workers," *Izvestiya*, October 5, 1968. Yu. Shpakov, "The Second Life of the 'Rabfak' Students," *Pravda*, January 24, 1969.

Table 4-2
PERSONAL PLANS OF 1963 GRADUATES OF SECONDARY
SCHOOLS* IN NOVOSIBIRSK PROVINCE, AND THEIR
REALIZATION
(in percent figures)

Intention	Total	Boys	Girls	Realization	Total	Boys	Girls
Go to work	8	8	8	Went to work 32	26	35
Combine work and				Combined work			
study	12	7	14	and study 3	2	3
Study full time	80	85	78	Studied full time 44	48	41
Other plans	–	–	–	Other† 21	24	21

*The 9,000 graduates surveyed by questionnaire probably represent those who completed what was then the full 11 years of secondary education in the regular daytime schools, although Shubkin did not make this entirely clear. A small sample of those who left school after eight years may have been included.

†Residual.

Source: Shubkin, 1965, p. 61.

Table 4-3
PERSONAL PLANS OF 1963 GRADUATES OF SECONDARY
SCHOOLS IN NOVOSIBIRSK PROVINCE, AND THEIR REALIZATION,
BY OCCUPATION OF PARENTS
(in percent figures)*

Occupation of Father (or of mother, if no father present)	Intention			Realization		
	Work	Combine Work with Study	Study Full Time	Worked	Combined Work with Study	Studied Full Time
Urban professional†	2	5	93	15	3	82
Rural professional	11	13	76	42	–	58
Industrial and construction workers	11	6	83	36	3	61
Transport and communications workers	–	18	82	55	–	45
Agricultural workers	10	14	76	90	–	10
Workers in trade and services	9	15	76	38	3	59
Others	12	38	50	63	12	25

*This was a 10 percent sample of the larger study, or about 900 graduates.

†This is a translation of the Russian term *intelligentsiya,* which in this context is probably a bit broader than "professional."

Source: Shubkin, 1965, p. 65.

the fall of 1969, some 200 "preparatory divisions" had been established under the aegis of various universities and institutes, including many of the most famous ones. Some 20,000 prospective students were admitted to either full-time or part-time study in them, and for the near future the figure is expected to climb to 100,000. The intention is that these students be working youth nominated by their employers at the recommendation of Party, Komsomol, and trade union organizations. Admission of the nominees is then the responsibility of a special commission within each preparatory division, composed of the division chairman and representatives of Party, Komsomol, and trade union organizations from the university or institute which sponsors the preparatory division. The commission interviews each nominee to establish his ability to embark on this route of admission to higher education. The ones who are selected then pursue an 8-month or 10-month course which prepares them for the regular university entrance examinations. But neither in their university admissions credentials nor in their subsequent performance as regular students do the students from these preparatory divisions have the benefit of lowered standards.

Minister of Higher Education Vyacheslav P. Yelyutin spoke plainly about the social import of this new system:

We all know perfectly well that up to now the young lathe operator, cattle breeder, or construction worker who has finished his secondary education in night school, even if his abilities are exceptional, was in a worse position to take university entrance examinations than the fresh graduate, let us say, of a ten-year school in Moscow, with his fresh store of knowledge. This inequality of opportunity was made even deeper by the so-called cramming system. What I am referring to is the special university preparation carried on at home, a method which has been used by many families in recent years.

Various means have been tried in an effort to equalize the chances of secondary school graduates. However, the partial and temporary benefits granted to young workers, and the lowering of entrance requirements were essentially of little use, for these did not add to their knowledge. Weak secondary education multiplied the difficulties of young workers who got into the universities, and the growing academic load often proved beyond his capacity. It is utterly clear that these are the main reasons why young people with a work record and experience in life still form an insufficient proportion of students in the daytime divisions.[75]

Table 4-3 shows that occupational mobility is impaired somewhat for the children of parents of some occupations, notably for the children of farmers. Of the farmers' children who had completed either 10th grade or 8th grade, three quarters intended to continue to study full

---

[75]O. Matyanin, "The Road to the University," *Pravda*, October 23, 1969; "For Future Students," *Izvestiya*, November 1, 1969.

time, but only 10 percent actually did so. While exactly the same proportion of the children of the "rural intelligentsia" (agronomists, other farm specialists, rural teachers, doctors, etc.) intended to study full time, well over half fulfilled this ambition. The children of the "urban intelligentsia" were the most ambition-satisfied of all: over 90 percent intended to continue full-time studies, and over 80 percent actually did so. Unfortunately, the survey gave no breakdown as between 8th-grade and 10th-grade graduates, which might have revealed further discrepancies. A geographically diverse sample of secondary school graduates examined by educational specialists in the Russian Republic supported Shubkin's findings as concerns aspirations: less than 4 percent of the sample wanted to work after graduation, while the rest sought full-time study either in the universities or the technicums.[76]

A complementary study of the social origins of the Soviet intelligentsia was carried out in selected institutions and enterprises in Sverdlovsk in the mid-1960's by M. N. Rutkevich, a philosopher oriented to empirical social research. The study showed two characteristics of admissions to higher education in that province: (1) the sons and daughters of specialists with a higher education occupied more than their proportionate share of places, and (2) the trend of admissions was in the direction of a social orientation distribution equivalent to that of the nation as a whole.[77] At Sverdlovsk city's largest institution of higher learning (the Urals Polytechnic Institute), the proportion of children of workers in the total admitted to the daytime division rose from 34 to 49 percent between 1958 and 1964; and while the latter proportion was close to the national proportion, it was still substantially under the proportion of workers in this heavily industrial region. At the city's mining institute the proportion of workers' children was appreciably higher than this (62 percent), but it was lower in the humanities, medicine, and at the Urals University. The children of salaried employees were overrepresented, in proportion, and within this group the children of specialists with a higher education were overrepresented to an even greater extent: At the Urals University their proportion ranged from 11 percent in economics to an overwhelming 58 percent in the prestigious subject of physics. Rutkevich did not hesitate to point out the factors which promoted

---

[76] *Shkola i proizvodstvo* No. 6 (June, 1966), p. 8.
[77] Rutkevich, 1967, pp. 15-23; condensed trans. in *CDSP* XIX: 35, pp. 14-17.

these disproportions: parents' income, education and occupation, and attendance at primary and secondary schools in large cities. In big-city schools the level of instruction, the physical facilities, and the opportunities for broadening the intellectual horizons of pupils are greater than in small industrial communities and the countryside.

During the debate of the early 1960's over the work experience requirement for university admission, the bulk of the publicly expressed opposition to this provision came from academic administrators and specialists, who clearly feared that admissions requirements had been debased to the detriment of educational quality.[78] Some Party officials who still favor the work requirement did not give up the fight even after it was modified in 1965 in the manner described above. The Party chief of industrial Chelyabinsk Province in the Urals charged that the recruitment of the children of workers' families for higher education was still being neglected. Correction of this situation, he believed, would have several beneficial results: it would increase the supply of skilled personnel in remote districts which presently are short of skills, and it would increase the proportion of university students whose occupational bent is already well established. For example, is there any justification in favoring one girl for admission to a medical institute directly from high school over another girl who already has several years of nursing experience, simply because the former has a slightly higher academic average? The Chelyabinsk official called attention to sociological surveys among university students which showed that in their choice of an educational path, many "had not been guided by an interest in a particular specialty but had come to study there only to obtain a higher education." It is the presence of such students which explains, he said, why such a large proportion of students in agriculture-related specialties—sometimes more than half—avoid going to work in their specialty after graduation.[79]

The director of admissions for Moscow University took the side of the quota proponents. Only 12 to 13 percent of the University's students, he pointed out, were from rural schools; hence, he advocated a "benign quota" proportionate to the number of graduates of rural schools nationally. Presently this is not permitted by law, but a legal precedent of sorts exists in the form of the places

---

[78]See the objections by Academician Alexander L. Mints in *Izvestiya*, September 14, 1962, and the Pro-Rector of Moscow University in *Komsomol'skaya pravda*, May 14, 1963.

[79]N. Rodionov, "Give Young People Revolutionary Tempering," *Izvestiya*, July 16, 1968; trans. in *CDSP* XX:29, p. 25.

reserved for applicants with work experience. Although many young people from the farms could be included under the quota for applicants with work experience immediately upon their graduation from secondary school, because they have put in the equivalent of two years or more of work on collective and state farms, the Ministry of Higher Education does not recognize this as work experience. Because of the lower quality of rural schools, only 23 percent of the rural school graduates passed the 1968 entrance examinations for Moscow University, as compared with 32 percent for urban graduates. Since this result is a typical one, according to the admissions director, rural school graduates confront a "psychological barrier" in addition to the barrier of their inferior preparation.[80]

Considering the content of this debate over admissions qualifications, it would be hard to demonstrate that either side has displayed a desire to promote class differences. Quite the contrary, it would appear to be to the advantage of both the top Party leadership and the educational establishment to equalize opportunity by any reasonable means not requiring an exorbitant outlay of resources (such as a universal boarding school system would require, for example). A self-perpetuating stratum of the privileged can be more of a liability than an asset to a regime in great need of scientific, technological, and managerial talent. Bringing young blood into the upper occupational strata is also one means by which the top policymakers can keep the habits and prejudices of one generation of high-level administrators from infecting the next generation. Mobility in the ranks assures maneuverability at the top. It is one thing to say that a "new class" has arisen which does everything in its power to bolster its prerogatives and to screen narrowly all those who want to join its ranks. A look at the caricatures in *Krokodil* is enough testimony by itself that this elite attitude must still be very prevalent. But it is quite another thing to say that the top policymakers promote the "new class" because they find it advantageous to their rule. The writer would guess that in the minds of the several dozen men who occupy the top Party posts, habitual elite attitudes mingle with the desire to keep fresh blood coming into the top occupational strata, and the convenience of administering policies through the same staid bureaucrats is tempered with the knowledge that fresh new faces may be needed to carry out new and controversial policies.

[80] A. Yemel'yanov, "The Road From the Village to Higher Education," *Pravda*, November 11, 1968.

The disadvantages of receiving one's education in a village or small town, in any case, reflect not an educational policy but rather the nation's uneven pattern of investment in nonindustrial facilities serving the population—in this case, schools. This problem, an all too familiar one to American educators, will be discussed further in Chapter 6. Data on educational investment levels by city and region are hard to come by, but some regional and country-city differences are obvious even to the casual visitor to Soviet schools. Why, for example, are the "special schools" which stress physics, mathematics, and English found only in the large cities? Physicists in Dubna, the major nuclear research center north of Moscow, calculated in 1960 that the entire supply of the nation's physicists came from particular areas of the country which together contain only 20 million people, or one tenth of the nation's population.[81]

The writer had a number of conversations in 1963-64 with Soviet students on the matter of the disadvantages of rural children. The Law Faculty of Moscow University had more than an average proportion of students from farm backgrounds simply because among the specialties taught in higher education, law is near the bottom in both prestige and difficulty of admission; consequently, farm children were better able to compete. Among the reasons given by students for the poor showing of farm youth in completing secondary school and entering higher education, the most common were the poor quality of rural schools, the lack of a cultured and stimulating environment, and the time and energy drained from studies by commuting long distances to school and working on the farm, including long hours devoted to tending one's family's garden plot. However, the farm-bred students were virtually unanimous in their opinion that farm parents are just as ambitious for the education of their offspring as are city parents; and that this is so because money and family background are in themselves no obstacle. Many of them had the impression—whether this is true or not—that respect for education is greater on the collective farms than it is among urban workers. They pointed out the number of cases they knew of, or had read about, in which urban families actually prefer to see their children drop out of school and earn money for the family in factory employment. A number of the law students had taken university entrance examinations in different faculties for

---

[81] Anatolii Agranovskii, "Before the Start," *Izvestiya*, November 14, 1968.

several years in a row, determined to get into higher education one way or another.[82]

As concerns the children of disadvantaged backgrounds generally, the relatively high level of their educational aspirations may be far more important in the long run than their lower level of realization. While their aspirations as shown in the Novosibirsk study were lower than those of the highest category of respondents (i.e., the children of the "urban intelligentsia"), they were lower by a fairly modest 17 percentage points. It was the *realization* of this ambition that was drastically lower for farm children.

Industrial and industrializing societies cannot avoid awakening career and status ambitions which, for a certain segment of the ambitious, they are unable to satisfy. This point is too obvious to need belaboring. Since foreign visitors to the Soviet Union do sometimes encounter Soviet young people who are embittered about career failures, we need a reminder now and then that this is not a peculiarly Soviet phenomenon, but simply a price paid by some citizens of any mobile, building society. It should also be said that the Soviet system has probably done more than other nations by way of fostering unrealistic expectations, for in Soviet ideology man's worth in society is very much a function of his contribution, direct or indirect, to production. One does expect an economic planning system of the Soviet type to be able to coordinate its system of education with job needs, and to guide its citizens into paths of education and training suited to their talents. What cannot be coordinated, unfortunately, is the impact of the Soviet work-and-talent ideology on those with little talent. The problem is further complicated where the talent search is carried on not only in the schools, but in the mass media as well, in fact every day on the front pages of the national press. The parallel publicity which glorifies the ordinary worker has apparently failed to evoke a better balance of aspirations.

---

[82]See V. Mordkovich, "No Leave-Taking Songs Are Sung In the Village," *Izvestiya*, January 5, 1962.

.5. *Equality and Incentives in Work Choices*

In any society which offers young people the possibility of moving far and fast up various career ladders, the transition from school to the world of work is a threshold which for many is psychologically hard to get across. You watch many of your coevals go on with their education, and they are a kind of threat. Does your decision to go to work put you in a blind alley? Will it offer you any kind of real satisfaction after 5 or 15 or 25 years? What is the alternative if the job is eventually abolished, or if the pressure to go elsewhere becomes overwhelming after you have built up some seniority? Does the employer's location isolate you from the major advantages of modern urban society?

The following pair of descriptions suggests that a young American steelworker who suddenly found himself employed in the steelworks of Magnitogorsk or Zaporozh'ye would find some familiar problems and choices, and some unfamiliar ones as well:

Of all the experiences I encountered during a summer at the steelworks none was as poignant as the exposure to the enormous pressure of job insecurity. Almost every man there, as he notices the crossed stripes on a novice worker's helmet, greets him with the words, "Don't work so hard.". . . . . The oldest group of workers rarely comes in contact with you, for their positions are established, and they are waiting for a worthwhile pension and for pension age. The middle men are also waiting, for jobs with a larger pecuniary reward or with more prestige. It is a time of acceptance. Some greasy machine or glowing ingot is your life, and you should make the best of it. But the most pathetic of all worker groups is the younger workers. When the axe falls [as automation reduces the work force] they will be the losers. They've just returned from the army or dropped out of high school, or tried college but failed, or married. And almost all have dreams of returning to college or going to computer programming or electronics school. Some make it too; but all too often the young steelworker drops out only to be back in a year or two (losing a couple of years' seniority in the process). These workers are your first and closest friends, and you see them being crushed by a system that offers virtually no escape.—From an account by an American college student of a summer spent working at a steel plant.[1]

. . . .

In comparing sociological survey data, you come to the conclusion that young people quit industrial jobs for two reasons, basically. A young man or woman who for the first time crosses the threshhold of a plant faces a multitude of new questions: whether the work will be interesting, what kind of friends there will be, how they will get along with the supervising workers, and so forth. Who is going to help the novice get through one of the complicated stretches of his career? A good supervisor, who will accept a young worker and guide him to the right tasks? But today's young worker has more education and far greater demands than the young workers of former times, while the supervisor, who sometimes has no grasp of the science of the "human approach," no longer fills the role which society expects of him. Meanwhile the problem of making the young worker part of the collective is becoming a matter of prime importance. If a young worker fresh out of secondary school is simply handed a shovel and told to get to work, he usually regards this as meaning that he is a failure in life, as the wreck of his dreams, and he tries to get another position in production. Here, as a rule, no amount of wages will help, not even a very high wage.—From an informal survey of the causes of labor turnover by a Soviet economist and a correspondent of *Izvestiya*.[2]

The situation of the restless young Soviet worker who is uncertain whether his job has anything worthwhile to offer him is different from that of his American counterpart in at least one important way: there are plenty of jobs elsewhere, including employers begging for his services in remote parts of the country who are able to pay very good wages as compensation for isolation and a hard climate. Loss of seniority in a given enterprise may well be a deterrent to job changing for workers who have already served 15 or 20 years. But for the younger workers, neither the sacrifice of a few years' seniority, nor the fear of not being able to find well paying jobs, represent any serious obstacle. In this sense, the employment choices of a young

---

[1]Neil S. Lutsky, "Of Summers of Steel and Sweat," *The New Wharton Account* (Wharton School of Finance and Commerce, University of Pennsylvania) October, 1968, p. 9

[2]E. Antonosenkov and V. Davydchenkov, "Turnover: Its Causes and Consequences," *Izvestiya*, October 18, 1968.

Soviet worker may be appreciably greater than those of a a young American worker, depending, of course, on his specialty, the industry he is in, and a number of other factors. If job changing and the geographical circulation of labor are an indicator of one important kind of freedom, the Soviet Union would surely rank high in this respect among the industrial nations of the world. Changing jobs and employment locations, to be sure, is only one labor relationship among many. Other relationships are beyond question restrictive by comparison with the analogous relationships in the United States and elsewhere, beginning with the Soviet prohibition on strikes. Yet the ease with which Soviet workers change jobs, and the problems which this creates for many employers, is having a strong effect on all the other relationships, and this fact has not been given adequate attention outside the Soviet Union.

The writer is aware that such a conclusion flies in the face of popular conceptions of the status of labor in the Soviet Union which are held in the West. Even as knowledgeable a student of Soviet affairs as Merle Fainsod wrote in the early 1960's: "The right to work is not a right to choose one's work freely, but a duty to work in disciplined subordination to state and party regulations. It frequently means working at the post to which one is assigned, at wages and in conditions which are determined by higher authorities over whom one has no control."[3] However applicable this judgment may have been to the labor practices of the Stalin era, it would be difficult to maintain today as a generalization. Not even the three-year job assignments given to university, technicum, and vocational school graduates really support his view: the education which entails the assignment is freely undertaken, and many graduates do leave their jobs and places of assignment with impunity before the three years are up. That wage scales are everywhere fixed by Moscow is true, but the implication that employers and employees alike have little room for maneuver within the wage system did not hold true even in the Stalin era. Strikes, to be sure, are prohibited now as then. But if one can imagine strikes being permitted in a labor situation like that of the Western Siberian Region, described below, would they necessarily be more effective in impelling national and local governments to improve working conditions than, for example, the mass desertion of important

---

[3] Merle Fainsod, *How Russia Is Ruled* (2nd edition; Cambridge, Mass.: Harvard University Press, 1965), p. 376.

construction projects in Kemerovo (described below) by workers disappointed with their low wages and poor work organization?

In the present Soviet Constitution, which was adopted in 1936, work is both a duty for every able-bodied citizen (Art. 12) and a right guaranteed for all citizens (Art. 118). Americans who wonder how the right to work is realized in a technical, legaĺ sense will search for a strictly legal mechanism in vain. Much of the 1936 Constitution, including both of these provisions, is declaratory. Soviet courts do not interpret these two articles directly, and furthermore the relationship between the Constitution and any given piece of legislation is not often specified in the legislation. The very wording of Article 118, in fact, suggests that the right to work need not be implemented by any kind of law specifying what legal recourse is open to the citizen in need of employment. Rather, the Constitution treats the very character of the Soviet economy as the one significant guarantee, for this Article continues: "The right to work is ensured by the socialist organization of the national economy, the steady growth of the productive forces of Soviet society, the elimination of the possibility of economic crises, and the abolition of unemployment." And five years before the Constitution was adopted, unemployment vanished from the nation's labor statistics; officially, it had been abolished for once and for all.

Rather surprisingly, the Soviet Union has no one all-purpose network of employment offices. On the other hand, there are definite employment services for given situations. These include the following: the relocation services of the Organized Labor Recruiting Service, known as *Orgnabor* (described below); the obligatory placement conducted for graduates of universities, technicums, and vocational schools (likewise described below); and employment services run by local governments. The latter operate with varying effectiveness, and do not necessarily have full information on jobs available in the localities they serve. The Commissions for Job Placement, one form of local employment service, commonly handle young people who are referred to them by the schools they have left, or by the militia (police). The Commissions for Cases of Minors can do the same thing in the course of dealing with young offenders who may thus be spared legal penalties. Neither of these bodies can compel a young person to take a job, it should be added.

The end of unemployment statistics was much more than a publicity gesture, for since the early 1930's there have quite literally been many more jobs than job hunters. Many Soviet economists have concerned themselves during the 1960's with ways of drawing housewives and others into the labor force. They and many others remain outside the labor force by choice, often in order to devote time to raising produce and poultry on their small individual plots of land. While these have never constituted more than 5 percent of the able-bodied population in the postwar period, nevertheless this proportion had risen nearly to the 5 percent level in the latter 1960's. Contrary to an impression which is widespread in the West, the Soviet housewife is under no formal obligation to take a job, regardless of the number or age of children in the family, if any. The high proportion of working wives and mothers in the U.S.S.R. may be explained by a combination of two factors: the advantage (or necessity) of having a second income for the family, and the fact that education and publicity have broken down the traditional barriers to the entry of women into many occupations, including medicine, science, and industrial technology.

It is one thing to determine that there are more than enough jobs for the able-bodied population; but the question of what kind of jobs may be had, and where they are located, is another matter. Such is also the case with any comparison between the unemployed able-bodied population in the United States, and what one finds in the "Help Wanted" columns of the newspapers in various localities. Many small towns of the Soviet Union do in fact have underemployment in some form, and many of their young people must migrate elsewhere after failing to find work locally. This is especially true of the western periphery of the U.S.S.R., which has had little industrial development in the postwar period. Teen-agers who leave school after eighth grade or still earlier find that enterprises frequently resist hiring them: they are an expense and a bother, they flit from job to job, and even if they stay on one job they will take some years learning to be productive, reliable members of the labor force. Such, in any case, is the view ascribed to many enterprise administrations in countless Soviet press items. While a variety of laws and regulations forbids discrimination in all hiring, including specifically discrimination against teen-agers and against pregnant women and nursing mothers, no law compels any enterprise or agency to create jobs for the benefit of employment seekers.[4]

Work-force reductions due to automation have become another

---

[4] See *Sbornik zakonodatel'nykh aktov o trude*, 1960, p. 65 ff.

familiar topic in the Soviet press and in professional economic journals. While numerous case histories are cited in which employers have planned successfully for retraining and job shifts, the recourse available to the worker whose job has been automated out of existence does not lie in the laws and courts. He may turn to the employment offices run by local governments as a convenience for employers within their jurisdiction, or to the local office of *Orgnabor* (explained below), the national relocation service. He may retrain at the expense of the state, although this will likely reduce his income considerably for a time, particularly if he has been in the upper wage scale grades as a skilled worker. So far, no comprehensive picture of the consequences of automation has emerged in the work of Soviet economists and other social scientists. Rather likely the automation of the 1960's has produced a mixed result of opportunity, inconvenience, and in some cases hardship for the workers affected by it.

If it is surprising to some foreigners that the *right* to work is not judicially enforced or enforceable, it may be even more of a surprise that there are no laws either to enforce the *duty* to work either, at least in any comprehensive fashion. The laws which do exist cover special situations, not the nonemployed generally. The one set of laws which did try to make a clean sweep of the voluntarily unemployed (housewives excluded, of course) was so problematic in its definition of voluntary unemployment that it had to be modified drastically: This was the so-called "antiparasite" legislation (described below), which was passed in various forms in the different republics during 1957-61. With this one exception, the legislation which affects the voluntarily nonemployed concerns not idleness itself, but the *means* by which one might gain an income to support his idleness. These might include speculation of some kind, or renting one's apartment or house in a manner forbidden by law. (Some private renting is legal.) There is nothing in the laws which would prevent a Soviet citizen from taking as long a vacation as he pleases on his savings or the savings of his family. Likewise, no law prevents a young secondary school graduate from living off his parents for a time, much as this is frowned on officially. A specialist or skilled worker who has been dismissed from his job, for whatever reason, will not ordinarily be subject to penalties for living off relatives and friends while waiting for an opening in his specialty, even though such jobs may be plentiful in other parts of the country. The organized social pressure which may be brought to bear in all these situations may be considerable, especially if it is applied through the Komsomol, but this varies from situation to situation.

Compulsory employment, and compulsory work without remuneration, is used in certain limited situations. The legal liability of all able-bodied citizens to labor service in emergencies, a practice sometimes called "labor mobilization," has not been much in evidence since the World War II period. In peacetime it can be used only in cases of natural disasters. The long-standing laws requiring participation by industries and farms in road construction and repair might be construed as compulsory labor, and a 1956 law ordering gypsies to stop migrating, settle down, and start working at regular jobs certainly imposed regular employment on a group which had shunned this for centuries.[5]

In sum, it may be said that the influences and pressures which bring a Soviet citizen into the labor force and keep him there have rather little to do with penalties for remaining outside the labor force. Rather, it is the general nonavailability of legal sources of income other than those from work which deters those who might otherwise seek the maximum possible idleness. As a practical possibility, the choice not to work is open to only a small minority of able-bodied citizens between 16 and 60. At the same time, the job choices which may be made *within* the world of work are very wide, and the very extent of this choice can create problems for a government which wants to influence them to make choices useful to the economy. The clearest example of this is found in the difficulty created for economic planners and administrators by the many young workers who flit from job to job freely, and just as freely migrate from area to area.

LABOR TURNOVER AND JOB CHOICE

Soviet economic planners and political leaders have regarded high labor turnover as a serious problem since the very beginning of the country's industrialization drive in the 1930's. Stalin's attack on wage levelling (*uravnilovka*) in 1931 used the turnover problem virtually as its key argument in support of introducing high wage and salary differentials. Narrowing the wage gap, said Stalin, would increase turnover; increasing it would reduce turnover. The unskilled

---

[5] *Vedomosti SSSR* 1956, No. 21; 1958, No. 34; *Trudovoye pravo*, 1963, p. 490; Conquest, 1967, pp. 32-34.

worker would have no motivation to become skilled if wages were equal; consequently, he has no motivation to stay with one job for any considerable period of time either. The skilled worker, said Stalin, would be motivated to migrate from enterprise to enterprise in hope of finding a work situation in which his skill is rewarded somehow, even if not with substantially higher wages. Factories and plants are seriously hampered where there is no steady "core" of skilled labor; retaining them is even more important than reducing the turnover of unskilled labor. Enterprises, continued Stalin, must pay far more attention to providing housing and assuring an adequate supply of consumers' goods for their employees; this is a major factor in reducing turnover.[6]

In 1940, under the threat of being drawn into World War II, the Soviet government instituted both a youth labor draft and a job "freeze" which was formally in force until 1956. Much evidence suggests that in the postwar years it was being enforced only sporadically, if at all. During the period 1940-45, in any case, workers guilty of job leaving or absenteeism could no longer be fired from their jobs, but instead were required to return to work and pay a fine of up to 25 percent of earnings for six months.[7] During the decade preceding adoption of these laws, the use of prison labor mushroomed in a fashion too well known to need recounting here. If Fainsod's judgment, cited above, is far too harsh as applied to the 1960's, it is also too mild to describe the position of much of the Soviet labor force in the 1930's and 1940's.

Statements by Soviet officials concerned with labor supply problems, and the whole tone of press commentary on labor turnover, all suggest that increasing the penalties for job leaving is not considered a possible policy alternative. "Administrative measures," as they are called, are considered to be of peripheral value at best by nearly all the public commentators on excessive labor turnover. Typical is the conclusion of a newspaper correspondent following a visit to the city-run employment service in Tomsk: "The city cadres division doesn't put pressure on anyone to go anywhere. Up to now, no one has managed to get rid of the excessive turnover of workers and specialists simply by means of administrative methods. What is important is to study the tendencies of this phenomenon, and to find those levers with whose help it would be

---

[6] Stalin, 1953, pp. 366-69.
[7] *Vedomosti SSSR* 1940, Nos. 20, 37, and 42; 1956, No. 10.

possible to solve the problem"[8] The chief legal or administrative restrictions on employment choice are those applied in special situations. Moscow, Leningrad, and other large cities of the European U.S.S.R. use the police registration system to control population influx. Cases have been known in which persons arrested in these cities for minor offenses, whether they are residents or not, have simply been delivered to the regular civilian labor placement agencies for relocation to remote parts of the country. Standard criminal penalties include "banishment" (*vysylka*) and "exile" (*ssylka*), the first a prohibition on living or working in a given area, the second entailing relocation to an area specified by the court, most usually one of the labor-hungry regions of Siberia. The "antiparasite" laws, already noted, provided for administrative resettlement for two to five years of the voluntarily unemployed at the request of meetings of ordinary citizens. This procedure has since been placed under a degree of judicial control. While all of these measures were drawn up partly with an eye to labor needs, we have no data from the 1960's from which to make a judgment about their role in allocating labor resources.

As for the obligations of graduates of higher education and the technicums, who after graduation are assigned to a given employer for three years, enforcement has proven nearly impossible. Quite aside from the problem of limiting the number of departures from job assignments *after* three years' service, which is a further problem, not even the device of withholding of university and institute diplomas until the graduates complete their assignments has been effective in inducing everyone to complete the required service. Enterprises are forbidden by regulation to hire graduates who have not finished their job assignments, for example those who drift back from Siberia to the cities of the European U.S.S.R. and look for work there. But according to numerous Soviet young people whom the writer has met who have seen the job assignment routine in action, enterprises in need of skilled labor usually ignore this. The formal requirement that such job leavers reimburse the state for the cost of their education (on the order of 4,000 rubles for a complete higher education) likewise remains a dead letter.[9] Graduating students have a certain choice in their assignments too. Those with top grades or a veteran's status get first choice of the jobs which are

[8]E. Shatokhin, "Work According to Preference," *Izvestiya*, August 29, 1968.
[9]*Sbornik zakonodatel'nykh aktov o trude*, 1960, p. 122; Sonin, 1966, p. 38.

offered. Those whose families live in the city where they are studying are generally offered jobs there.

Employers are not in fact penalized either for helping graduates to avoid completing their job assignment. Under a decree of 1948, enterprises may not employ higher education and technicum graduates who have not been assigned to them by their respective ministries. Although industrial administrators are criminally liable for violating this rule, its application is ignored in practice, according to the top Russian Republic official responsible for these placements. Those enterprises which have sponsored some of their own young workers for admission to higher education and the technicums, he wrote, usually insist that these workers return to serve them as specialists after graduation, even in cases where the circumstances suggest a different employment. While the enterprises in such cases can pretty well dictate job assignments, graduates are not in practice penalized for leaving their assignments, legally or otherwise.[10]

Whether Soviet labor turnover is large or small by comparison with turnover in other industrial economies is not important here. The excellent comparative study by Mary Harris of Glasgow University suggests that the difference between the Soviet and British turnover rates may not be great; it also poses the question of whether the costs of reducing present turnover could be justified economically in either country.[11] Actually, average Soviet turnover rates may be comparable to those in the United States, besides which Soviet sources indicate that average turnover in the early 1960's was a fraction of that prevailing in the early 1930's.[12] In the Far North of the Soviet Union, in spite of the high wage differentials (described below) and other benefits which are offered for these areas, a high turnover rate is probably accepted as normal by economic planners. At least, these areas are little mentioned in writing and studies on the turnover problem. The point is that Soviet political leaders, economic planners and industrial administrators do regard the present turnover level in many economically important areas as undesirably high, that during the 1960's they have urged steps to reduce it, and that they appear to be agreed on a policy of manipulating incentives rather than devising new means of compulsion.

---

[10]K. Savichev, "Duty and Personal Wishes," *Molodoi kommunist* No. 3, 1967, pp. 78-81.

[11]Harris, 1964, pp. 400-404.

[12]Brown, 1966, pp. 33-34; Fakiolas, 1962, passim.

Soviet analysts of labor turnover data have very little to say about the positive aspects of turnover, except that they do mention the proportion of job leavers who return to full-time education, or who move in order to work near an evening technicum or university. There are no specific data on job leaving by secondary school graduates who have completed the two years of production work which helps qualify them for admission to higher educational institutions. But certainly part of the job-to-job turnover among workers under 25 or under 30, who form the vast majority of job leavers, also has to do with their finding a satisfactory work situation, or with making basic career decisions. Does an individual enterprise, or the economy as a whole, lose by seeing a worker leave when the alternative is to retain a dissatisfied and ambitionless worker for some years? If the Soviet government for some reason were to enact an employment-control system similar to that of 1940, one of its principal effects would be to keep a lot of "square pegs in round holes," so to speak. A varied work experience may also serve as the strongest kind of motivation to a young worker to improve his qualifications. It may take four or five different jobs to convince him that in order to get ahead (however he may define this in his own case) he has to get more education, or at least to stick at one job long enough to acquire more on-the-job training before better positions will be open to him.

Changing jobs and changing residence may bring psychological benefits as well. It is better, certainly, for young people to work off their restlessness, love of change, and desire to travel and get acquainted with different parts of their country by working their way from place to place, than by more socially disruptive means. For some, the work experience may simply mean a much-needed break during studies, or a chance to accumulate savings and goods.

THE CASE OF THE WESTERN SIBERIAN REGION

A look at one of the Soviet Union's areas of highest labor turnover will show the character and extent of the problem, the policy recommendations under consideration for dealing with it, and perhaps also the limits of national manpower policy. The Western Siberian Region (WSR) has been much studied by economists and other social scientists at the Siberian Division of the U.S.S.R. Academy of Sciences in Novosibirsk. This is an area of some 947,000 square miles, over 10 percent of the nation's total, embracing five provinces: Altai (technically a *krai* or territory), Kemerovo, Novosibirsk, Omsk, and Tomsk. The low overall density indicated by its population of 12.1 million (1966)—a mere 5 percent of the Soviet Union's people—must be seen in the light of its urban concentrations. The WSR is 59 percent urban as compared with the national ratio of 54 percent. Rapidly growing Novosibirsk City, with a population of just over a million, is followed in size by Omsk (746,000), Novokuznetsk (484,000), Barnaul (395,000), Kemerovo (358,000), and Tomsk (311,000). All these cities except Tomsk, and most of the WSR's urbanized area, lie within a radius of 150 miles of Novosibirsk City. As of the mid-1960's, only 17 percent of the labor force was engaged in agriculture. The WSR's vast coal deposits, together with its iron and nonferrous metallic ores, have furnished the basis for building an important metallurgical complex during the past four decades, as well as for chemical industries, machine building, and other metal-working industries. Large oil and gas reserves, together with a modest hydroelectric energy production and potential, assure the WSR of a long-term energy base for continued industrial development. Electric power production costs in the coal-fueled steam plants of the WSR, like those of Siberia generally, are 50 to 75 percent below those of the European U.S.S.R. Coal production costs in the WSR's Kuznetsk area are 50 percent lower than those of Donets coal in the Ukraine, and those in its Ekibastuz area 83 percent lower.[13] The WSR's main cities are located along—or on short branch lines of—the Trans-Siberian railway, and air communications to both the European and Far Eastern portions of the nation are likewise good. Novosibirsk city itself, though physically not the most attractive of Soviet cities, has been the beneficiary of efforts to turn it into a capital, so to speak, of one large part of Siberia, the Chicago of a booming Soviet heartland. Symbolic of these efforts was the location in 1958 of the Siberian Division of the Academy of Sciences there, in an attractively designed "research city" in the suburbs.

Economists frequently make comparisons between indices of various kinds for the WSR and those for the Central Region, which includes Moscow and 10 surrounding provinces. In many respects they suggest that this part of Siberia, at least, is not far behind

---

[13]Mikhail G. Pervukhin of *Gosplan* in *Ekonomicheskaya gazeta* No. 45, (November, 1967). Trans. in *CDSP* XIX:46, pp. 3-4.

well-developed European Russia in output and living standards. The high emigration rates from the WSR seem puzzling in view of this. At first glance, there is little but the somewhat colder climate, and remoteness from the nation's more popular resort areas, which might discourage migrants to urban areas from settling in the WSR.[14] A further puzzle is to determine whether the high rate of emigration has any connection with the similarly high migration rates *within* the WSR, or with job changing within given communities.

Studies done at Novosibirsk's Institute for Economics and Industrial Production Organization (of the Academy of Sciences, Siberian Division) showed a net population outflow from the WSR of 370,000 persons during the period 1957-63. To be sure, 200,000 of these came from the largely agricultural Altai Territory rather than from the industrial regions. For 1965 alone, the net outflow was 100,000, which suggests that the rate has been rising. Interregional population movement for the WSR for recent years has been 1.3 times that of the average for the Russian Republic, and 2.1 times that for the Central Region.[15] While the WSR's urban population has been having a substantial net immigration from outside the WSR, this positive balance is due almost entirely to immigration from rural rather than urban regions (see Table 5-1). This means that a high proportion of the new urban residents are entering industrial and other nonagricultural occupations for the first time, and that their average level of training is low.

Table 5-1
NET INTERREGIONAL MIGRATION BETWEEN THE WESTERN
SIBERIAN REGION AND ALL OTHER REGIONS OF THE
SOVIET UNION
(in thousands of migrants)

Type of Migration Balance	*1962*	*1963*
Urban population of the WSR	+56.0	+ 79.0
(a) With urban areas of all other regions	- 3.5	+ 5.6
(b) With rural areas of all other regions	+59.5	+ 73.4
Total population of the WSR	- 40.0	- 119.0

Source: Akademiya nauk SSSR .... *Zapadno-sibirskii ekonomicheskii raion*, 1967, p. 181. A plus sign indicates a new inflow of migrants to the territorial unit or units indicated, a minus sign net outflow.

---

[14] A detailed account of the WSR's economy and resources may be found in Akademiya nauk SSSR . . . *Zapadno-sibirskii ekonomicheskii raion*, 1967, pp. 19-57.

[15] *Ibid.*, p. 182.

A substantial proportion of the outflow, on the other hand, consists of trained industrial workers.[16] The emigrants from both urban and rural areas of the WSR move, for the most part, to Central Asia, Kazakhstan, and the Ukraine, the nation's warm-climate areas, many parts of which are labor-surplus areas in one sense or another, the surplus being mainly unskilled and lowskilled labor. Of the immigrants to the WSR, a large proportion (just how large is impossible to say) are transferring residence under the auspices of one or another organization: university, technicum and vocational school graduates sent for their three-year assignments following graduation, personnel transferred among industries, farmers arriving under the agricultural resettlement programs, and transfers arranged through *Orgnabor*, the resettlement agency described below.[17] Actually, the very fact that a large proportion of immigrants came under programs of formal job assignments may account to some extent for the heavy emigration. Many of the recent university graduates sent to the WSR on their three-year postgraduation assignments often consider that they are simply doing their duty by working for several years in Siberia or other remote areas, after which they intend to seek employment in the western or southern parts of the nation. Enterprises in the European U.S.S.R., eager to obtain skilled labor from any available source, compound the problem by luring migrants back to the areas they originally came from, and for this purpose they too pay transportation and resettlement expenses.[18]

Data gathered during the first half of the 1960's in Novosibirsk and certain cities of Kemerovo Province showed the following characteristics of workers who had left their employment for any reason: One quarter to one third of them left the city as well as the enterprise, while most of the remainder switched jobs without changing their place of residence; they were young, about half of them under 25 and three quarters of them under 30; and family status was such as to facilitate mobility, 55 percent of them being either single persons or families with no dependents, with a further 18 percent belonging to family units with one dependent only. Further data for Novosibirsk alone showed that among skilled workers, 25

---

[16] A survey done in the machine-building industries of Novosibirsk supports this conclusion. *Ibid.*, p. 181.

[17] *Ibid.*, p. 182.

[18] L. Denisova and T. Faddeyeva, "Some Data on Population Migration in the U.S.S.R.," *Vestnik statistiki* No. 7 (July, 1965), pp. 20-21.

percent of the job changes involved a change of specialty as well. The survey attributed this circumstance much more to poor hiring and work organization procedures rather than to lack of perseverance on the part of the workers. For many of these workers, immigration to the WSR had meant shifting to tasks below their skill levels. Among all those who entered into new employment during the period under study, about one quarter had quit work within five months. Within this entire group of new employees, the proportion of those quitting was highest among unskilled workers—33 percent—as compared with 23 percent for skilled workers, 18 percent for engineering and technical staff plus white-collar employees, and 15 percent for apprentices.[19] Data on the average time spent between jobs are spotty, but a survey by the municipal employment office in Tomsk showed an average of 46 days.[20] Such an average may reflect both lack of centralized hiring information and the preference of workers who turn the time between jobs into their summer vacations.

Among the professions, part of the personnel turnover may be the result of inadequate accommodations, consumers' goods, and amenities. Such was the conclusion in the early 1960's of a group of national and local medical administrators concerning the turnover of doctors in the Kuznetsk Basin. Hospital construction there had been slowed as a result of transferring responsibility for such construction from enterprises to local governments. Production of pharmaceuticals, in a region expected to produce its own, had been held up because of supply problems. One result of the shortage of both personnel and supplies was that local public health statistics had shown some negative trends in recent years.[21]

Tables 5-2 and 5-3 are typical of the various surveys of reasons given by workers for leaving their jobs in the WSR. The reasons surveyed are interesting, but as studies they must be viewed with caution. Their categories of reasons differ, and most surveys fail to classify responses systematically according to age of respondent, industry, type of work, earnings levels, and change of residence. Doubtless, many of the respondents would not have left their job because of one adverse factor alone, but only because of a combination of them. None of the surveys take into account the impact on newly hired workers of the rate of turnover which they

[19] Adakemiya nauk SSSR . . . . *Zapadno-sibirskii ekonomicheskii raion*, pp. 183, 188.

[20] E. Shatokhin in *Izvestiya*, August 29, 1968.

[21] *Izvestiya*, December 7, 1962, p. 5.

see about them. From the point of view of labor force morale, high turnover itself may be regarded as a cause of yet more high turnover.

Table 5-2
REASONS GIVEN BY THE LABOR FORCE OF MACHINE-BUILDING ENTERPRISES
IN THE WESTERN SIBERIAN REGION FOR VOLUNTARY
TERMINATION OF EMPLOYMENT
(in percent of total responses)

| | | *Novosibirsk City, 1959* | | |
| | | | *Having Worked at a Given Enterprise:* | |
Reasons Given	*Kemerovo Province and Altai Territory, 1960*	*Total*	*Less Than 1 Year*	*5 to 10 Years*
1. Unsatisfactory wages	11.4	18.7	20.9	13.4
2. Working conditions, including:	14.4	17.85	18.2	18.0
(a) Lack of jobs suited to specialty	4.8	2.4	,2.5	4.5
(b) Lack of possibility for skill improvement	2.2	0.05	0.1	0.0
(c) Dissatisfaction with own profession	4.6	9.1	9.4	9.0
(d) Dissatisfaction with work conditions	1.6	2.7	2.4	3.0
(e) Dissatisfaction with character of work	1.2	3.6	3.8	1.5
3. Living conditions, including:	20.8	24.65	23.1	25.4
(a) Inadequate housing	13.8	10.3	11.1	13.4
(b) Housing too far from job, or inadequate transportation to job	2.6	8.1	7.8	3.0
(c) Inadequate preschool facilities	4.4	6.2	4.1	9.0
(d) Dislike climate	0.0	0.05	0.1	0.0
4. Family and personal circumstances, including:	32.6	22.4	21.2	20.9
(a) Marriage	2.0	1.8	1.2	0.0
(b) Rejoining family or relatives	23.5	12.4	13.3	7.5
(c) Health (worker or family)	6.8	6.7	6.1	11.9
(d) Childbirth	0.3	1.5	0.6	1.5
5. Other reasons, or reasons not stated	21.0	6.0	5.4	10.4

Source: Akademiya nauk SSSR ... *Zapadno-sibirskii ekonomicheskii raion,* 1967, p. 189.

Table 5-3
COMPARISON OF SURVEYS OF REASONS GIVEN FOR VOLUNTARY
TERMINATION OF EMPLOYMENT, BY SELECTED MAJOR
CATEGORIES ONLY
(in percent of total responses for each survey)

Reasons Given	Kemerovo Province	Novosibirsk City	Krasnoyarsk Province	Leningrad City	Institute of Labor
Wages	11.4	18.7	17.5	23.5	13.8
Work and working conditions	14.4	17.85	13.9	37.4	17.4
Living conditions	20.8	24.65	19.4	29.9	15.9

Source: Brown, 1966, p. 37, sources cited in footnotes 81, 82, and 83 on p. 347.
Kemerovo and Novosibirsk data from Table 5-2.

As a guide for policymakers, these data are useful mainly as a reminder that a whole variety of circumstances must be corrected and improved in order to bring about greater labor force stability. The fact that few emigrants mentioned dislike of the climate as a principal reason for leaving should give heart to economic planners, since this is the one thing that cannot be changed. On the other hand, those who actually may have left because they couldn't stand the weather probably preferred to cite other reasons. The policymakers should also learn that the quality of life in the plants and factories counts for something too. For all that has been written in Soviet newspapers about lack of housing, day-care facilities, shops, good transportation, and other amenities as primary reasons for Siberia's labor problems, the surveys do indicate that wages and working conditions weighed somewhat more heavily among the complaints than did living circumstances.

The lesser availability in parts of Siberia of housing, services (particularly medical), preschool facilities, and other necessities is the subject of frequent Soviet press comment. Table 5-4 compares the availability of these items as between the WSR and the Central Economic Region as of 1962 according to indices based on averages for the entire Russian Republic.

The WSR's lower real wages are surprising at first in view of the favorable wage coefficients established for some industries. However, coefficients exist only for certain branches of industry (not for construction, transportation, or services) and in some cases for individual enterprises rather than for industries as a whole. The

Table 5-4

INDICATORS COMPARING THE STANDARDS OF LIVING IN
THE CENTRAL ECONOMIC REGION* AND THE WESTERN
SIBERIAN ECONOMIC REGION
(as a percent of averages for the Russian Republic, per thousand population,
i.e., Russian Republic = 100)

	Economic Region	
Indicator	*Central*	*Western Siberian*
Real wages of workers and employees†	100	92
Housing space	105	93
Number of schools‡	89	105
Number of kindergartens‡	157	81
Number of nurseries‡	124	83
Number of physicians (except dentists)	135	83
Number of dentists	123	71
Number of auxiliary medical personnel	118	84
Number of places in sanatoriums§	86	62
Number of places in rest homes	143	71

*Moscow Province and a number of surrounding provinces in European Russia.

†Does not include collective farmers.

‡Presumably this means the number of places rather than the number of institutions.

§ This simply reflects the fact that sanatoriums are clustered in the warmer southern provinces.

Source: Akademiya nauk SSSR ... *Zapadno-sibirskii ekonomicheskii raion,* 1967, p. 185.

heightened intraregional differentials, while they may help stem job leaving from major industries in the WSR, also have the effect of promoting turnover *within* the region. No studies have been made of high turnover, but such a conclusion would be the exact opposite of Stalin's argument in 1931, already cited.[22] Furthermore, many foodstuffs are more expensive in Siberia than elsewhere due to transportation distances and special problems of storage and preservation. A family budget survey done by the Labor Institute in the early 1960's found expenditures on foodstuffs in the WSR to be 7 percent higher than in the Central Economic Region, clothing and footwear 17 percent higher, and fuel more than twice as high. These differences are not the result of the U.S.S.R.'s zonal price system, since the WSR and the Central Economic Region are both in the same zone, but of climatic factors plus a certain "slippage" in price

[22]Akademiya nauk SSSR .... *Zapadno-sibirskii ekonomicheskii raion,* pp. 187-188.

administration.[23] One Soviet correspondent reported from Irkutsk that while Siberian production costs for meat and dairy products are lower in Eastern Siberia than in the Central Economic Region, prices for these products are in fact higher in Eastern Siberia, even though both are located in the same price zone. Imagine, he wrote, an animal slaughtered in Siberia whose carcass is divided and the halves put on sale in Moscow and Irkutsk. It will still command a higher price in Irkutsk, regardless of the long journey in a refrigerator car required by the half delivered to Moscow.[24] Meanwhile, not only the industrial heart of the WSR, but other industrial areas of Siberia along the Trans-Siberian Railroad are covered by increased wage differentials only in a limited and uneven fashion.[25]

In some cases, it is simply the growing pains of new industries which are responsible for high labor turnover, since inefficiency and disorganization in the use of labor may accompany construction in new areas, and the first years of a new plant's operation. The USSR State Construction Bank's representative for Kemerovo Province blamed the high labor turnover among construction workers on the scattering and inefficient use of resources in that branch of the economy. The Kemerovo Chemical Industry Construction Trust was seriously behind in its construction targets in 1961-62; but instead of concentrating its manpower and material resources on the most important chemical plants, it took on a number of civil construction contracts on the side. In 1961 the Trust lost two thirds of its personnel, who "quit in droves, fed up with the chaos and the low wages," since spasmodic work patterns made it impossible to organize a rational system of incentives.[26]

The consequence of all these shortcomings for the WSR's urban labor force during the 1960's has not been a shortage of labor in simple numerical terms. It is primarily the engineers, technicians, and skilled workers who are in short supply as a proportion of the total labor force. Much of the skilled manpower comes and goes on in the manner described, while unskilled labor builds up in the cities. The villages of the WSR have been drained of labor as urban jobs increase in number, and it is the ex-villagers who form a substantial

---

[23]Akademiya nauk SSSR . . . . *Zapadno-sibirskii ekonomicheskii raion*, 1967, p. 185. See also Perevedentsev, 1964, p. 82, and Gordeyeva, 1964, pp. 85-88.

[24]L. Shinkarev, "The Blacksmith's House," *Izvestiya*, March 27, 1968.

[25]Batkayev and Markov, 1964, pp. 165-69.

[26]F. Artamonov in *Sovetskaya Rossiya,* November 11, 1962; trans. in *CDSP* XIV:46, p. 13.

proportion of the WSR's unskilled urban labor.[27] The shortage of
child-care facilities plus shortcomings in the availability and retailing
of consumer goods has meant that a greater-than-average proportion
of the working-age population is engaged only in domestic chores,
the most important of which is raising food on family plots during
the summer. Although according to 1964 data the proportion so
occupied was only 10 percent in Novosibirsk City, it averaged 25
percent in other urban areas of Novosibirsk Province, and was high as
40 percent in some towns.[28]

What are the policy implications of the turnover problems? Having
encouraged young people of talent to move as high on the
occupational ladder as they are able, and having provided them with
rewards in status and compensation, Soviet economic and educational planners have refrained from advocating use of the force of
law to induce them to repay the state for their education in any
fashion. The workers of low skill and middle-level skill, those who
have not been able to get onto the upper rungs of the educational
ladder, are not prevented by any law or policy from wandering from
place to place (save to certain of the largest cities) in search of the
best compensation that is open to them, or from interrupting their
working lives with further attempts to get ahead through education.
So policymakers must seek the solution to what they consider
excessive migration (which includes occupational and educational
"migration" as well as the geographical variety) in better social
planning. This means specifically: (*a*) environmental planning which
will equalize living conditions in various parts of the country and
which will also make the city dweller feel "at home" even in a
burgeoning new industrial city in a remote area; and (*b*) occupational
and employment planning of a kind which will provide meaningful
guidance at the crucial turning points of a young person's education
and career "ladder."

In wage and earnings policies, a basic policy choice for greater
equalization was made in the latter 1950's which is described below.
While living with the consequences of this decision has not always
been comfortable for Soviet policymakers, it is doubtful that this
decision will be altered in the foreseeable future. In environmental
and occupational planning, some of the most important difficulties
are "programmatic," having to do with running programs rather than

[27]Perevedentsev, 1965, pp. 17-19.
[28]Zykov, 1964, p. 68.

with making policies. It is easy, for example, to write central directives telling enterprise administrations to set up "big brother" programs which will bring young workers into a fruitful relationship with older workers and thereby ease their entry into industrial work; it is quite another matter to make sure that such a program is successfully run, something which depends much more on the temper of the enterprise administration than on the thoughts of policymakers in Moscow. On the other hand, where such basic environmental improvements as housing and services are concerned, *Gosplan* the central ministries and the economic policymakers of the Party Secretariat are faced with a clear alternative of making investment of this kind keep pace with industrial growth in the high-turnover areas of Siberia and elsewhere. Criticism of the lag of civil construction investment is a familiar theme in the press.[29]

POLICIES FOR ORGANIZING POPULATION MOVEMENTS

The rulers of Russia have been concerned with large-scale population movements since the 16th century. The deportation of suspect ethnic and social groups to remote areas, the binding of agricultural laborers to the soil, the use of conscript labor gangs for long-term construction and mining in remote areas—all of these were used by the Tsars. In this respect the Stalin regime was simply solving old problems which had recurred in modern form by using harsh means familiar to Russian governments of other eras.

Today the instruments for organizing the geographical distribution of the industrial labor force, outside of the incentive system itself (see below), are these: (1) the State Committee for the Use of Labor Resources, which in 1967 succeded *Orgnabor*, the Organized Labor Recruiting Service whose history is summarized below; (2) the work assignment system for graduates of higher education, the technicums, and the vocational schools; and (3) mass campaigns for bringing young people to areas of new industrial or agricultural investment. The first two channels of recruitment include both long-term settlement and assignments of limited duration; the new State Committee deals not only with permanent resettlement, but also with the three-year contracts for work in the Far North, where recruits are not really expected to settle permanently. The assign-

---

[29] See L. Shinkarev, *op. cit.*

ment system for graduating specialists has already been described. In itself, the assignment obligates graduates for only three years, but assignments are handed out in the eternal (and often disappointed) hope that the young specialists will settle permanently where they have been sent. The third device, the mass campaigns, include the Komsomol's annual student expeditions to the Virgin Lands area of Kazakhstan, a program which now embraces many different kinds of summer employment in all parts of the country. While the students—ordinarily the equivalent of juniors—stay only for a summer, other campaigns have been aimed at permanent resettlement of young people. There were revived in 1954 after a lapse of two decades, with the much-publicized "public summons" (*obshchestvennyi prizyv*) to young people to join in starting new state farms in the Virgin Lands area of Kazakhstan.[30] There were other such campaigns later in the 1950's, but the 1960's did not see extensive use of this type of appeal, certainly not as a device for effecting permanent resettlement.[31]

What evidence is there that compulsion is used today in the process of resettlement? We have already seen the absence of any effective sanctions for compelling graduating specialists to fulfill their job assignments. In the case of the Komsomol's summer work programs for students, considerable pressure has been used in the past, at least, even if the Komsomol can compel no one. Refusal to take part in at least one summer expedition to Kazakhstan or elsewhere might result in an inconvenient black mark on one's record, affecting both further studies and subsequent career choices. The writer recalls a student at Moscow University who in the spring of 1964 gravely informed foreign students that "The Virgin Lands recruitment is going to be voluntary from now on—and that's official."

One way of removing alcoholics, petty criminals, suspect parolees, and other undesirables from Moscow and the other cities of the European U.S.S.R. is the choice sometimes offered them by the militia (police) of taking a jail sentence or reporting to *Orgnabor* for resettlement. In 1962 *Izvestiya* published complaints by officials in the Siberian hardship areas that *Orgnabor* was sending them recruits of dubious background and motivation. Some of them had been pressured to take work assignments through *Orgnabor*, including a

[30]Described by Sonin, 1959, Ch. 9.
[31]Dol'skaya, 1959, pp. 97-98.

number of alcoholics. Several Moscow enterprises confirmed the reporter's impression that the ones who left their employment included a fair number of problem cases whom their employers were glad to be rid of. In the north of Irkutsk Province, the militia detected several thousand workers who had come in an attempt to avoid alimony payments. But part of the reason why *Orgnabor* was dealing with the dregs was that it was doing so little to promote and publicize job opportunities.[32] In this respect it was no competition for the Komsomol, whose success in recruiting young people by the tens of thousands for crash projects is well known. In spite of these indications that pressure and compulsion have been used in recent times, the writer has found no evidence that during the 1960's either *Orgnabor* or its successor have depended mainly on these methods for gaining recruits.

Part of the problem of supplying Siberia with labor through migration and resettlement is that, in spite of the many laws and regulations providing benefits for migrants, there has been such poor governmental coordination of the actual employment process. *Orgnabor* was performing a marginal role at best by the first half of the 1960's. It remains to be seen whether the defects of this loosely coordinated agency will be made up by the new administrative structure which replaced it in 1967, the State Committee for the Use of Labor Resources. *Orgnabor's* job notices have been a familiar sight on bulletin boards in the cities and towns of European Russia and the Ukraine since the early 1930's, but the volume of its placements declined greatly after World War II. During the first decade following its establishment in 1931, *Orgnabor* made as many as 5 million job placements annually, mainly in the unskilled and semiskilled categories. In 1958 this volume had declined to 700,000, of which 200,000 were seasonal placements. The jobs offered at this point were largely in the Siberian north and other hardship areas.[33] Part of these totals were collective farmers from the labor-surplus areas of the European U.S.S.R.—the western fringes of the Ukraine and Byelorussia, and some south-central provinces of the Russian Republic. One of *Orgnabor's* basic programs was that of resettling these farmers in the agricultural areas of Siberia, though of course nothing prevents them from migrating to the Siberian cities later on, as many do.[34]

---

[32]*Izvestiya*, September 15, 1962.

[33]Brown, 1966, pp. 29-33; Sonin, 1959, Ch. 7.

[34]Dol'skaya, 1959, pp. 97-98.

The results of the decline of organized recruiting were shown in the studies of migration patterns in the WSR carried out by the labor resources specialist Viktor I. Perevedentsev at the Novosibirsk branch of the Academy of Sciences. These showed that for the early 1960's, at least, 85 percent of the migration in and out of the Region was accounted for by individuals not under the auspices of any organization or resettlement service. Perevedentsev assumed that the percent of nonorganized migration throughout the country was over 50 percent at least.[35]

These shortcomings should be seen not as the failure of an existing policy, but rather as the consequence of the failure to devise and implement any kind of comprehensive policy at all. Comprehensive regional planning of labor resources has yet to be realized, even for the areas of Siberia which would stand to gain most from its application. Even the availability of information on manpower needs and manpower supply is limited. Apparently *Orgnabor* did little to systematize and make public the data gathered from its own operations.[36] Perhaps more important than any of these factors was the fact that *Orgnabor* was geared primarily to dealing with the demand for unskilled and semiskilled labor. It was scarcely equipped to coordinate the kind of information which would lead to satisfactory placements for skilled labor and technicians, who are understandably more demanding about the positions to which they are referred. Probably it was the Soviet economy's steadily declining need for unskilled and low-skill labor that dealt the death-blow to the old recruiting system.

No comprehensive nation-wide hiring system, or even the complete centralization of employment information, has ever been attempted, even within separate industrial branches. Indeed, there would be hardly any practical way for Moscow to stop casual hiring by labor-hungry enterprises even were it the policy to do so. While no comprehensive data are available on the channels through which hiring is carried out, the writer's impression from many conversations on the subject with Soviet citizens is that most enterprises hire most of their work force below the technician level without using an employment service or intermediary organization. This is often done

---

[35]Perevedentsev, 1964, p. 80.

[36]This, in any case, is the opinion of Vladimir I. Markov, a research economist with the Russian Republic Gosplan, who has specialized in labor resource problems. See his article in *Planovoye khozyaistvo* No. 10 (October, 1965), pp. 1-8. Trans. in *Problems of Economics* IX:2 (June, 1966), pp. 37-43. The relative lack of economic data by region was noted by L. Shinkarev, *op. cit.*

by placing job notices in the local press, and by posting them at the factory gates. Exceptions may be those enterprises in hardship areas and remote places which are not near any population centers which might provide a source of labor.

Yet another cause of the problems of organized recruiting has been the lack of proper motivation to use it rationally, both on the part of the employer and on the part of *Orgnabor* personnel themselves. Employers in need of labor that is not available locally have tended to inflate the requests they send in to *Orgnabor* and its successor, requests which *Orgnabor*, at least, was unable to verify independently. Promises concerning wage levels and nonwage benefits have been similarly inflated; as a result, skilled workers would arrive at their new jobs only to find themselves placed in jobs beneath their skill level, at lower wage grades than they had expected, and housed in temporary structures rather than in the new apartments they had been promised. The enterprise administration in such cases was not even under an obligation to hire the persons sent to it by *Orgnabor*, and it paid nothing for *Orgnabor's* services. The staff of *Orgnabor*, for its part, received bonuses according to the number of workers it sent, and not according to the number actually hired. However, neither the employers nor their prospective employees were under any obligation to work through *Orgnabor*. The head of the new State Committee for the Utilization of Labor Resources for the Russian Republic stated in 1968 that these abuses still needed to be corrected.[37]

It remains to be seen whether *Orgnabor* has been effectively reorganized or simply renamed. The State Committee for the Use of Labor Resources is actually 15 separate organizations operating in each of the 15 Union Republics; of these the Russian Republic is by far the largest, and contains the bulk of the nation's hardship employment areas. The Russian Republic's Committee inherited from *Orgnabor* the whole pyramid of provincial and local offices. Appointed as the new chairman was Konstantin A. Novikov, the former First Party Secretary of Archangel Province and long a top official in this northern area, which doubtless had had labor supply problems of its own.[38] In the first year of its existence, the Russian

---

[37]"Who will Go To New Places?" *Izvestiya*, September 18, 1963; Yulia Vus, "To New Places," *Izvestiya*, December 19, 1963; *Literaturnaya gazeta*, May 15, 1968; "Whom Does Organized Recruiting Offer Us?" *Izvestiya*, February 24, 1968; reply by K. Novikov in *Izvestiya*, July 9, 1968.

[38]*Vedomosti RSFSR* 1967, Nos. 8 and 13.

Republic's 13,000 local offices placed 873,000 persons. More important was the fact that the Committees began participating in the drafting of plans for industrial location and siting, and in policy decisions concerning the training of industrial workers. All this was in with the recommendations of Perevedentsev, who stressed that all aspects of labor distribution be coordinated by republic-level agencies.[39]

Some initial problems of the new agency were observed by an economist and an *Izvestiya* reporter who jointly did some spot checks. As of the fall of 1968, the number of applicants in many places was still low, due to lack of publicity. Also, the local offices were forbidden to give job information to anyone already employed, clearly a regulation made in the hope of not encouraging further turnover. This means that employed workers are obliged to tour other cities and enterprises themselves if they want to change jobs, which means a loss of working time. Finally the employment offices do not operate on the basis of economic accounting.[40] In short, what has been the Soviet Union's largest employment agency, far from being an instrument of regimentation or compulsion, has been used less and less as a result of its not having found a suitable role in the nation's economy during the last quarter-century.

POLICY ALTERNATIVES FOR BETTER LABOR PLACEMENT AND DISTRIBUTION

The possible courses of action for reducing turnover in a region like the WSR are these: (*a*) penalties, (*b*) central administrative control of hiring, nationally or by economic branch, (*c*) special incentives, (*d*) equivalence of conditions with other areas, and (*e*) building of morale. Penalties can be of the legal variety, but those which have been discussed have been largely deprivation of various benefits which workers normally receive. Special incentives may include extraordinary wage rates at all grades for the hardship areas, or extraordinary fringe benefits for these same areas. Equivalence may include extra outlays, for example, transportation subsidies to cover vacation transportation for workers in remote parts of Siberia, who must make long and expensive journeys to the resorts of the

---

[39]Manevich, 1968; Perevedentsev, 1965, p. 95.

[40]Ya. Antosenkov and V. Davydchenko, "Turnover: Causes and Consequences," *Izvestiya* October 10, 1968.

south. Such was the complaint of the director of a metallurgical plant in Temirtau in the Kazakh desert, who was losing skilled workers to another metallurgical plant in the climatically favored Sea of Azov area; and round-trip air ticket to the Black Sea costs 220 rubles.[41]

The public discussion of policy alternatives in the latter 1960's has focused largely on psychological and sociological factors. Hardly any mention is made of using penalties, and there is little stress on disincentives. Most interesting of all, much of the discussion concerns the types of human contact which should be promoted. For example, a group of academic figures proposed in 1962 that higher educational institutions provide some kind of follow-up program for their graduates during their three-year assignments. They recommended first that institutions specialize in a geographical area in making their assignments, to give the opportunity to their graduates to keep in touch with one another and feel the continuing support of the "collective." This is particularly important where the graduates are schoolteachers, for example, assigned to isolated rural localities. This degree of geographical concentration would in turn make possible consultations, refresher programs, and other means of retaining meaningful ties between the graduate and his alma mater. Above all, it is important that these ties not be broken off, as normally happens at the time the job assignment procedure is completed. The "collective" must continue its psychological and professional support.[42]

One particularly intriguing policy proposal would link advantages in purchasing cooperative apartments to stable employment records. Under this plan, workers would contract with their savings banks for an advance, made after a specified period of time, covering part of the down payment on a cooperative apartment; and in return, the depositors would continue their deposits, and in general show themselves to be reliable credit risks, with no tendency to flit from job to job. The same could be done for time purchases of automobiles and other consumer durables.[43] There is probably some truth in the argument that in the United States, consumer credit has

---

[41]*Literaturnaya gazeta*, May 8, 1968, p. 10.

[42]P. Barkov *et al.*, "The Institute and Its Charges," *Izvestiya*, February 9, 1962. Trans. in *CDSP* XIV:6, p. 10.

[43]Ya. Zhukovskii, "Get Your Apartment at the Savings Bank," *Literaturnaya gazeta*, November 1, 1967.

been promoted consciously by business as a means of keeping the labor force stable.

An increasing amount of the public discussion of turnover and employment choices concerns the importance of a smooth, planned transition from secondary school to work, and of the human adjustment of young workers on their first industrial jobs. Advances in both of these areas are not likely to be the object of central legislation or of major central policy decisions, simply because they depend so much on local initiative and on evoking proper human initiative and attitudes. Where employment of secondary school graduates is organized locally, it takes the shape of placement plans drawn up by the district or provincial government, working in consultation with employers, the trade unions, and Party officials. Graduates apply to their district department of public education for assignments to specific employers. The success of any such arrangement naturally depends on the cooperativeness of employers, which according to many newspaper accounts is not to be taken for granted.[44] The very idea of reserving jobs for secondary school graduates and school leavers is the result of the enterprises' conviction that teen-agers cause far more than the usual amount of expense and trouble for reasons described above. The one central policy decision which might serve to reduce the resistance of enterprises would be instituting a system of subsidies to enterprises in proportion to the teen-agers they hire; but during the last dozen years the thinking of economic reformers has tended so strongly in the direction of eliminating subsidies that this does not seem a likely step at present.

Even less amenable to solution through central policy measures, but of importance for labor force stability and the worker's whole attitude toward his career, is the lack of attention to young workers newly arrived on the job. In the account of the American steelworker quoted above, it was the differences in levels of job security and insecurity that accounted for the gulf between the novices and the workers with seniority. While technological unemployment has begun to appear in the Soviet Union, as everywhere else in the industrialized world, it is still of limited scope. Furthermore, workers released because of reduction in staff do not lose their uninterrupted

---

[44]Some typical items are: K. Zakaliuk, "After the Graduation Dance," *Izvestiya*, February 8, 1968; V. Shuboderov *et al.,* "Where Are Teen-Agers To Work?" *Pravda,* May 28, 1965; "Show More Concern For Adolescents," *Pravda*, December 26, 1964.

work record for social insurance and pension purposes.[45] Nevertheless, to judge by the volume and content of the public discussion of
inattention to young workers, their occupational and psychological
adaptation remains a problem. Failure to deal with adaptation
problems is held to be a major cause of frequent job changing and
career changing among young people. A correspondent observed
after a survey of enterprises in Khabarovsk: "Often teen-agers have
just stepped across the threshhold of an enterprise when every kind
of indication is made to them that they are unwelcome guests. . . . In
doing this, adults forget that even the most 'ill-bred' boy feels both
anxiety and joy when he first comes into a workers' collective."[46]

The system of "patronage" (*shefstvo*) exercised by experienced
workers over newly employed young workers has long been in
existence; the function of the "patron" is that of watching over
training and adaptation to work relationships. At least it has long
been encouraged in the mass media, though at the same time no data
have come to the writer's attention which would indicate the extent
to which it has actually been practiced. Leningrad's large "Elektro-
sila" plant recently experimented with an extension of this system.
Its 300 patrons were renamed "counselors" (*nastavniki*), and each of
these was either assigned three or four workers, or placed in charge
of a brigade consisting of young workers. The special feature of this
counselor relationship, which was set up with the assistance of
educators and psychologists from the Leningrad Pedagogical Institute, is that it is meant to foster a set of small social units rather than
only work relationships. While Soviet social researchers have displayed some interest in the interaction of social and work relations,
this is a new field even by comparison with the country's very young
field of empirical social research generally.[47]

Industrial societies offer their citizens opportunities for expressing
their satisfaction or dissatisfaction with their lot which can be more
potent and revealing than the use of the ballot box. To enable the
individual to find his place amid the complicated array of roles which
an industry-based society requires, he must be offered choices in
order to assure his finding a role in which he will perform
adequately. Talent, even talent for humble occupations, cannot be

[45]Brown, 1961.

[46]Zh. Chesnokov, "I Would Like A Job," *Pravda*, December 1, 1967. Trans. in *CDSP* XIX:48, p. 29.

[47]S. Vipchenko and A. Kubikov, "Counselors," *Izvestiya*, March 24, 1968; Platonov, 1965, Ch. 10; Zdravomyslov *et al.*, 1967, Chs. 2 and 3.

commanded to appear and develop; it must be nurtured, and to do this means offering possible talents a chance to prove themselves. Once the talent is discovered and trained, it must be induced to cooperate, to adapt, and, at the higher job levels, to innovate. While pressure and restrictions may be used to get a steady performance of routine tasks out of a given labor force, improvement of skills and adaptation to increasingly complex processes depends heavily on the human environment and human organization. Central policymakers may pull a great number of policy "levers" without improving this environment appreciably. Local initiative and individual example must, if they are permitted to do so, come to the fore as a major force for change. Here, just as in the educational policy problems described in Chapter 4, the time may have come when Moscow's central labor policy planners are willing to make room for much greater diversity of labor practices among enterprises, localities, and industrial branches.

"THE POWERFUL LEVER OF MATERIAL INTEREST"

Assume that a young worker who has tried several employers in more than one region of the country has decided to commit himself to a particular enterprise and a particular specialty. What kind of concrete rewards await him for using and improving his skills, and for becoming a steady performer on the job? Wages and salaries may be used to reward performance on the job, loyalty to the job, or the attainment of a particular skill level, or they can be used simply as recognition of the worker's right to a living because he contributes to the economy, to the best of his ability, eight hours a day. The first three of these may be used to some extent in combination; none of them can be combined easily with the egalitarianism of the last principle. If any one of them is applied in an extreme fashion, it rules out the use of the others in any but a marginal way.

Certain comrades feel that the movement for a communist attitude to labor is "something loftier than material interests." Such opinions cannot be considered correct. V.I. Lenin categorically noted: "Shock work is preference, but preference without consumption is nothing. . . . Preference in shock work is also preference in consumption. Without this, shock work is a dream, a figment, while we, after all, are materialists."—V. I. Yagodkin, economist and labor specialist.[48]

. . . . .

———
[48]*Pravda*, November 23, 1964. Trans. in *CDSP* XVI:47, p. 4.

For some reason or other, uninterrupted work at the same enterprise has ceased to be appreciated here in the past few years. And there is the same price, i.e., the identical wage according to the rate scale, for a man who has just come to the collective and who has changed his place of work dozens of times and for an old worker who has given half his life to one plant or construction organization. People must be materially rewarded for many years of conscientious work in one collective.—S. Tikhonov, brigade leader of a construction trust in Almet'yevsk.[49]

. . . .

The wage adjustment measures (made since 1955) reflected the Party's line of gradually eliminating the difference between high incomes and relatively low incomes among the working people. However, the process of bringing wage levels closer together has nothing in common with leveling. It is directly related to reducing differences in qualification levels and labor productivity and with the replacement of unskilled labor with skilled labor. . . . . It must be said that full use is not yet being made everywhere of the favorable opportunities for implementing the principle of equal pay for equal work created as the result of the introduction of the new wage payment terms. Some economic officials reduce the problem of material incentives to a matter of mechanical increases in rates of pay. . . . . —Alexander P. Volkov, chairman of the U.S.S.R. State Committee on Labor and Wages.[50]

. . . .

The elite was ready to accept equality because [as a consequence of the lavish fringe benefits considered necessary to sustain their top performance] they no longer cared about income, and ordinary people because they still did care about it. Mr. Roberts' Equalization of Income Act of 2005 married the interests of all classes in society in a most singular way. Since that time every employee of whatever rank has received the Equal (as emoluments are officially called) simply by virtue of being a citizen, and the differences between grades have been recognized not any longer by salaries but by the payment of such varying expenses as could be justified by the needs of efficiency. Employers have, of course, been allowed to give benefits to technicians, too, if they wished. . . . . Technicians have a mere seven-hour stint and so naturally cannot claim the same consideration as professional staff who are in effect on the job for twenty-four hours a day. . . Equalization of income has brought to an end much of the old, wearisome argument about differentials.—Michael Young, *The Rise of the Meritocracy*.[51]

Even the drastic solution discovered by Michael Young's "merito-cracy" of the 21st century made a certain concession to the seniority principle, let it be said, in allowing periodic wage increases for the

---

[49] *Trud*, February 8, 1963. Trans. in *CDSP* XV:6 p. 35.
[50] *Pravda*, April 4, 1962. Trans. in *CDSP* XIV:14, pp. 6-8.
[51] Pp. 158-59.

workers ("technicians" now, all of them) because they had been used to it and because it helped keep up morale. But most interesting is the fact that wage egalitarianism in this perhaps-not-so-fictitious society was *not* the result of agreement on equal per capita rewards as a good principle. It stemmed, rather, from the same basic philosophy expressed in the Volkov quotation above: the purpose of rewards is to maximize the performance of the economy, and even the egalitarianism of the communist future is justified only if this is its effect. So of the three quotations above, only the first advocates pay as a reward for human qualities or behavior which are not necessarily related to work performance, in this case loyalty to the job.

How Wage Differentials Began. The history of Soviet labor reward policies shows a fairly complicated "mix" of rewards promoted by central policies, which range from highly differentiated money rewards to purely psychological rewards.[52] Wage differentials, both within and among industries, have been present throughout the history of the Soviet labor force as performance and skill-improvement incentives. Bonuses have constituted a significant portion of wages throughout, and are drawn both from enterprise wage funds and from the "Enterprise Fund" (earlier the "Director's Fund," established in 1936), whose size varies with enterprise profits. Nonmoney rewards for extraordinary labor performance by individuals and groups have been a constant feature of the reward system, though they have passed through peaks and troughs as campaign succeeded campaign: the voluntary work days (*subbotniki*) of the 1920's; socialist emulation (*sotssorevnovaniye*) in the form of contests among enterprises and work groups; shock work and Stakhanovism in the 1930's; the "Brigades of Communist Labor" during the Khrushchev period; and numerous honorific reward devices—"Certificates of Merit," "Red Banners," "Rolls of Honor," and the like.

Wages, salaries, and money rewards for labor of all kinds have been subject to tight central control since the beginning of the Soviet regime, however much these have been modified by administrative "slippage" or improvised modifications. Consequently, wage differentials have a distinct national policy history of their own. This history began with a brief and unsuccessful attempt in 1917-18 to reduce all administrative and managerial salaries to the level of

---

[52]For the history of Soviet wage policies, as well as for more comprehensive data on recent wages, see: Bergson, 1964, Ch. 6; Conquest, 1967, Ch. 2; Brown, 1966, Ch. 10.

earnings of the average worker. Differentials both within wage scales and among wage and salary scales were on the increase until the mid-1920's, when trade-union chief Mikhail P. Tomskii pushed for radical application of a Party directive calling for a narrowing of differentials. In Moscow, Leningrad, and the Urals some worker enthusiasts were going even further by banding together in voluntary groups, pledging to increase output, and pooling their pay in order to redistribute it in equal sums, with some accommodation made for dependents.[53] Stalin, as we have seen, put a sudden end to these pressures in 1931. The vastly increased wage scale and interindustry differentials of the 1930's and 1940's were justified publicly in terms of their consequence for output, and for no other reason. During this entire 1931-53 period there is no hint that Stalin and the top administrators of Soviet industry had any other effect in mind.

A 1960 study by Murray Yanowitch (of Hofstra University) found in the wage differential increases of the 1930's a political motive commingled with the economic motive of directing skilled labor to vital industries: this was the need to maintain the political loyalty of critical portions of the labor force at a time when average real wages were declining. If there was a serious question of political loyalty in the 1930's, by the mid-1950's the political problem could scarcely have occupied as large a place as it did earlier.[54]

While one is always tempted to try to identify social and political motives in the midst of economy-oriented motives, this particular suggestion is a vulnerable one. Why, in this case, should the Soviet government have favored a minority at the risk of further increasing the dissatisfaction of the majority with its living standards? For such a theory to stand up, one would have to assume that the skilled workers of the 1930's were also those most capable of being led or organized in some manner which could have endangered Stalin's political system. While Stalin and the political leaders of the 1930's may have been impressed with the special political potential of the upper stratum of workers from their experience in the Russian Revolution, neither they nor we have much evidence for assuming that this potential was present in the early five-year plans as well.

What had happened in fact was that wage differentials as among industrial sectors, which had been greatly heightened in the 1930's in order to direct labor to priority sectors of the economy, were being

---

[53]Wesson, 1963, p. 205.

[54]Yanowitch, 1960, pp. 190-91.

heightened still further by the actions of industrial ministries and by individual enterprises as well. The fact that between the mid-1930's and mid-1950's nearly three quarters of the man-hours expended were compensated by piece-rate systems enabled enterprises to manipulate earnings through constant readjustment of the work norms of which piece rates were based. Further manipulation of earnings was made possible by the complicated system of bonuses, which varied greatly from one industrial sector to the next, but was (and still is) applied to piece-rate and wage-rate workers alike. By the mid-1950's nearly half of all earnings were being paid out in the form of bonuses of various kinds. Wage scales, which had remained unchanged since the early 1930's, had lost much of their meanings as the basis of work norms, consequently, the norms themselves were rigged so as to provide automatically large bonus payments.[55]

The "Wage Revolution" of 1959-63. In November 1958 the Khrushchev administration announced its intention of raising the proportion of basic wage rates in overall earnings to 70 or 75 percent for piece-rate workers, and to between 75 and 85 percent for time-rate workers.[56] The great variety of bonuses which make up the balance of earnings may be augmented from the Enterprise Fund, which is accumulated by enterprises in proportion to their profits. While the Fund serves a number of purposes, premiums can be paid from it as long as their total does not exceed 5.5 percent of the enterprise's annual wage bill (7 percent for some industries).[57]

During this same period of the late 1950's, the proportion of time-rate to piece-rate jobs was increased in most branches of industry. In the industries for which data are available, time-rate workers were not more than half of the total in any in 1956; by 1961, only the woodworking and shoe manufacturing industries retained less than 30 percent of their workers on time rates, while time-rate positions formed 91 percent of the total in oil refining, 82 percent in oil extraction, 61 percent in the chemical industry, and 51 percent in the coal industry.[58] This measure too permitted the State Committee on Labor and Wages to keep closer watch over actual

---

[55] See report of Lazar' M. Kaganovich at the 20th Party Congress in 1956. *XX S" yezd KPSS* Vol. I, pp. 527-29.

[56] *KPSS v rezolyutsiyakh*, Vol. 4, p. 353.

[57] *Sbornik zakonodatel'nykh aktov o trude,* 1960, Ch. 6.; Conquest, 1967, pp. 63-67.

[58] Gendler, 1961, p. 65, *Vestnik statistiki*, No. 6, 1962, pp. 94-96. Cited from Table 1 in Yanowitch, 1963, p. 689.

earnings levels, which had been generally less predictable under piece rates than under time rates.

Thus, control over industrial earnings had in some respects slipped from the hands of the policymakers, one result being that unforseen increases in the wage bill contributed to inflation in the 1930's, The creation in May 1955 of the U.S.S.R. State Committee on Labor and Wages marked the beginning not only of a largely successful effort to restore order to wages, but also the beginning of a new policy on wage differentials.[59] The Committee was first headed briefly by Lazar' M. Kaganovich, then from 1956 to the present by Alexander P. Volkov. Shortly after its founding, Khrushchev and Mikoyan, at the 20th Party Congress in 1956, called for a reduction in earnings differentials. They advocated both an increase in the lower earnings categories and a reduction of some of the top industrial earnings. Mikoyan, particularly, called for "liquidation of the excessive gap which can be seen in our country between the wages of low-paid and high-paid workers and employees." The gap had been justified, he continued, during the earlier period of industrialization because of the pressing need for skilled workers. But now, because of rising educational and training levels, "although differences must be retained, still they will be reduced."[60]

Significantly, the spokesmen for a reduction in differentials did not justify this policy in terms of a philosophical ideal of distribution, but quite simply in terms of its effect on productivity. Khrushchev's statement on the subject set the tone for other policymakers: "We must persistently improve and perfect the forms of earnings in all branches of the economy, place earnings in direct dependence on the quantity and quality of each employee's work, and make full use of the powerful lever of material interest for the purpose of increasing labor productivity."[61]

"Material interest," for the individual worker, was henceforth to be reckoned much more in terms of stimuli for improvement of skills than it had been in the past. Consequently, the worker's most important incentive would be the prospect of rising from one grade (*razryad*) to the next along the wage scale (*tarifnaya setka*) of his particular industry. Moving from grade to grade depends much more on skill improvement than on work performance alone, and not at all on seniority. For example, basic wage rates in the machine-building

[59] *Vedomosti SSSR* 1955, No. 8.

[60] *XX S''yezd KPSS* Vol.1, pp. 74-75, 307.

[61] *XX S''yezd KPSS*, Vol 1, p. 75.

industry following the 1959-63 wage reforms looked as follows:

		Wage	
		Lowest	*Highest*
Grade	*Coefficient*	*Scale*	*Scale*
I	1.00	48.00	68.00
II	1.13	54.24	76.84
III	1.29	61.92	87.72
IV	1.48	71.04	100.64
V	1.72	82.56	116.96
VI	2.00	96.00	136.00

Payment of bonuses can add roughly an additional 25 percent to each wage; these depend on individual and group performance, and to a limited extent on enterprise profits. The more important industries generally used several base rates, within the limits set by the lowest and highest permissible wage for Grade I; the larger enterprises get the higher wages, but all within the industry use the same system of coefficients. A few heavy industries use seven-grade systems, and the iron and steel industry uses 10 grades.

At issue in the work of the Committee on Labor and Wages were two coefficients: that between the highest and lowest grades on any given wage scale and that between one grade and the next. The ratio of the lowest to highest grades had risen from the very narrow confines of 1:1.6 in the early 1920's to 1:2.8 in 1927 and 1:3.6 in 1932, with many individual exceptions among the large number of scales in use, which by the 1950's numbered some 2,000.[62] Yanowitch's reconstruction of maximum differentials for piece-rate workers only shows them to have risen from 1:2.85 in 1932 to 1:3.6 in 1940-44, then to have been cut to 1:2.42 in 1946, only to have risen to 1:2.8 in 1956, when the Committee on Labor and Wages began issuing its own scales.[63] In the latter 1950's the Committee began using scales of 6, 7, and 8 grades having a maximum differential of 1:2.8. By the early 1960's its scales typically used a 1:2.0 ratio for nonpriority heavy industry branches and nonfood light industry, plus a slightly lower 1:1.8 for food industries.

Table 5-5 shows the consequences of the post-1956 changes for a number of leading industrial branches. The comparatively high differentials accorded to mining and metallurgy reflect both the

[62]Maier, 1963, pp. 96-97; Kapustin, 1962, p. 26.

[63]Yanowitch, 1960, pp. 180-81.

continuing importance of these branches, the difficulty of the work, and the need for an assured labor supply. The remaining differentials are on the order of 1:2.0, which actually represents a slightly greater postreform differential in the case of some of the wage scales in consumer industries.[64] This table supports the conclusion of Yanowitch that on the whole there has been a moderate reduction of differentials.

Table 5-5
MAXIMUM BASIC WAGE RATE DIFFERENTIALS BEFORE AND AFTER THE
WAGE REFORMS OF 1956-63, AS COEFFICIENTS OF GRADE I, BY
INDUSTRIAL BRANCH

Branch	Prereform Differentials			Postreform Wage for Grade I, Lowest and Highest Scales in Rubles
	Wage Scale with Smallest Differential	Wage Scale with Largest Differential	Postreform Differentials	
Coal mining	3.14	3.76	3.75	52.70 and 82.00
Ferrous metallurgy (basic production)	3.34	4.06	3.2	52.70 and 65.50
Ferrous ore mining	2.52	3.14	3.2	64.80 and 67.80
Nonferrous ore mining	2.53	3.68	2.85	64.80 and 73.50
Nonferrous metallurgy (basic production)	2.47	3.62	2.6	52.70 and 67.80
Cement	2.38	3.05	2.4	n.a.
Chemicals and chemical extraction	2.01	3.24	2.3	52.00
Oil	2.46	3.09	2.0	52.00 and 69.00
Machine-building and metal-working	1.86	3.56	2.0	48.00 and 68.00
Glass	1.79	3.26	2.0	n.a.
Building materials	1.79	3.26	2.0	n.a.
Woodworking	2.07	2.72	2.0	n.a.
Paper and cellulose	2.11	2.59	2.0	n.a.
General foodstuff processing	1.85	2.17	1.8	45.00
Fish processing	1.38	2.63	1.8	45.00
Meat and milk processing	1.25	2.20	1.8	45.00

Source: Batkayev and Markov, 1964, pp. 65-67; Maier, 1963, pp. 141-44, 150.

Differences among the lowest basic wage rates (Grade I of each of the various wage scales) of different industries were substantially reduced as well. Where in 1956 the highest such rate (that of the coal industry) was 50 percent above the lowest rate (that of some food industries), this difference had been reduced to less than 20 percent

---

[64]Yanowitch, 1960, p. 186 and Table 7, p. 184.

by 1963.[65] This has the effect of grouping the wages of unskilled and low-skill labor for all industries at roughly the same level.

The policy of "closing the gap" between low and high earnings in the labor force as a whole, which would nevertheless stop short of the type of wage levelling promoted in the early 1920's, was expressed in a Central Committee resolution of 1958 and confirmed in the control figures for the seven-year plan of 1959-65.[66] This approach was finally enshrined in the Party Program of 1961:

Ever larger masses of unskilled workers and employees will become skilled, while diminution of differences in levels of labor skill and productivity will be accompanied by a systematic reduction of differences in pay levels. As the welfare of the entire population rises, low income levels will rise towards the higher income levels, and gradually the differences will be reduced between the incomes of farmers and workers, low-paid and high-paid workers, and among the incomes of the population of various regions of the country.[67]

In raising the wage levels of the lowest-paid workers, the makers of wage policy rejected a proposal by the State Committee on Labor and Wages for larger percentage increases among the lower grades of each scale than among the higher grades.[68] According to this proposal, the lower-paid workers would get a proportionately larger reward than those in the upper half of each scale for increasing their skills and/or their productivity. However, most of the scales which were actually adopted after 1956 typically display percent increases from grade to grade which increase somewhat toward the top of the scale.[69] The actual effect of these new scales on earnings depends very much on the policy of the enterprise and the kind of work norms which it sets. For one thing, the tendency to keep only a small proportion of the work force in the lowest grades has prevailed in many enterprises after the wage reforms just as it did before.

There has been little specific policy emphasis on seniority as a basis for additional earnings. According to Alexander P. Volkov, head of the State Committee on Labor and Wages, bonuses specifically for length of service at a given enterprise are distributed

---

[65]Kapustin, 1964, p. 291.

[66]*KPSS v rezolyutsiyakh*, Vol. 4, p. 323.

[67]*XXII S"yezd KPSS*, Vol. 3, p. 296.

[68]This had been proposed in the Committee's magazine, *Sotsialisticheskii trud* No. 9, 1956, p. 5.

[69]See the samples given by Conquest, 1967, p. 48.

only to part of the workers: only one fifth of the nation's workers and employees ever received them at any given time in recent years. It would cost too much to introduce this for the entire working force. Hence, from now on rewards for a long and unbroken labor record will be paid only from that part of profits earmarked for incentives. At the same time, Volkov has repeatedly stressed the necessity of a firm link between productivity and bonuses.[70] To be sure, seniority may be quite important to workers in determining their eligibility for nonmoney benefits, first of all their priority in housing assignments. Changing jobs may be somewhat disadvantageous for those in the higher wage grades, who may find themselves in lower grades when they begin work elsewhere. If one compares the effect of *overall length* of one's work record on pension and social security benefits, with the corresponding effect of an *unbroken work record* at a given enterprise (and "unbroken" admits of many exceptions), one must conclude that the money incentives for staying at the enterprise are intended to play only a modest role as compared with incentives for work performance and skill improvement.

Managerial Rewards. Personnel from foreman on up are grouped for statistical purposes as "Engineering and Technical Personnel" (ETP). The ratio of ETP salaries to workers' wages is of some interest. When salaries and wages are each averaged for all industry, the most striking thing is that the ratio of ETP salary averages to wage averages declined from roughly 2.5:1 in the early 1930's to 1.5:1 in the early 1960's, at the conclusion of the major wage-reform drive of the Khrushchev period.[71] Differentiation within the ETP can still be rather high, however, even after the reforms. In 1963, according to one Soviet economist's data, the lowest differential between average technicians' salaries to average plant directors' salaries was a mere 1:1.6, while the highest (in the high-priority industries and those with difficult working conditions) was 1:4.2.[72] Technicians receive salaries whose levels are roughly those of wage rates in the upper half of wage scales for their industries; consequently, they often earn less than skilled workers. Between technicians' salaries and those of the director fall the salaries (in ascending order) of engineers, foremen, shop chiefs, chief specialists, and

---

[70]*Pravda*, November 14, 1965; May 15, 1967.

[71]Maier, 1963, p. 98; Bergson, 1964, p. 114; Yanowitch, 1963, pp. 688-91.

[72]Maier, 1963, p. 159.

directors of departments. Tables 5-6, 5-7, and 5-8 show some of the few salary scales available by individual industry in ruble figures. They do *not* include bonuses for the enterprises' production performance, which are considerable in the case of the directors and

Table 5-6

BASIC MONTHLY SALARY RATES FOR MANAGERIAL, ENGINEERING, AND TECHNICAL PERSONNEL IN THE ASBESTOS AND GRAPHITE INDUSTRIES, 1959

(in post-1960 rubles)

Position	Category I Enterprises	Category III Enterprises
Director	250-280	190-220
Chief specialists and directors of departments	180-200	140-160
Chiefs of basic shops	180-200	140-160
Chiefs of other shops	140-160	110-130
Mining foremen; production foremen	130-150	110-130
Other foremen	110-130	90-100
Engineers	100-120	90-110
Technicians	70- 90	70- 80

Source: Bergson, 1964, p. 113. Bonuses are not included in these rates, of course.

Table 5-7

COMPARISON OF WORKERS' BASIC MONTHLY WAGE RATES WITH BASIC MONTHLY SALARIES OF MANAGERIAL, ENGINEERING, AND TECHNICAL PERSONNEL IN THREE INDUSTRIES, FOLLOWING THE 1959-63 WAGE AND SALARY REFORMS

(in rubles)

Position	Basic Wage or Salary Rate		
	Machine-building Industry	Textile Industry	General Foodstuff Processing Industry
Director	330*	n.a.	210-280*
Shop chief (highest group)	150-180	130-150	
Shop chief (lowest group)	130-150	110-120	100-115
Foreman (highest group)	115-125	110-120	95-105
Foreman (lowest group)	90-100	90-100	75- 85
Engineer	85-100	80-100	80-100
Technician	70- 80	70- 80	70- 80
Time-rate worker in the 6th (highest) grade	96	86	81
Time-rate worker in the 1st (lowest) grade	48	51	45

*Computed from approximate ratios of the lowest technician's salary to the director's salary given in Batkayev and Markov, p. 143. This may be supplemented by the "personal salary" described in Chapter 3.

Source: Batkayev and Markov, 1964, pp. 139, 143; Table 5-5.

Table 5-8
BASIC MONTHLY RATES OF PRODUCTION AND NONPRODUCTION
PERSONNEL IN CONSTRUCTION, 1969 SCALE*
(in rubles)

Position	*Basic Wage or Salary Rate†*
Within a trust: ‡	
Chief of production department, also chief specialist	160-190
Chief of planning and economic department	150-190
Chief of personnel department	135-170
Within an administration:	
Chief of administration	170-190
Chief of supply office, chief of production department	150-190
Chief of planning and economic department	150-180
Senior work superintendent	180-200
Work superintendent	160-180
Foreman, shop mechanic	135-150
Engineer	120-160
Technician	100-125
Accounting and related personnel	90-145
Typist, clerk, cashier, and similar positions	70- 80
Time-rate worker in the 6th (highest) grade	137
Time-rate worker in the 1st (lowest) grade	76

*Applies to all construction organizations, regardless under what auspices they work.

†The first six rates shown are differentiated by size and type of construction organization. This table shows the total span.

‡The trust (*trest*) is the largest unit of organization in the construction industry. The administration (*upravleniye*) is a smaller production unit, often operating under the auspices of organizations outside the construction industry proper.

Source: *Ekonomicheskaya gazeta* No. 5 (January 1969), p. 19.

upper salaried personnel. In 1958 an attempt was made to legislate a 350-ruble ceiling on the monthly salaries of managerial personnel.[73] However, the writer heard from several Soviet officials in 1963-64 that this had been widely ignored or circumvented in practice. The wage reform did effect a certain reduction in maximum differentials both within the ETP, including enterprise directors, and within enterprise personnel as an entire group, including both ETP and workers. In the salaries for the machine-building industry, shown in Table 5-7 at their postreform levels, the ratio of a plant director's

---

[73] *SP SSSR*, 1958, No. 3. However, this did not affect existing salaries above the 350-ruble level.

salary to the lowest technician's salary used to be 7:1 instead of the present 4.7:1; in the textile industry, it was formerly a maximum of 5:1 instead of 4:1.[74]

As the last two columns of Table 5-5 suggest, earnings differentials among industries represent a careful appraisal of labor skill priorities, together with an estimate of the relative difficulty of maintaining a stable labor force in various industries. The coal industry's average earnings, for example, rose from 14th place among Soviet industrial wages in the late 1920's to first place by the end of the 1930's, and has remained there ever since. Simultaneously, iron ore mining and ferrous metallurgy rose from 12th and 9th place, respectively, to 2d and 3d place. In 1956 they were followed, in order, by petroleum, paper, metalworking, electric power, and chemicals, after which came the light industries, with food processing and clothing manufacture in the last two places.[75] At about this same time, average earnings in the coal industry were 48 percent above the average earnings for all industry, and food industry earnings were 31 percent below it. Gertrude Schroeder's 1966 survey of differentials in other leading industrial nations (France, Italy, Great Britain, and the United States) shows that interindustry differentials among Soviet industries are just about the same as those on the European continent generally, although no industry in Great Britain or the United States has average earnings of more than 25 percent above the national average.[76]

Regional Differentials. Most of the Soviet Union from the Urals and Western Kazakhstan eastward is assigned wage differentials which apply to the basic wage rate. The WSR's maximum differential of 1.2 for example, would increase a 100-ruble basic monthly wage to 120 rubles, with the usual bonuses added to this. In most areas, however, two or more differentials are applied according to the type of industry. Workers in extractive industries usually receive the highest differential for that area, and workers in heavy industries the various lower differentials. In Central Asia and those parts of southern and eastern Siberia which do not qualify as hardship areas, workers in light industry and consumers' goods enterprises generally are assigned no coefficient at all. Basically, the coefficient is meant

---

[74]Batkayev and Markov, 1964, p. 143. (See Table 5-7)

[75]Bergson, 1964, p. 115.

[76]Schroeder, 1966, pp. 316-17.

to do two things: to provide compensation for a higher cost of living occasioned both by higher prices on foodstuffs and certain nonfood products, and by the extra clothing and dietary needs required by the more severe climate; and to direct more workers and specialists into the labor deficit areas. The following differentials were in effect in 1964:[77]

(1) Urals, Western Siberia, Kazakhstan . . . . 1.10 to 1.20
(2) Far East, southern portion of Eastern Siberia,
      certain parts of the European North . . . . 1.20 to 1.30
(3) Central Asia . . . . 1.15 to 1.30
(4) Murmansk Province . . . . 1.40 to 1.50
(5) Areas similar to the Far North . . . . 1.30 to 1.50
(6) Certain European areas of the Far North . . . . 1.50 to 1.80
(7) Siberian areas of the Far North . . . . 1.60 to 2.00

For certain climatic hardship areas (e.g., deserts and remote mountainous areas) which are not in (6) and (7), there are differentials of roughly the level of those in the Far North.

State *price differentials* are assigned according to three broad zones: the lowest prices are in the Ukraine, the Caucasus, Central Asia, and the black-earth zones of the European U.S.S.R. generally; next come the nonblack-earth zone of European Russia (including Moscow), the Urals, the WSR, and some other southern portions of Siberia; the highest prices are in the Far North and parts of the Far East. But the differentials for state prices are not great: less than 1:1.2 between the lowest and highest for foodstuffs (except milk, vegetables, and others for which no state zonal prices are set) and just over 1:1.1 for nonfoodstuffs. However, a price comparison of the purchases made with a minimum worker's budget shows an actual differential for the Far North, all types of prices considered, of 1:1.5. In some parts of the Far North this is even greater, 1:1.7.[78]

In the hardship areas of the Far North, and in the slightly less favored belt of hardship areas immediately to the south of this (item 5 above), a *wage supplement* is paid in addition to the differential wage rate. The supplement, like the differential, is derived from the normal basic wage rate. In certain regions of most severe climatic hardship along the Arctic Ocean, it adds a further 10 percent to the wage rate every six months, up to a rate of 100 percent of earnings

---

[77]Batkayev and Markov, 1964, p. 184.
[78]Maier, 1963, pp. 260, 263.

or 300 rubles per month, whichever is less; the supplement in other Arctic fringe areas increases somewhat more slowly after the first three years, and the other hardship areas south of the Arctic fringe receive a 10 percent supplement every 12 months. Thus, an engineer in a mining enterprise in the Noril'sk area who for similar work in the European U.S.S.R. would get a basic salary of 120 rubles per month can receive as much as 240 rubles in salary alone with the differential reckoned in, and at the end of three years a further 120 rubles monthly in supplements, or somewhat more if his share in bonuses is reckoned into basic earnings. For skilled workers, engineers, and technicians, total earnings of as much as 500 rubles are not uncommon in such area.[79]

While the lure of earnings is great in the Far North, the makers of wage and labor policies clearly do not expect any considerable portion of the labor force to settle there permanently. The latest law on benefits in these areas, in fact, reduced the normal labor contract period from five to three years. Industries in parts of the Soviet Far East (Khabarovsk Province, chiefly) have been having some success in attracting a permanent labor force.[80]

A common labor service dating even from before the official change to three-year contracts has been the three-year stint in which workers and specialists serve for two and a half years on the job without significant interruption, then take the six months of paid vacation they have accumulated during this period and relax in the southern vacation areas, or look for other work. These and other hardship area benefits are not unlike those enjoyed by workers in northern Scandinavia (at Sweden's iron mines at Kiruna, for example), northern Canada, and equivalent areas. In the Soviet Union these princely earnings are popularly known as the "long ruble," and are sometimes the subject of moralizing in the press in view of the fact that the money incentive seems uppermost in the motives of a large part of the northern labor force.

IS A NEW PHILOSOPHY OF WORK EMERGING?

While the Soviet management of wages, salaries, and other work compensation is a most complex field of study, and one bedevilled—

---

[79] *Vedomosti SSSR* 1967, No. 39, Art. 519.

[80] See, for example, Maria Ivannikova, "Results of the Experiment," *Izvestiya,* February 6, 1969.

at least for foreign observers—with large gaps in information, the direction of Soviet policies since the 1950's is clear. Compensation of all types at all levels is to remain geared to productivity for the foreseeable future, and this policy will continue to be justified publicly in terms of productivity. The raising of the lowest earnings, some of which represented less than a living wage for an individual or a one-income family, has been simply an administrative hastening of a process which was already taking place in industry. The decline in the ranks of unskilled labor in proportion to the total labor force, together with competition among industries for labor of all kinds, had been emptying the lowest wage grades anyway. The low-paid service occupations, including teaching, whose "output" cannot be measured in money or things, benefited from an analogous raising of the "floor" only when the consequences of not offering a greater reward threatened to be a numerical or qualitative decline in these occupations. Such a decline would have had a bad effect on the portion of the labor force engaged in production. A skilled labor force needs a better basic education, and deficiencies in everyday services had turned out to be a major factor in promoting high labor turnover. Meanwhile, an effort was made to curb some of the very highest wages and salaries. But probably, if there were enough data to provide an exact answer, it would turn out that raises in the lowest wage categories were paid for, so to speak, not by cutting down managerial salaries, but by holding the line on the highest wage categories as productivity rose.

From a philosophical point of view, the small circle of men which has made these major decisions has been "speaking the language" of conventional money incentives. The "language" of appeals to other human instincts and satisfactions has occupied them, too, but its role has been a subordinate one. These men have assured the Soviet labor force repeatedly that it is not their intention in the foreseeable future to reduce the length and height of the money reward "ladder" any further. What was done in the 1950's and 1960's to bring the lowest-paid members of the industrial labor force up off the ladder's bottom rungs, and to eliminate these low rungs altogether, was grounded primarily in economic common sense. The actual minimum income needed by an individual to keep body and soul together settled at around 60 rubles during these two decades; and this had to be taken into account in making provision for the dwindling ranks of unskilled laborers. The younger of these eventually learn skills and improve their incomes, but they had to be provided for meanwhile. They had to be given a substantial incentive to leave their home towns and settle permanently in the country's most labor-hungry areas. Above all, they had to be motivated to improve their skills, which might mean sacrificing profitable overtime pay in order to work to finish high school at night, and then train at an enterprise-sponsored technicum. The regularization of wage scales, and the increased role of basic wage rates in overall earnings, seem calculated to intensify the motives for skill improvement by comparison with the motives for quantitative output on a given job.

Soviet Marxist ideology has long maintained that it is socialism's particular nonmaterial incentives that make the difference between the behavior of labor forces under socialism and capitalism. The "combined use of material and moral stimuli" became the leading work-motivation principle of the Khrushchev period. To the writer, it seems that the real emphasis of this period was on adjusting and refining individual material rewards. Even the 1961 Party Program stated bluntly that during the 1960's and 1970's, until the foundations of communist society are complete, "the building of communism should rest on the principle of material interest." In spite of the planned expansion of the social wage, according to the Program, earnings from labor are to remain the basic mechanism of consumption until the 1980's at least.[81] Moral stimuli were used mainly in the form of public honors for high performance, including the banners issued to labor teams for attaining high performance standards under the "Movement for Communist Labor," now 10 years old. The effect of concrete rewards has been much analyzed, but that of nonmaterial rewards is only now beginning to get attention. *Gosplan*, industrial ministries, and professional economists have long devoted attention to the use of wage differentials and other money rewards in shaping the labor force's composition and performance. The first study of the effect of nonmaterial stimuli on performance was that of Andrei G. Zdravomyslov and V.A. Yadov of Leningrad University, who in the mid-1960's studied the performance correlates of some 2600 workers in 25 Leningrad enterprises.[82] The results are described below.

Actually, the notion of a "material" stimulus is not sharply

---

[81] *XXII S"yezd KPSS*, Vol. 3, 1961, p. 296.
[82] The final results are embodied in Zdravomyslov, *et al.*, 1967.

opposed to that of a "moral" stimulus in Soviet ideology. The category of moral stimulus excludes rewards in the form of money earnings, whether for individual performance or group performance. But from the 1950's on, especially, with the increased emphasis on public welfare, *moral* stimuli were interpreted in the mass media and official statements as *concrete rewards of the near future* in the form of the social wage and the increasing availability of consumer goods. These rewards include those social wage items whose abundance and quality depends on the profitability of the enterprises whose workers they serve. Consequently, it is hard to draw any clear line between the moral and the material. Hence, "moral stimulus" may be translated as instilling awareness of very tangible consumption increases which do not happen to take the form of increased earnings. There is nothing inappropriate about the desire of Soviet economic planners to create this particular awareness, except that the use of the term "moral" to describe it is somewhat curious.

One noted economist at Moscow University wrote in *Pravda*, that he would eliminate the distinction between the two types of stimuli altogether by positing that what is good for the worker's pay envelope is good for the welfare of society as well: "The personal material interest of each worker in the result of his labor is at the same time his interest in developing society's productive forces. The harmonious conjoining of personal and social interest is the basic characteristic of material interest under socialism."[83] Some months later, *Pravda* carried a strong rejoinder by the writer Grigorii A. Medynskii, who has written extensively and with considerable perception on the motivational problems involved in crime and juvenile delinquency. Moral stimuli, he argued, must not be debased by assuming that they are by-products of material stimuli. The latter are a means to an end, while "ideals are a source of action, a mainspring, an inner motor of human conduct, the impulse for the truest and most powerful stimuli."[84]

In some ways, Soviet labor policies have long recognized the role of work performance correlates which are neither material rewards on the one hand nor saturation with slogans on the other. From the time of the earliest five-year plans to the present, the mass media have stressed the role of the labor "collective" as an important factor in shaping the attitudes and personal growth of its members. The

---

[83]V. Yagodkin, "Labor and Its Stimuli," *Pravda*, February 10, 1967.
[84]Grigorii Medynskii, "Stimuli and Ideals," *Pravda*, August 2, 1967.

collective is recognized by Soviet law, in fact, in a much-used provision which permits wrongdoers to be released to the custody of their working collectives as an alternative to conviction and punishment, the collective then assuming responsibility for its wayward fellow worker both at work and in leisure hours.[85] Another probable correlate of good work performance, the intrinsic interest of work, is recognized in the many official prophecies that the monotonous jobs and heavy physical labor will eventually be abolished, thanks to further mechanization and automation. Jobs of the future will be sufficiently complex to sustain interest and pride in achievement.

Aleksei M. Rumyantsev, an economist, Party official, and Central Committee member who is considered the chief promoter of empirical research in the social sciences, recently painted the following optimistic picture of the relation of man and work:

All labor will be intellectual, which will require a high level of education and intelligence. This labor by its very nature will be creative, and not for a minority but for the masses, for everyone. A substantial proportion of former working time will be converted to free time. Gradually the other prerequisites necessary for the manifestation of all the people's creative forces will be created. "The service of man" will begin to play an ever more important role in administration, and increased attention will be paid to satisfying the full range of his requirements—scientific-production, consumption, and everyday, cultural-esthetic and medical—and to developing truly human relations in production and in daily life. The sciences dealing with the needs and behavior of people—the economics of consumption, sociology, psychology, hygiene, etc.—will become more important.[86]

Significant recent labor-motivation findings by social scientists in both the Soviet Union and the United States may, if they are accepted by Soviet policymakers, render centrally legislated motivation systems a good deal more problematic. Theodore Herzberg, a psychologist at Western Reserve University, has developed a "motivation-hygiene theory" according to which efforts to manipulate work motivations through money rewards and tangible fringe benefits are dealing with a very small segment of the motivation question. Honorific rewards, furthermore, have a negligible effect. Of the two sets of needs which Herzberg identified, man's "need as an

---

[85] Art. 52 of the RSFSR Criminal Code of 1960, with corresponding provisions in the other republic codes.

[86] A. Rumyantsev and P. Bunish in *Izvestiya*, November 16, 1967. Trans. in *CDSP* XIX:46, p. 5.

animal to avoid pain" (hygiene component) and his "need as a human to grow psychologically" (motivation component), earnings constitute only one of a varying number of components of the first set. The placing of earnings among the avoidance-of-pain components rather than among the positive motivators was the result of numerous studies in which earnings turned up far more frequently as a source of job dissatisfaction than as a source of positive feelings toward work. Even this role of earnings as "dissatisfiers" turned out to be considerably less important than such factors as company policy and administration, and relations with one's superiors.[87]

One wonders, after studying the numerous trials and replications of Herzberg's survey, how any one experienced in setting wages and salaries, whether nationally or in a single shop, could possibly regard his task as related in any direct sense to work performance or employment behavior. The concern of Soviet leaders and wage administrators to avoid wage "levelling" seems largely unnecessary; indeed, a nation with such a strong egalitarian component in its official philosophy and popular thinking may be well advised to imitate Michael Young's "meritocracy" in avoiding certain dissatisfactions by pursuing a more egalitarian wage policy, and concentrating instead on intrinsic work satisfactions and work-oriented fringe benefits.

Herzberg believed his findings to be confirmed by the preliminary report of the Yadov-Zdravomyslov survey of the motivations of 2,600 young workers in industries in the Leningrad area, carried out in the mid-1960's.[88] The final report of this survey (1967), however, did claim to establish a high correlation between earnings and work performance. At the same time the report explains the survey's low correlation between "work content" and work performance (except at the extreme upper and lower ends of the work performance scale) in terms of special circumstances. But the conclusions which the authors draw, once these circumstances have been taken into account, are like those of Herzberg as regards the content of the work itself in terms of interest and meaningfulness. There are high correlations with work performance in the case of longer periods of work in one's specialty as opposed to shorter periods; and there are high correlations with Party membership, participation in civic

---

[87]Herzberg, 1966, pp. 71, 125-27, *et passim.*

[88]Preliminary results of this were published in *Voprosy filosofii*, No. 4 (April, 1964), pp. 72-84; the full report is Zdravomyslov, *et al.*, 1967.

activities outside of work, and participation in the "movement of communist labor," a system of intergroup competition on the job. The variety of high-correlation factors led the survey's authors to conclude, unlike Herzberg, that "it is first of all *social circumstances* which determine the social essence of the worker's relationship to his work."[89] By "social circumstances" is meant the ideals of Soviet society generally, which permeate the consciousness of all workers living in this society, but in varying degrees. These are measured in terms of participation in service-oriented organizations outside of work and in voluntary activities for improving work performance. Once these factors are regarded as constants, however, then work satisfactions and motivations stemming from the character of work itself occupy the place which Herzberg assigns to them. On the basis of these data, the Leningrad team concluded that it had refuted Herzberg's view that motivations within the work process operate in the same way no matter whether the factories are owned by socialist governments or private investors.[90]

Gennadi V. Osipov, head of the Soviet Sociology Association, contended that recent research pointed to good relations among groups of workers—the "collectives"—as a key correlate of good production performance:

From a sociological standpoint, the central question of management is the regulation of relations within the collective. The point is that the solidarity of the collective depends on the state of these relations, as does its readiness to fulfill production assignments. Research conducted in the mining industry of the Northeast, for instance, has shown that labor turnover is less and indices are better where the so-called "collective-spirit coefficient," i.e., the strength of the ties within the production group, is highest. This strength has often been achieved not through raising wages but through the presence of the necessary qualities on the part of the leader and the selection of brigade members united by common interests.

This conclusion has been tested against the experience of other industrial enterprises; the same results were obtained everywhere. . . .[91]

No matter whether these potentially significant codicils to Herzberg's findings can be verified by further surveys in the Soviet Union, the United States, and other industrial nations, both

[89]Zdravomyslov *et al.*, 1967, pp. 288-89.

[90]Yadov, 1965.

[91]G. Osipov, "Man, Labor and the Collective," *Pravda*, January 11, 1969. Trans. from *CDSP* XXI:2, p. 19.

Herzberg's conclusions and those of the Leningrad team suggest that the promotion of both work satisfactions and good work performance is becoming less and less a matter of manipulating material rewards, including fringe benefits and various amenities. "Hygiene" motives, that is, will be of less use as a means of preventing excessive labor turnover, of stimulating good work performance, and of spurring workers to improve their qualifications and to make creative contributions to the work process. The most that can be done from Moscow is to assure that the "hygiene" factors are kept above a comfortable minimum throughout the country, to provide special compensation for work in hardship areas, and to prevent affluent enterprises from manipulating their labor rewards in a way that would give them a large advantage over other enterprises which are competing for the same people and the same skills.

Stress by enterprises on the intrinsic interest of work, while it is not necessarily incompatible with central control of work compensation, may not be compatible with central control over the size and skill level of an enterprise's work force. The 1965 reforms did indeed give enterprises more autonomy on both these scores. The labor-motivation findings described above lend weight to the case for enterprise-level determination of the progress of automation, consequently also of labor force specifications. In fact, if the volume of case histories reported in the Soviet press and professional journals indicates a trend, it appears that after the 1965 reforms many enterprises did in fact make use of this autonomy.

Even more significant, probably, is the impetus which the Yadov-Zdravomyslov study and others like it are giving to the social sciences themselves. The idea of survey research in the area of human satisfactions and dissatisfactions swiftly gained acceptance in the early 1960's. If the 1970's produce some kind of Soviet policy decision concerning further investment in this research, it may be over the question of whether to pour massive resources into investigating human satisfactions, wants, and drives. If the answer to this is positive, the Soviet Union will have an unparallelled opportunity to break new ground in studying man as worker and creator.

.6. *Organizing the Urban Environment*

Urban planners and officials everywhere have had to face increasingly the question of how far they can or should attempt to shape social relations through shaping the urban physical environment. It is safe to say that there is no consensus on this question in any country. Among professional planners in the West, one need not look far to find many who are sometimes called "ecological determinists." For them the man-made physical environment is fundamental both to the interactions of men and to men's reactions to the society they live in. However, this outlook is not necessarily shared by the officials, municipal councilmen, and legislators who must approve the things the planners plan and allocate resources for them. Among these officials and legislators, especially in the United States, one is far more likely to encounter the opposite outlook, namely, that urban social behavior has causes of its own which are not directly related to whatever the planners might plan. In this country, the conviction is widespread that public demand for different types of housing and residential environments will on the whole evoke an appropriate response from governments, builders, zoning boards, and planning officials; therefore, organization of the physical environment by professional planners should concentrate on whatever things are most sought by city and suburban residents, whether it happens to be low residential density, convenience of services, good accessibility to other areas, proximity to city centers, or whatever. Only in large city centers, and in certain other areas with respect to which

187

there cannot be public "demands" in the usual sense of the word, should governments and the planners who serve them regard themselves as determiners of the environment in any comprehensive sense.

Such a view may be buttressed with the argument that social interaction in modern urban areas is no longer place-oriented anyway. Therefore, it cannot be affected by the actions of urban planners, at least not by using the means of planning which are available locally. The citizen's reaction to his physical environment and the people who inhabit it, one may argue further, are related to his ability to choose from among a variety of environments, and to his ability to extend his friendships and activities over a wide geographical area if need be. What he wants from the immediate environment of his residence is a rather limited, but to him quite important, group of features which vary with family status, age, and individual preference.

At the time of the Russian Revolution, the discussion of these problems as they apply to large industrial cities was only in its beginnings in the United States and the West generally. At that point in history, the most prominent specific theories about the relation between physical environment and society had to do with creation of small ideal communities apart from the large cities. England, during the century that preceded World War I, had provided especially fruitful soil for proposals and projects of this sort, beginning with the model communities of the industrialist Robert Owen (1771-1858) and ending with the garden cities of Ebenezer Howard (1850-1928). But as concerns the planning of existing large cities and the growth of new cities, there were as yet no well-developed theories applicable to the problems of the 20th century which the young Soviet government might have used as a point of departure.

The writings of Marx and Engels devoted scant attention to urban physical planning, save for some comments on specific evils which these two founders of Marxism saw around them in the industrial cities of Britain and Europe. Friedrich Engels as a very young man had published a 300-page study of the economy, society, and living conditions of Manchester (*The Condition of the Working Class in England*, 1845) which among other things interpreted the city's physical organization as the result of the needs of the great industrialists and the upper middle classes. But the remedy for these ills which Marx and Engels proposed was little more than a throwback to the strong antiurban strain in utopian social thought of the early 19th century. The *Communist Manifesto* (1848) called for "gradual abolition of the distinction between town and country by a more equable distribution of the population over the country." Engels' elaboration of this statement 30 years later sustained its antiurban character while stressing that distribution of industry over the countryside was essential for the further development of industry itself, as well as for the development of agriculture. His main point was that there would be no justification at all for large cities under communism because, he asserted, it is impossible under any economic system to maintain hygienic surroundings within them.[1] Thus, from the Marxian classics Lenin and his government inherited a rudimentary planning outlook which strongly favored a highly industrial society but opposed large concentrations of population.

From his own experience in promoting revolution, however, Lenin had learned to place emphasis on large concentrations of industrial workers not only as the most appropriate seed-beds for a proletarian revolution, but also as the social environment in which the social relations of the communist future were being shaped in the capitalist present. From this premise, Lenin and his colleagues understandably drew the conclusion that the urban society which his regime inherited, small as it was in proportion to Russia's population, had already been shaped decisively. Lenin, like other Marxists, believed further that the relation of the individual to the society around him was a function of his economic relations with this society, specifically of his role in production and his reward for productive labor. If large urban population concentrations had been important in carrying out the Russian Revolution, the fact of concentration was beside the point after the Revolution. For that part of the population which consisted of urban workers, the role of urban planning would be subordinate to the proper organization of economic relationships. For the rural population, however, the manner in which cities grew and developed was to have a decisive social impact. The urban way of life must ultimately spread throughout the countryside, Lenin believed, and the collectivization of agriculture would be only a transitional step in this regard.

It was certainly to the advantage of the Soviet regime that it did *not* inherit any rigid guidelines for urban planning, and that it dealt

---

[1] Friedrich Engels, *Herr Eugen Dühring's Revolution in Science* (New York: International Publishers, 1939), pp. 322-23.

flexibly with the views of Marx and Engels on the subject. A ready-made philosophy, embedded either in Marx's own thought or in Soviet Marxist ideology, might easily have inhibited creativity in the same manner in which, for example, it so long obstructed creativity in economic thought. Soviet architects and urban planners have consequently been less inhibited about borrowing ideas from the capitalist West than their colleagues in economic planning have been. In seeking the answer to a given problem, they are under no obligation to identify the problem strictly in Marxist terms, even if this is often done in fact. For example, Soviet urban planners during the past decade have been concerned about the increasing tendency of city dwellers to withdraw into their private lives. Also, much has been written about the aimless, unorganized use of free time by a certain proportion of teen-agers and young people generally, a phenomenon which Soviet criminologists associate with delinquency and crime. Is a different kind of "microdistrict" part of the answer? Or the widespread introduction of the "commune-type" apartment house? In the 1960's, Soviet architects, urban planners, and (most recently) sociologists have produced an abundance of designs, experiments, and studies which may lead to answers for these problems.

This is not to say that the work of urban planners has been unaffected by strong preferences on the part of the top political leadership. A recent example of this was the preference of the Khrushchev administration for five-story walk-up apartments over high-rise apartments. A similar example is the ideological preference for apartment living over individual houses as a means of creating a proper setting for social interaction at places of residence. But actually this preference is buttressed more often with economic than with doctrinal arguments: Apartment living in properly equipped microdistricts makes it possible for housewives and mothers to work; it enables residents, whether employed or not, to volunteer their time to help sustain an even higher level of services—in recreation, for example—than state budgetary funds provide for. But the absence of formal ideological structures on the individual house has meant that in small towns, rural areas, and small isolated industrial communities ("workers' settlements" or "urban-type settlements") one may get a state loan for building an individual house. The contribution of the individual garden plot—which is one of the advantages of having a one-family dwelling unit—to the economy has been publicly acknowledged during the last 15 years. The various analyses of the Western Siberian Region (see Chapter 5) which point out the high proportion of housewives who labor in their garden plots rather than industry do not blame such families for harboring socially backward attitudes, but rather criticize the trade and supply network for not maintaining the kind of food supply which would render garden plots superfluous.

A boon to the early Soviet leaders in formulating urban planning policies lay in their thoroughly positive attitudes toward the city and toward urban life generally. To Americans, because of the vast growth of concern with urban problems in the United States in the 1950's and 1960's, this seems to be merely stating the obvious. Actually, much of our own serious lag in attention to urban problems, in a nation which was 50 percent urban by 1920, can be ascribed to a social outlook mistrustful of cities and city life, which was widely shared by political and economic leaders until fairly recent times. This same outlook held the qualities of life in rural and small-town society to be the desired norm; life in large cities tended to alter these qualities for the worse. Cities could serve the economy but not society, for their effects on society were largely negative: increasing impersonality in human relations, indifference of man toward his fellowmen, the breakdown of primary-group controls, the increased need for external controls, and the proliferation of huge, impersonal organizations. This image of the city may have been either vastly oversimplified or simply wrong, but the important thing is that, in many separate versions, it was widely believed in the United States.[2] With this belief went a fatalistic attitude toward the circumstances that produced all these undesirable social effects in the city. The norms of the small town might perhaps be re-created in a suburban setting, but few Americans believed that the inner city could sustain them.

The victory of the Bolsheviks in 1917 was among other things the victory of an urban-oriented political movement over a rural-oriented movement. The political defeat of the Social Revolutionary Party in 1917-18 brought to an end some 35 years of debate among the leftwing political groupings over the economic future of Russia. Industrial workers, though a small proportion of the working

---

[2] See Harold L. Wilensky and Charles N. Lebeaux, *Industrial Society and Social Welfare* (New York: Russell Sage Foundation, 1958), Ch. 5, for a critique of these beliefs about the city.

population at the time of the Revolution, were now considered to represent the future society in microcosm. Soviet leaders saw in them that vital part of the population most capable of creating a new social and physical environment, and most responsive to this environment after its completion. Rural attitudes and rural living conditions would ultimately be abolished as such, they believed, for the progress of the countryside would henceforth be measured in terms of the infusion into it of urban attitudes and conditions. Some urban planners of the 1920's advocated dispersion cities and linear-type layouts as suitable means of pumping, so to speak, the ideas of the cities into the country.[3] The farms would become enormous food factories; those who worked them would live in comfortable apartment communities and commute to their mechanized occupations just like any industrial worker.

Consequently, there remained little room in the outlook of the new leadership for a Tolstoyan appreciation of rural Russia. Rural attitudes and habits would change slowly, at best, and this would require the guidance of city-oriented organizers. The figure of Davidov in Sholokhov's *Virgin Soil Upturned* (1932) is the literary prototype of the 25,000 urban communists sent out to organize collective farms during the early 1930's. But the rural population would stay refractory until its way of life had been changed decisively: in the eyes of the Party leadership it was slothful, suspicious of change, steeped in religion and superstition, and given to drinking and to dissipating its energies.

Even if part of the leadership of the United States and the Soviet Union did not share the attitudes ascribed to them here, on the whole it may be said that the early Soviet leaders had an enormous advantage of outlook in dealing with the problem of structuring the urban environment. The realization that urban planning should be used to effect social change was accepted by the Soviet leadership some four decades before it took hold among American governmental and business leaders. Undergirding the confidence of Soviet leaders in this respect was a central investment planning system which permitted them to locate industries with an eye to their effects on population distribution and employment needs. In the United States, this type of control was available only in the location of Federal installations and projects. Also, Soviet leaders and economic planners of the early decades were confident of their

---

[3] Parkins, 1953, pp. 20-29.

ability to control and even limit absolutely the growth of the largest cities. It is true that this confidence has been rather shaken by many experiences with population targets which had to be scrapped a few years after they were established. Nevertheless, one wonders whether Moscow today would be the same size as London or New York had there been no central control over the location of new industries.

If Soviet policymakers were largely free from idealizing rural and small-town life, they were long hampered in urban construction by the nation's particular economic priorities, and also by administrative problems. Industrial ministries under great pressure to put their new plants into production were apt to press for locations and sites which best suited this short-run objective. The same pressure for output caused plants to organize their environment in ways which frustrated efforts to create more livable surroundings for the population. In overall investment allocation, the high priorities for heavy industry and defense meant serious lags in housing and other urban construction. Where money was available for large-scale civil construction, both national and local officials often preferred to spend it on individual projects and complexes of colossal scale, built in a wastefully ornamental style which was later (in 1955) to be condemned. The resources of local governments were often slender, so industries built their own haphazard, plant-oriented environments around them, as have so many plants in other countries.

Another obstacle, which may also have been a peculiar sort of advantage, was the lack of a Russian sociological tradition. Sociology did not emerge as a discipline until the 1960's, and Soviet urban planners and social scientists long regarded urban sociological studies in the West as not relevant in a socialist nation.[4] However, it must also be said that the impact of American sociology on the thinking of urban political leaders and planners in the United States is difficult to find before the post-World-War-II period. Even today it is hard to generalize about the effect of sociological research on urban planning.

There was no lack of awareness among Soviet architects and urban planners of leading planning concepts in the West and elsewhere during the 1920's and 1930's. At the time the Moscow Master Plan was in preparation in the early 1930's, the Moscow Architectural and Planning Administration gave consideration to proposals by

---

[4] See Fischer, 1964, for a detailed account of the emergence of Soviet sociology, also the two-volume *Sotsiologiya v SSSR* 1965, as well as *Marksistskaya i burzhuaznaya sotsiologiya segodnya* (Moscow: Nauka, 1964) for fundamental statements of the character and direction of Soviet sociology as of the mid-1960's.

Le Corbusier and Frank Lloyd Wright, and in other ways as well brought itself up to date on the latest concepts of large-scale urban development in other countries.[5] In the end, perhaps it was just as well that Soviet political leaders and urban planners did not bind themselves to any particular concept from abroad during the first four decades following the Revolution. Instead, they forged ahead pragmatically, usually rejecting the more novel and untried planning philosophies.

One specific factor retarding the growth of interest in the sociological aspects of urban planning has been the scarcity of published demographic data by cities and industrial areas. Particularly needed are data on the type and extent of employment, sex and age characteristics, migration patterns, family size, and other categories which if projected into the future would be invaluable for urban planners. Recently a Khar'kov economist engaged in urban planning work urged specifically that this data be included in the reporting of the 1969 census.[6] The first comprehensive demographic survey of an individual city since the early 1930's was in fact done in Khar'kov, and published in 1968.[7] The work done on labor and migration patterns in Novosibirsk by the Siberian Branch of the Academy of Sciences was noted in Chapter 5. The Computer Center of the Ukrainian offices of *Gosplan* has recently been working out demographic projections for the year 2,000 for Kiev and the Ukrainian Republic as a whole.[8] Hopefully, such research will be undertaken on a nationwide scale in the near future.

In the late 1950's investment in housing and services rose appreciably from its former level. Actually, the *proportion* of investment in these categories to total investment stayed at about one third during the entire 1950's and 1960's. But investment in housing and services more than doubled between 1955 and 1960 alone.[9] From 1955 on, there was a renewed interest in further developing basic urban planning concepts. But missing in discussions of this period among architects and city planners were the interesting sociological considerations which figured in the debates of the 1920's and early 1930's. The presentations at the All-Union Conference on

---

[5] Parkins, 1953, Chs. 2-4.

[6] *Vestnik statistiki* No. 7 (July, 1967), pp. 34-35.

[7] Kurman and Lebedinskii, 1968.

[8] O. Gusev, "Machines Make Predictions," *Pravda*, November 24, 1968.

[9] U. S. Congress, Joint Economic Committee, *Soviet Economic Performance, 1966-67*, p. 42.

Urban Planning, held in June 1960, show this gap clearly. While the late Vladimir A. Kucherenko, then head of the USSR State Construction Committee (*Gosstroi*), criticized earlier planning practice for not considering the "wealth of social content of the Soviet city," neither the keynote addresses nor the discussion which followed really delved into the question of urban society. Instead, the emphasis in urban structure was on three planning components: (*a*) the optimization of construction and operating costs, (*b*) the distribution of services, including the grouping of services in microdistricts, and (*c*) maintenance of proper health and recreation norms.[10] While all three are vital to urban planning anywhere, the major spokesmen of Soviet city planners assumed—though their assumption may have changed during the 1960's—that realization of proper norms under these three headings would itself do all that any urban planning could possibly do to promote good social relationships.

This, too, was the sentiment that the writer discovered in numerous conversations with Soviet planners and architects in 1963-64. Most of them, when pressed on the matter, denied that spatial planning itself could have any specific social effect other than that of liberating city dwellers from the inconveniences which might restrict their possibilities for social involvement and the enjoyment of their leisure. Social relations, nearly all of them asserted, are basically the fruit of men's relation to their work and of the manner in which the state and nongovernmental organizations channel their activities. The task or urban planning is a supplementary one. These same architects and planners, however, laid great stress on the function of planning in shaping the aesthetic perceptions of ordinary people, which can in some way influence man's appreciation of society as well. No one in the field of urban planning with whom the writer talked thought that the country's new sociological research facilities would change the goals or methods of planning substantially. At best the sociologists might suggest some improvements of detail. Typical was the response that "If these people [the sociologists] have some suggestions to make to us on the basis of their research, for example in designing apartments better suited for family living, of course we shall consider them." Reflected in these attitudes is the long-standing Soviet confidence in the positive social influence on the urban environment generally.

---

[10] *Vsesoyuznoye soveshchaniye po gradostroitel'stvu, 7-10 iunya 1960 g.*, p. 21 *et passim.*

An interesting dissenting opinion was voiced in 1965 by the director of the Institute for the Theory, History, and Long-Range Problems of Soviet Architecture:

The residential district, and even more the city as a whole, is not the mere mechanical agglomeration of microdistricts. We must take a careful look at the social interconnections of the city's various parts within the context of the entire organism. If we fail to do this, it will be difficult for us in the future to attain urban social unity. We should look at the socialist city in its organic social, functional, and architectural unity.

It must be said that, unfortunately, we still have no rounded theoretical concept of the communist city; there is a glaring deficiency in this branch of science. We should take all possible steps toward solving this problem, for otherwise serious mistakes in our urban construction will be inevitable.

I would like to stress in addition that those vital processes which go on in a city are not merely composed of, or restricted to, the sphere of services. We should not forget that the main social basis of our society is labor. The activity of our people in the sphere of labor is the determining basis of social life. For this reason we have no right, in resolving urban problems, to deal with them only from the point of view of consumption and services. We must pay more attention to scientific development of the system of cultural and everyday services in the sphere of productive activity, in its interconnections with the sphere of consumption and everyday life, i.e., the sphere of residential districts . . . . [11]

Other dissenting opinions have come from designers of the revived "commune-type" apartment buildings of the latter 1960's, described below, whose most prominent supporter has been the noted economist Stanislav G. Strumilin.

Four areas of choice for Soviet urban planners in the 1960's are discussed in this chapter and the next: the size and dimensions of cities and urban areas, the concept of the neighborhood, the recently revived idea of a new way of life in specially designed dwelling complexes, and the question of equality in distributing urban investment.

THE CONTROL OF URBAN SIZE AND GROWTH

In 1960 the Soviet Union joined the family of nations whose population is more than half urban, and by 1967 the share of urban

---

[11] Statement by K. I. Trapeznikov at the Scientific-Technical Conference on the Planning and Construction of Residential Districts and Microdistricts, December 1-3, 1964, reported in *Arkhitektura SSSR* No. 2 (February, 1965), p. 3.

population was already 55 percent, or 128 million out of a total of 234 million.[12] Naturally, the definition of "urban" varies from country to country. Soviet urban population figures today include over 700 communities of less than 3,000 population each, because the principal occupations of their residents are nonfarm; all communities over 3,000 are by definition urban. At the time of the Revolution, the urban share had been less than 20 percent, which at the time amounted to less than 30 million population. In spite of the great economic disorder inherited by the new regime, the long-range opportunity for shaping a new type of urban environment was a golden one. The Soviet regime could not, of course, start with a "clean slate" in existing large cities. There was, nevertheless, a plan of the 1920's to build a completely new Moscow to the northwest of the existing city, while preserving old Moscow in museum fashion; but it was rejected in favor of step-by-step reconstruction which would preserve Moscow's basic layout, while extending the city's territory in most directions.[13] Later on, the vast destruction of World War II did offer opportunities for the radical redesigning of many cities of European Russia and the Ukraine.

Another planning advantage for the young Soviet government was that it had only a small number of large cities. In 1917, only Leningrad (then called Petrograd, still earlier St. Petersburg) and Moscow numbered in the millions, with 2.5 and 1.8 million inhabitants, respectively. Kiev and Odessa were approaching the half-million mark, Khar'kov was over 300,000, and seven other cities were over 200,000. But that was all. Besides, the distribution of urban areas in Russia at the beginning of the present century was such that these were unlikely to grow together to produce any massive conurbation or "supercities" within any short space of time. The distribution of the nation's vast power resources was and is such as to favor the dispersion of urban growth to many regions of the Soviet Union's vast territory. For one thing, as of the 1960's some 80 percent of the nation's power potential lies east of the Urals, 15 percent in the European U.S.S.R., and 5 percent in Central Asia.[14] While many types of heavy industry need not be located near the supply of raw materials and power, nonetheless the location of raw

---

[12]Estimate as of January 1, 1967. Tsentral'noye statisticheskoye upravleniye . . . , *SSSR v tsifrakh v 1966 godu*, p. 7.

[13]V. E. Poletayev, *Na putyakh k novoi Moskve* (Moscow: Izdatel'stvo AN SSSR, 1961), p. 48.

[14]L. Melent'yev in *Izvestiya*, October 14, 1961, p. 3.

Table 6-1
POPULATION GROWTH SINCE 1939 OF SOVIET CITIES HAVING
OVER 500,000 POPULATION BY 1967
(in thousands)

	1939	1959 (Jan. 15)	1967 (Jan. 1)	Percent Increase from 1959 to 1967
Moscow*†	4,542	6,040	6,507	8
Leningrad†	3,385	3,321	3,706	12
Kiev	847	1,104	1,413	28
Tashkent‡	556	927	1,239	34
Baku†	775	971	1,196	23
Khar'kov	833	934	1,125	20
Gor'kii	644	942	1,120	19
Novosibirsk	404	886	1,064	20
Kuibyshev	390	806	992	23
Sverdlovsk	423	779	961	23
Tbilisi	519	703	842	20
Donetsk	466	699	840	20
Chelyabinsk	273	689	836	21
Kazan'	398	647	821	26
Dnepropetrovsk	527	660	816	24
Perm'	306	629	796	27
Odessa	602	667	776	16
Omsk	289	581	774	33
Minsk	237	509	772	52
Rostov-on-the-Don	510	600	757	26
Volgograd	445	592	743	26
Saratov	372	581	720	24
Ufa	258	547	704	29
Riga	348	580	680	17
Yerevan	204	509	665	31
Alma-Ata	222	456	652	43
Voronezh	344	448	611	36
Zaporozh'ye	282	435	595	37
Krasnoyarsk	190	412	576	40
L'vov	340	411	512	25
Krivoi Rog	189	388	510	31

*Within its present boundaries.

†Includes population centers under municipal jurisdiction outside the contiguous area of the city.

‡The 1967 figure for Tashkent includes 35 population centers outside the city limits which were placed under city administration in December 1966.

Source: Tsentral'noye statisticheskoye upravleniye . . . , *Strana sovetov za 50 let,* 1967, p. 21.

materials and power is such as to promote the establishment of new industrial centers far away from the large cities of the European U.S.S.R. Many of the completely new cities of Siberia and Kazakhstan are indeed resource-oriented, however.

The name of Magnitogorsk (pop. 352,000 in 1966) is probably the most familiar among the newly founded cities, but there are many others: Bratsk, Angarsk, Komosomol'sk-on-the-Amur, Novokuznetsk, Noril'sk, Temirtau, and a number of others. Other important present-day industrial centers were small towns 50 years ago, but grew to a half million or a million during the Soviet period, including Novosibirsk, Donetsk, Chelyabinsk, Yerevan, Alma-Ata, Zaporozh'ye, Krasnoyarsk, and a good many others.

Soviet political leaders and urban planners have focused their attention on three aspects of urban size and growth. The first is the matter of population size. What limits can or should be sought for the largest cities, those of over a million? For cities of less than a million, is there an optimal size which could serve as a growth target or ceiling for planners? The second is the problem of setting limits to the physical spread of cities by establishing greenbelts around their periphery, and by separating adjacent cities, or segments of the same city, through parks and other areas of nonurban land use. The third is the problem of planning *for* population increases, including unforeseen increases, by controlling the manner in which urban areas grow rather than working within arbitrary limits. Up to the 1960's, these problems were considered mainly from the point of view of environmental hygiene. During the 1960's, however, specialists from several professions who are concerned with urban life began to devote attention to the sociological aspects of urban size and growth.

Population Growth Control. The various aspects of population growth control must be distinguished. One of these is the attempt to maintain a growth ceiling on a few of the very largest cities, those whose populations number in the millions. The second is the effort to make accurate population growth estimates for cities of lesser size. The third is to regulate the pace of their growth by controlling the number of large new industries, research and educational institutions, and other "city-forming" employers which are established in these cities over a given period of time, as well as the expansion of existing facilities. The fourth is the problem of working out an optimal size, or range of optimal sizes, for cities which are being planned from the very beginning, and over which a greater degree of control can be exercised. The advocates of optimal size sought criteria applicable to cities of under a half million. Much of the discussion about diverting prospective industrial investment away from cities in the 250,000-500,000 range has been occasioned not so much by a philosophy of growth limitation as by the desirability of using this investment to develop economically static towns under 100,000 or 50,000. The most common argument for locating industries (or other major employers) in small cities and towns is that, in the absence of major employers, their populations are often underemployed. Using their labor force on the spot is considered by many economists and planners to be far preferable to inducing them to relocate to the large cities, where housing and other facilities must be provided for them anew.

Ever since the 1920's, these discussions have been underscored by the conviction on the part of Soviet planners that the U.S.S.R. would be the first industrial nation to regulate urban growth. Particularly, they believed that the growth of giant urban agglomerations such as New York, London, and Tokyo could be prevented, and the negative consequences of very great urban concentration avoided. Planners elsewhere have watched this experiment with interest, and have observed a mixture of successes and failures. As will be clear from the discussion below, there is no reason to judge the failures harshly, and every reason to pay close attention to the evolution of Soviet urban growth policies during the 1970's.

Of the reasons put forward by Soviet urban planners and political leaders for growth limitation of any kind, few can be called sociological in the sense of resting on a theory of what is desirable in human association. The writer has been unable to discover a single Soviet statement to the effect that large population concentrations as such promote alienation or dissociation from society. Assertions of this kind have not been demonstrated anywhere, of course, however much they have been put forward as impressions. However one may define "alienation" in the American setting or anywhere else, it remains to be shown that this is the special product of the very largest cities as compared with medium-sized cities or small towns. Soviet commentary on the subject, as one would expect, does not even concede the possibility of alienation as a phenomenon of socialist society. This is partly the result of Marxist thinking about social relations, according to which alienation is a product of property relations and their immediate consequences, and not of population concentrations. The Soviet citizens with whom the writer raised the question of scale, whether urban planners or laymen, seemed unconcerned about its social implications. Muscovites who were aware of the efforts made to limit the city's size were concerned first of all about overcrowding in stores, transportation, and other facilities. As one Soviet law school professor put it: "As far as I'm concerned, there could just as well be 12 million Muscovites as 6 million. As you can see, we get along together in large masses, and there would be no social problem. The only thing I'm afraid of is that if they ever let the city grow that much, then no matter how many new stores and subway lines they build, things would still be twice as crowded as they are now." The Harvard study of Soviet emigres from the World War II period concluded, among other things, that the Soviet citizen identifies easily with large social groupings, and that group size itself does not make much difference to him.[15] Actually, Soviet planners are becoming increasingly aware of the social *benefits* of very large cities—the opportunities they present, the stimulation, and the clustering of people with talent, imagination, and ambition. In so doing, they are confronting one aspect of the problem of equality in environmental benefits and opportunities: If it is the largest cities that offer more than cities in the smaller size ranges, how is it possible to compensate for the difference?

The arguments advanced by Soviet urban planners, economists, and political leaders *against* letting cities grow beyond the one million mark are these: the increasing transportation and utility costs per inhabitant beyond a certain acceptable limit; the increasing difficulty of maintaining environmental hygiene, and the costs associated with it; and the increased commuting distances to work, as well as increased travel distances to recreational areas. All these arguments, but particularly the first two, have been applied in attempts to determine optimal city sizes as well. Those planners and economists who have put forward optimal size criteria, however, have devoted their calculations much more to the problem of lower limits rather than upper limits. Both the eminent architect N. V. Baranov and the economist Vladimir G. Davidovich placed emphasis on the scale of housing expenditures and public services, and came to the conclusion that at a given population level these items become economical.[16] Davidovich used a system of population variants measured against expenditures in three categories at various population levels: expenditures per inhabitant on housing and all types of services, transit time from the urban periphery to the center, and physical volume of service establishments. He found that while all

[15] Raymond Bauer, Alex Inkeles, and Clyde Kluckhohn, *How the Soviet System Works* (Cambridge, Mass.: Harvard University Press, 1956), p. 141.

[16] Baranov, 1962, pp. 48-56; Davidovich, 1960, pp. 150-60.

per capita expenditures rise fairly slowly up to a population level of 200,000, from that point on per capita transportation expenditures begin to rise steeply. Separate calculations based on two different levels of public services yield approximately the same result. Thus, Davidovich arrived at an optimal size range of 50,000-200,000, while Baranov by less intricate calculations (which included, however, optimal relations among types of employment) discovered a 140,000-250,000 range.[17] Thus far the writer has discovered no such calculations which include expenditures for control of environmental pollution. But the greater flaw in both the calculations above is that neither takes into account the economies obtained by grouping industries into aggregates which result in population concentrations well over a half million; that is, an optimum must not rest on economies in nonproduction investment and operation costs alone.

High-level action to limit the growth of the largest cities began with a Party Central Committee resolution of June 1931, which attacked the problem at its roots by forbidding construction of new industries in existing large cities, first of all in Moscow and Leningrad.[18] A decree of 1935 then supplied some hard guidelines which from that time on became standard as techniques of growth limitation.[19] It called for limiting Moscow's population to a maximum of 5 million, while providing for the city's progressive territorial enlargement, and specifying the basic direction of urban growth (toward the south and southwest, in this case). The city's control over undeveloped land in its land reserve was assured, and the plan laid out a six-mile-deep forest belt girdling the city beyond these reserve lands.

The 1959 census showed just over 5 million inhabitants in Moscow, although an enlargement of the city's limits which took place in 1960 increased this figure by a million. The mid-1966 figure of 6.4 million suggests that a substantial annual growth is still taking place.[20] However, the planning guidelines approved in 1966 foresee an increase to only 6.8 million by the 1980's.[21] It is harder to judge

---

[17]Davidovich, 1960, pp. 155, 157; Baranov, 1962, p. 51.

[18]*KPSS v rezolyutsiyakh*, Vol. 3, p. 123.

[19]Decree of July 10, 1935, in *SZ SSSR* 1935, No. 35, Art. 306.

[20]*Narodnoye khozyaistvo SSSR*, 1965, p. 35. Table 6-1 gives Moscow's 1939 and 1959 populations within its post-1960 boundaries.

[21]*Arkhitektura SSSR* No. 6 (June, 1967), p. 7.

the success of a Party resolution of 1939[22] forbidding the construction of new enterprises in Kiev, Kar'kov, Rostov-on-the-Don, Lor'kii, and Sverdlovsk; the first three were restricted in growth during the next 20 years by massive wartime destruction, and the last two had to develop industrially because of the war. But all of them have grown at a rapid rate in the 1960's (see Table 6-1).

In 1958, Khrushchev stated flatly in a major address that "it is necessary, at long last, to put an end to population growth in the big cities through the influx of people from other areas of the country." His confidence found expression in the "Standards and Norms for Urban Planning and Construction" issued by *Gosstroi* in December 1958.[23] In this unusual document, all cities over 250,000 were classified as "largest" (*krupnyi*) and were prohibited from accommodating further industrial plants, major expansion of existing plants, and other major new employers save for those serving the local population. The distinction between "local" industries and organizations and those which are more than simply local is necessarily an arbitrary one. Moscow planning officials explained to the writer, for example, that the Bolshoi Theater was classified as a "major employer" rather than a "local" operation, while certain smaller theaters in Moscow were "local." Analogous distinctions, they said, are used with industries as well.

Under the 1958 "Standards and Norms," cities of 100,000 to 250,000, classified as "large," were to be kept below a ceiling of 250,000 or 200,000. But most new industrial construction (new plants or expansion of existing plants) was to be directed to cities classified as medium-size (50,000-100,000) and small (under 50,000). In the forest belts, where they are established around any given city, all construction was prohibited save for that relating to agriculture, recreation, transportation, and maintenance of the forest itself. Satellite cities, where they were to be built, would be located in the part of the suburban zone beyond the forest belt; the term "suburban zone" embraces both the forest belt and the zone of restricted construction beyond it. Thus, the largest cities, and those

---

[22]Cited in Khauke, 1961, p. 19. See also Molotov's report to the 18th Party Congress in *The Land of Socialism Today and Tomorrow* (Moscow: Foreign Languages Publishing House, 1939), p. 134.

[23]*Pravda*, March 15, 1958. *Pravila i normy planirovki i zastroiki gorodov*. Moscow: Gosstroiizdat, 1959.

threatening to pass the 250,000 threshhold into the "largest" designation, were to be limited territorially in the strictest way by the forest belt.

But today, a decade after the forthright policy statements on city growth limitation and ratification of these unparallelled national rules, the necessity of permitting growth well past these arbitrary limits has been generally recognized among Soviet planners, and apparently acquiesced in by political leaders. The largest cities—all those over 250,000—are under constant pressure from industrial ministries in Moscow which are seeking urban sites for new enterprises and the expansion of existing enterprises for reasons which are described below. In 1960 the chief architect of Moscow, the official primarily responsible for coordinating the city's development plans, said: "We are still subjected to great pressure on the part of the state committees, ministries, and other agencies in charge of various branches of the economy which are seeking to carry on construction in Moscow by any means possible." Not only the city proper but the forest belt too was affected by this pressure, he indicated. The chief architect of Leningrad similarly deplored the number of exceptions which were still being made to that city's ban on new "city-forming" employers for the benefit not only of new industries, but of major research establishments as well.[24] Latvia's top economic planner told of a drawn-out bureaucratic struggle between officials of Riga and two plants, automotive and chemical, which were attempting to expand their complexes with new structures in spite of a firm municipal policy against this.[25] Numerous other examples could be cited. In 1958, Khrushchev had directed attention to the Moscow enterprises which were still importing labor from the outside, and circumventing the registration restrictions (described below) in so doing. By and large, these workers came to do the unskilled "rough" work in a city whose unskilled and low-skill labor force is a smaller proportion of the whole than elsewhere.[26]

While administrative control over migration into the big cities is peripheral as a means of limiting population growth, it is important

---

[24] Statements by I. I. Loveiko and V.A. Kamenskii, then chief architects of Moscow and Leningrad, respectively, at the 1960 conference on city planning. *Vsesoyuznoye soveshchaniye po gradostroitel'stvu*, 1961, pp. 269 and 297.

[25] M. Raman, "Within City Limits," *Izvestiya*, April 29, 1966.

[26] *Pravda*, March 15, 1958.

from the point of view of labor supply and deserves a word of explanation. The system of militia (police) registry, which is so important to newcomers to the large cities of the European U.S.S.R., serves as a deterrent to permanent settlement by many casual migrants. Too many of these, drawn simply by the lure and overall advantages of the big cities rather than by a definite job, would contribute to housing problems and might form a floating labor force which in turn might impel industrial ministries to press for building new enterprises there. In Moscow, at least, jobs would be available for such migrants in the service occupations, which are still understaffed.[27] Registry with the police, which is the receipt of a registration authorization (*propiska*) on presentation of one's internal passport and verification of one's job status, entitles a migrant both to hold a local job and, possibly more important, to receive local housing to the extent it is available. Control over labor force size by this means is far less certain than control by regulation of housing space assignments in a given locality. Employers in need of labor may ignore the failure of a job applicant to receive his *propiska*, and may even help him make housing arrangements. Rental of housing space by private agreement, which itself is fully legal if rate ceilings are observed, is frequently a way of solving the housing problem for those without registration. While these loopholes do permit a certain amount of population "leakage" into Moscow and the other big cities, still the system acts as a deterrent to many others.

Viktor I. Perevedentsev, the migration specialist, expressed doubt that restricting issuance of the *propiska* is even marginally effective: "One thing is clear: if towns have no jobs to offer, there is no reason to restrict issuance of the *propiska*, for people will not move there anyway. If new jobs are offered, there should be personnel to fill them. No limitation of the *propiska* will be of any use in such cases. One can only compel people to live dozens of kilometers away from their work. But is this the best result?"[28] Here he was referring to the fact that many migrants to Moscow avoid registration problems by settling in outlying communities and commuting long distances to their jobs in the city; and the same happens around other large cities in the European U.S.S.R.

---

[27] Interview with N. F. Yevstratov, Director of the Master Plan Institute of Moscow, January 1964.

[28] V. Perevedentsev, "Cities and Years," *Literaturnaya gazeta*, February 26, 1969.

Besides its use as a means of migration control, the Soviet *propiska* may be cancelled in connection with certain penalties under criminal law. Banishment (*vysylka*) as a penalty involves a prohibition on residing, for a specified number of years, in a given city or cities. From Soviet legal specialists the writer gained the impression that denial of the *propiska* is sometimes applied at the discretion of the militia as a means of removing undesirable elements from Moscow and the larger cities, or as a way of preventing former inhabitants of these cities with criminal records from resettling there.

By the 1960's, not only the practical difficulty but also the negative economic consequences of the ban on major industrial and other "city-forming" investment had become evident. In 1966 Moscow's chief planner referred to this construction ban as one of the mistakes of the past. Compilation of the basic guidelines for a new master plan, consequently, made provision for over 60 industrial and depot zones, and for the design of a number of large-scale industrial complexes, which among other things will replace a much larger number of small-scale enterprises. The new policy for Moscow is to limit construction of production units and of scientific and educational establishments to "those connected with the city for economic or governmental reasons."[29]

Meanwhile, the problem of the majority of other large industrial centers has been that of unanticipated rates of growth. Target population figures for given periods—usually 20 years—have been surpassed before half the target period was up; master plans, where they were drawn up, had to be shelved a few years after they were ratified. There is no problem compiling a long list of examples of this from the post-World-War-II period. Here are a few at random:

Sverdlovsk: In 1954, over the protests of the city administration, the population target for 1975 was set at 800,000 by *Gosplan*; this level was reached in 1960. In 1958, *Gosplan* foresaw 1 million inhabitants in 1980; by 1966, the city was only 40,000 short of this level and growing by 30,000 annually.

Angarsk: When construction began on this new Siberian city in the early 1950's, near the site of a major new hydroelectric project, the 20-year projection was for 80,000 people. Ten years later it already had 134,000, and the 1966 figure was 179,000.

Khar'kov: Development of urban housing and services was based

[29]G. Fomin, "The Face of the City," *Pravda*, May 16, 1966.

on a population target of 1 million, set during the mid-1950's. This level was reached in 1962, and growth has continued at the rate of 30,000 annually during the 1960's.

Novosibirsk: After World War II the population target for 1970 was set at 850,000; but by 1960, population had reached 918,000.[30]

The main reasons for the growth of cities in the 250,000-to-1,000,000 range are two: the desire of ministries to build their plants, research establishments, and other facilities in areas where public services are to some extent already provided, and to which it will be relatively easy to attract a skilled labor force; and the desire of local political leaders to have more industries and other "city-forming" organizations. Major industries contribute to cities in three ways: they strengthen the case of city governments for large budgetary assignments, they contribute directly to city budgets through fixed rates of taxation, and they build housing and service facilities which are increasingly being turned over to municipal jurisdiction soon after they are built. (All this is quite aside from the income received by cities from their own industries, which are nearly all small-scale consumer-goods operations.) While in past decades industries kept under their own control the housing and other facilities they erected for their own employees, the practice in most larger cities—and indeed this is required by regulation—is to deliver all these to the city within a short period of time, either 12 or 6 months. Thus, an industry which puts up an apartment building may fill it initially with its own employees, often with newly hired specialists who are attracted to the job with offers of new housing; but after it has done this, the city assumes jurisdiction and may fill future vacancies from its own waiting lists.

The same factors promoting growth are operative in cities in the 100,000-250,000 range. Here unforeseen industrial and population growth continue in spite of many exhortations to the industrial ministries from officials in *Gosplan, Gosstroi*, and the central Party offices to develop the cities under 100,000, particularly those in the 10,000-50,000 range. Thus, an intensive drive for population growth has been occurring in precisely those cities whose populations now approximate the various optimal sizes discussed in the late 1950's and early 1960's.

---

[30] *Vsesoyuznoye soveshchaniye po gradostroitel'stvu,* 1960, pp. 93, 282-83; *Narodnoye khozyaistvo SSSR* 1965, pp. 30, 37, and 39; Korzh, 1964, p. 8; *Trudy VI sessii Akademii stroitel'stva i arkhitektury*, 1961, pp. 319-20.

Among Soviet city planners, the writer met few advocates of any kind of sweeping policy of urban population growth limitation. The one significant group which did (in the writer's 1964 interviews, at any rate) advocate strict adherence to size norms consisted of officials in the Russian Republic's State Committee for Civil Construction. Their answers indicated that their counterparts at the national level shared these views. Given their responsibility for spatial planning throughout the vast Russian Republic, it is understandable that these officials are advocates of a carefully planned distribution of industrial and population growth, and that they reflect the view of the top political leadership on this score. As the administrators of central policies in civil construction, they are particularly concerned with the consequences of industrial concentration for housing and services, and with the hygienic consequences of urban size. The chief architects of large cities other than Moscow and Leningrad took a more relaxed view of growth and size. One planner in Minsk told the writer in 1964: "Quite frankly, I am for big cities, even for those over 1 or 2 million. With our best efforts, we can never make cities under a half million quite as attractive as places to live, compared with the biggest ones. [Minsk had just surpassed the half-million mark in 1959, and was growing fairly rapidly.] The point is to design our newer big cities by learning from the defects of the existing ones."

During the 1960's a new trend of thinking emerged in the public discussion of the city size question. Some urban planners now consider it a mistake to concentrate on the question of size by itself, since the root of the "size problem" lies not in size itself, but in the proper structuring of broad urban areas, however large. It is now argued by some planners, economists, and others that the proper articulation of growing urban areas can do away with the whole question of growth limitation, as this question has been understood up to now. A growing large city need not remain bound to its single traditional center for its major cluster of services, nor to old established industrial areas. It is the radical division of urban areas into separate massive components for industry, housing, transport, and other functions which is creating congestion and other undesirable side effects. The city should be articulated into "complex districts" each of which would unite these functions. While the city center with its city-wide functions and services would continue to expand somewhat territorially, new centers would be created in each of the complex districts, each providing most of what the traditional center provides. Growth will continue, no arbitrary population ceilings or targets will be employed, but qualitatively new forms of growth must be found. Volgograd (formerly Stalingrad), Novosibirsk, and Sverdlovsk are cited as large cities based upon complex districts; Volgograd, actually, has become a classic example for Soviet planners of a "dispersion city" originally created out of five semi-independent urban units.[31] The increase in the number of Moscow's boroughs in 1968 from 16 to 27 may represent an effort to articulate the city into smaller planning units, most of which might one day be able to offer employment for the bulk of the population within their various individual limits.

Limitation of Spatial Growth. Following acceptance in the 1920's of the idea of halting or limiting population growth by limiting the introduction of further major employers, the further idea of an outer physical barrier to urban territorial expansion emerged from discussions of the Moscow city plan in the 1930's. The idea of the "greenbelt" as such a barrier had already gained popularity in Britain and the West, thanks largely to the work of Ebenezer Howard. Moscow's 1935 master plan attempted to lay the groundwork for a suburban zone (*prigorodnaya zona*) with the city limits (then situated 8 to 10 miles from the city center) as the inner radius, and with an outer radius about 30 miles from the city center. The innermost portion of the suburban zone, a ring of land about six miles wide, was set aside as a forest belt. Here further major construction was forbidden. Permitted uses outside of existing built-up areas were to include primarily recreation, agriculture, and the preservation of forests and open space which would preserve both the supply of fresh air and the beauty of the city's immediate surroundings. The goals of planning in the remainder of the suburban zone were not specified. If any kind of integrated plan for this large zone has emerged meanwhile, the writer has not yet discovered it. Construction of almost every kind has been permitted in the suburban zone beyond the forest belt, although the intention of 1935 appears to have been that of preventing unnecessary encroachments on agricultural lands. A 1940 amendment to the master plan increased the maximum outer radius of the suburban zone to 60

---

[31]Pchelintsev, 1961; Bocharev and Rabinovich, 1962. Sketch maps of the development plans of Volgograd are available in Parkins, 1953, pp. 25 and 74.

miles, a 1950 revision reduced this to 30 miles, and the guidelines approved in 1966 increased it again to 45 miles. Diagram 2 shows the present state of affairs, the city limits having been extended in 1960 to the circumferential highway as shown.[32]

Diagram 2
MOSCOW'S SUBURBAN ZONE AND FOREST BELT

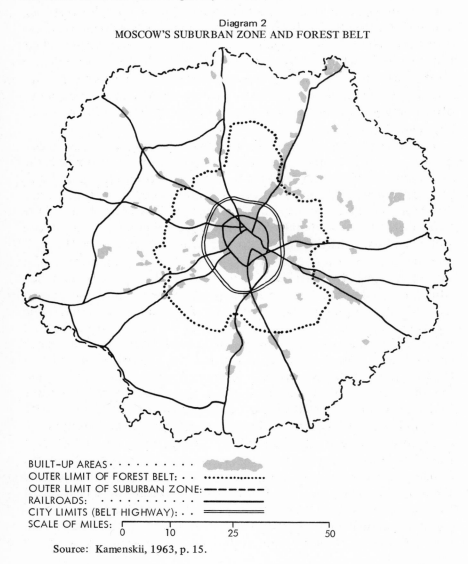

BUILT-UP AREAS · · · · · · · · ·
OUTER LIMIT OF FOREST BELT: · · ················
OUTER LIMIT OF SUBURBAN ZONE: ───────
RAILROADS: · · · · · · · · · · ══════
CITY LIMITS (BELT HIGHWAY): · · ══════

SCALE OF MILES:

0   10   25   50

Source: Kamenskii, 1963, p. 15.

[32]Parkins, 1953, p. 40; Kamenskii, 1963, p. 28; *Arkhitektura SSSR*, No. 6 (June, 1967), p. 7; Khauke, 1960, pp. 18-19.

Plans for suburban zones in other cities began to emerge after World War II. Khar'kov's plan was issued in 1947, and by the 1960's a number of other major cities of the European U.S.S.R. had adopted at least the boundaries of suburban zones, among them Leningrad, Kiev, Minsk, and Riga.[33] The dimensions of these zones vary with the contours of the cities they embrace and the landscape in which they are located. Moscow's zone extends as far as 45 miles from the city's center, Kiev's 22 miles, and Leningrad's 35 miles in places. In no case, however, has the jurisdiction of the hub city extended to the entire zone. With the extension of Moscow's city limits in 1960, planning of the forest belt was brought under the city government's direct jurisdiction even though this belt remained outside the city's formal boundaries. Comprehensive planning in the remainder of the suburban zone is to be carried out by agreement between city and provincial planning authorities, and it is possible that coordination between the two is one of the administrative problems which has so far hampered strict observance of zoning.[34] Baranov expressed his opinion at the 1960 urban planning conference that the skeleton plans for suburban zone development (*skhemy prigorodnykh raionov*) often appended to city master plans are of little use in practice. In vain did the late Vladimir A. Kucherenko, then head of *Gosstroi*, call for placing all construction and development in the suburban zone under the authority of the hub city.[35]

The Moscow city boundary extension of August 1960 added 107 square miles of city territory to the 234 square miles already encompassed by the 1935 plan (see Diagram 2). The new boundaries, which provided considerable additional construction space to the north and south, coincided with a planned circumferential highway which was completed a few years later. Beyond the highway, the city was accorded direct jurisdiction over a forest belt of 700 square miles, and from that time on has borne direct responsibility for the preservation and development of its most important recreational areas.[36] The remaining suburban zone outlined by the Moscow

[33] Kamenskii, 1963, Chs. 1 and 2.

[34] The writer was unable to obtain interviews with planning officials at the provincial level anywhere. Security considerations may have been responsible for this, since planning at this level deals much more with questions of industrial location and communications than with matters of housing, distribution of services, and the like.

[35] *Vsesoyuznoye soveshchaniye po gradostroitel'stvu*, 1960, pp. 31, 101.

[36] *Izvestiya*, August 19, 1960. Trans. in *CDSP* XII:35, p. 19-21.

Master Plan Institute in the early 1950's and revised in 1966 remains a planning rather than administrative unit; thus, the realization of a suburban zone plan rests on voluntary cooperation between city and provincial planning offices. Baku solved much of its jurisdictional problem by gaining administrative control over the entire Apsheron Peninsula, Tbilisi also undertook some annexation on adjacent mountainsides not particularly suited for construction, and Kiev followed the example of Moscow in annexing an entire forest and open-space belt up to 22 miles from the city center.[37] Tbilisi is favored by its geography from the point of view of restricting territorial growth; the surrounding mountains permit additions to the built-up areas only in a scattered handful of places. Yet the city's chief architect stated that it was virtually impossible for the city government substantially to limit population growth, which was 18,000 annually by the mid-1960's.[38]

The forest belt and its recreation facilities are meant to be an extension of the municipal park system of any given city; it accommodates primarily daytime visitors, not long-term vacationers. Leningrad's chief architect estimated a peak weekend use of his city's forest belt in the near future by 1.5 million city dwellers, nearly a third of the population.[39] Both the forest belt and the remainder of the suburban zone beyond it include a number of formally designated recreation areas. Those outside the forest belt will ultimately be provided with overnight facilities and equipment for vacation use. However, extensive modern overnight facilities are provided in Moscow's model recreation area on the Klyazma Reservoir, 10 miles north of the city center, even though it is located within the forest belt.[40] Erection of private dachas within these recreation areas is either forbidden or else discouraged.

Moscow's forest belt should be the envy of urban planners anywhere who are concerned with obtaining massive recreational space within easy reach of large cities. The environs of the city, in their sheer natural beauty, the unspoiled character of large contiguous forest areas, and the recreational potential of natural waterways

---

[37]*Vsesoyuznoye soveshchaniye po gradostroitel'stvu*, 1960, pp. 321 and 350; Kamenskii, 1963, p. 28.

[38]*Vsesoyuznoye soveshchaniye po gradostroitel'stvu*, 1960, p. 349. *Narodnoye khozyaistvo SSSR* 1965, p. 38.

[39]Kamenskii, 1963, p. 270.

[40]*Ibid.*, pp. 67-95.

and large reservoirs, offer the city dweller a complete change from the pace of the busy capital. Yet the Soviet Union's system of central economic planning offers no guarantee in itself that the forest belt can be developed as planned, for definite problems have already arisen.

The enactment of laws by itself does not guarantee preservation of recreational and open space in the Soviet Union any more than it does in the United States. Zoning variances in the Soviet Union are not decided by a specialized agency, but rather granted by the political unit which originally approved the land-use plan. In the case of Moscow and Leningrad, this is nothing other than the U.S.S.R. Government itself, in the form of its Council of Ministers (or cabinet). The major industries and research facilities whose top representatives are cabinet ministers understandably use their influence when they need land; and in the lesser cities whose plans are approved at lower levels, the influence of these same bodies is even greater.

Furthermore, the suburban zones and their forest belts are by no means sparsely populated. Moscow's suburban zone according to the 1959 census contained a population of nearly 2.4 million, of which some 930,000 lived in the 700 square miles of the forest belt alone.[41] Roughly half of the employed population of the total suburban zone commutes to jobs in Moscow; in the early 1960's this was in the vicinity of 400,000 persons, and by 1967 it had risen to a half million.[42] Within the forest belt, several important suburban communities occupy locations along the main lines of communications to the hub city: Mytishchi (98,600 in 1959), Lyubertsy (91,000), Balashikha (57,600), Krasnogorsk, Vnukovo, and many lesser communities. The guidelines approved in 1966 foresee an increase in population by the 1980's, to a total of 1 or 1.1 million.[43] Leningrad's suburban zone displays a similar population pattern and planners in that city estimate that during the foreseeable future, some 20 percent of the population of the entire area (city plus total suburban zone) will continue to reside in the suburban zone.[44] Planners who have studied the problem of encroachments into

---

[41] Lappo, 1961, p. 93.

[42] Interview with N. F. Yevstratov, Director of the Moscow Master Plan Institute, January 1964; Yevstratov and Matveyev, 1967, p. 66.

[43] *Arkhitektura SSSR* No. 6 (June, 1967), p. 7.

[44] Kamenskii, 1963, pp. 270-71.

Moscow's forest belt noted early in the 1960's that the time was fast approaching when half the belt would be built up. Building in areas not zoned for structures was taking place particularly along the arterial rail and highway routes which for a century have provided the skeleton of the city's radial pattern of spread. The truly open areas both in the forest belt and beyond it come in the form of great wedges pointing toward the city; they are far more spacious to the west of the city, where comparatively little industrial development has occurred.[45]

One may well wonder how it is possible that the zoning requirements laid down by Soviet urban master plans are so often altered and violated in practice. One of the important functions of *Gosstroi* is to enforce master plans, and it constitutes an administrative hierarchy with offices at all levels of the Soviet political structure—national, republic, provincial, and local. Its agents in the localities are the chief city architects and their staffs. Operating within *Gosstroi* at all levels is a components structure called *Gosarkhstroikontrol'*, the State Inspection Agency for Architecture and Building, whose reports form the evidence on the basis of which judicial penalties may be imposed for violations of zoning. Violations which do occur are of three kinds: those committed by industries on territory under their administrative control, those committed by municipalities themselves in making or condoning arbitrary exceptions to the master plan, and those committed by squatters who build individual homes without first receiving a plot assignment. Squatters are no longer a great problem, except in some new industrial communities where squatting is encouraged and protected by industries which have not had time to put up apartments for their employees. What is done by both industries and cities is simply the Soviet version of the universal problem of spatial planning in rapidly growing industrial economies: the production needs of the moment are supported by powerful organizations, while those who speak for the nonproduction needs of the future find it difficult to provide an equally well-organized counterweight to this pressure.

Ordered Growth in Urban Areas. The world's first modern satellite cities were born of the efforts of Ebenezer Howard, already mentioned, the founder of Letchworth (1903) and Welwyn Garden City (1920), both located in what were then the exurbs north of

---

[45]Khauke, 1961, p. 24; Lappo, 1961, p. 102.

London. The list of Britain's satellite cities, now called "new towns," is by now a long one: Stevenage, Harlow, Basildon, Crawley, and a dozen more both outside of London and outside of other cities. While Howard stressed the need for local industries, just as contemporary Soviet planners do, he saw the garden city as an alternative to the large industrial city, and not as an urban unit having close economic and other ties with a hub metropolis. To this extent the garden city concept bears some relation to the *Communist Manifesto's* call (1848) for an even distribution of population over the countryside; but in this respect, as even the Fabian socialists pointed out, Howard was a century or more too late. Interestingly, his optimal figure of 30,000 inhabitants per garden city is identical with that suggested by the somewhat utopian proposals of 1960 made by Stanislav G. Strumilin (see below). In the post-World-War-II era it was not the garden city idea, but rather the "new town" which depended to a large extent on its relationship to a hub metropolis— sometimes in the form of "bedroom communities" only—which took hold in Europe and elsewhere, Stockholm's Vallingby and Helsinki's Tapiola being among the best known examples.

It was the German architect Ernst May who in the 1930's introduced the satellite city concept in the Soviet Union.[46] Khrushchev and many of the nation's leading planners strongly backed the idea in the 1950's as a means of deconcentrating the population of the largest cities, or at least of safeguarding established population ceilings by accommodating any further migration into the area. By the early 1960's Soviet planners realized that as a deconcentrator of population, the satellite city would have slight effect. Partly for this reason the term was dropped in 1963 as a planning category, although it is still used informally to characterize some of the newly built communities in suburban zones. At the same time, emphasis was shifted from the planning and building of totally new towns in the suburban zone to developing existing towns fairly rapidly up to the desired population targets.

Soviet planners were determined from the beginning that their satellite cities not become bedroom communities. That, among other things, would simply increase the burden on rail and bus transport. Their residents were to work in local enterprises, and at the same time share the advantages of big-city cultural facilities evenings and

[46]Parkins, 1953, p. 23.

weekends, thanks to good transportation into the hub city. Their principal employers would not be newly established ones, for that would defeat the aim of growth limitation in the urban area. Instead, the satellite cities would receive those employers which could be moved out of the hub city; with them would go their working forces. Together with the more or less "clean" industries would go research facilities, institutions of higher learning, and other similarly "clean" facilities which might actually prove more practicable to move than industries.[47] Satellite cities, whether newly built or based on existing suburban towns, were to be built in the suburban zone beyond the forest belt, at distances which could vary with local plans. Population estimates were generally in the 50,000-75,000 range, and proposed distances from the center of the entire urban area 40 to 50 miles. Moscow led the campaign with the construction of Kryukovo, which began in 1960, a completely new community along the railway line to Leningrad 22 miles from the center of Moscow, with a projected population of 65,000.[48] In the late 1950's much publicity was accorded to Sumgait, near Baku, and to the "Academic City" near Novosibirsk built to accommodate the staff of the new Siberian Division of the U.S.S.R. Academy of Sciences.[49] Kryukovo, the much-advertised prototype, was to be provided with light industry, both transferred from Moscow and newly established. Population projections made for other satellites of Moscow at the height of the enthusiasm for them are shown in Table 6-2. Most were to be based on existing small cities, and their total projected population meant accommodating something approaching a half million people.

At least part of the reason for cutting back the satellite city program was the old problem of ministerial reluctance to see new enterprises shoulder the first burden of creating a new city, wherever this could be avoided. According to the chief planner of Khar'kov Province, Khar'kov city's plans for Cheryomushnaya, a projected satellite city of 80,000 at a distance of some 30 miles from the city, hung in the balance in the mid-1960's while the problem of distributing expenses was being resolved. The industries planned for Cheryomushnaya were linked to those of Khar'kov and normally would have been sited in or near the hub city. But unless special

---

[47]Statement by V. A. Kucherenko, chairman of *Gosstroi*, at the June 1960 urban construction conference. *Vsesoyuznoye soveshchaniye po gradostroitel'stvu*, 1960, p. 23.

[48]*Ogonyok* No. 15 (April, 1958), p. 15.

[49]*Pravda*, November 3, 1957.

Table 6-2
SATELLITE CITIES OF MOSCOW PROJECTED AS OF 1960

	Population as of January 1960	Projected Population (no dates specified)
Cities to be based on existing communities:		
Dmitrov 34,500		50,000
Mikhnevo 5,100		70,000
Chekhov 13,900		70,000
Volokolamsk 8,600		60,000
Novo-Petrovskoye 2,900		70,000
Gzhelo-Rechitsy 10,400		50,000
New cities:		
Kryukovo . . . . —		65,000
Voronovo . . . . —		n.a.
Kamenka . . . . —		n.a.

Source: Vsesoyuznoye soveshchaniye po gradostroitel'stvu . . . *Planirovka i zastroika goroda kryukovo,* 1960, p. 3

financing were provided, the first industry to settle in the satellite city would bear not only a major portion of the cost of housing and service facilities, but the cost of utilities and communications as well.[50] Indeed, if construction economies are a primary guideline for creating additional built-up areas somewhere within the orbit of a large city, the best way to proceed may not necessarily be a ring of new towns. One Soviet geographer pointed out in 1961 with respect to Moscow that if the primary goal is to unburden the city of a million of its population together with certain industries, in order to provide healthier living circumstances for everyone, then a single additional urban territory would do. A single city of a million to the south of Moscow, connected to the old city by monorail or conventional rapid transit lines, would not only accommodate twice the population projected for all the projected satellite cities combined, but would be much better suited to Moscow's radial pattern of development.[51]

The function of satellite cities as population deconcentrators was the first feature to be abandoned. Two high *Gosstroi* officials pointed out in 1960 that in order to reduce the population of Moscow by one million 10, 15, or 20 satellites would have to be

[50]Korzh, 1964, p. 9.

[51]B. B. Rodoman in *Goroda-sputniki.* 1961, p. 172.

constructed, which both officials considered feasible at that time, even if a long process.[52] Furthermore, population deconcentration means deconcentration of major employers if people are to work in the communities where they live and avoid suburban commuting. The chief planner of Khar'kov Province reported in 1960 on the impossibility of moving any of Khar'kov city's major employers out of the city to the surrounding small towns. Not even one of the small industries, those which could be moved, had been relocated in the entire post-World-War-II period. If industrial deconcentration is to be a national policy, he suggested that 5 percent of all new industrial investment be set aside for relocation program.[53] While the present policy of *Gosstroi* emphasizes the use of existing small towns within a 50-mile or 60-mile radius of a large city, development of these towns is treated simply as a special case of the efforts to develop small towns generally. Specifically, towns of less than 50,000 within commuting reach of large cities are to be developed to a point between 50,000 and 100,000.[54] While growth in these towns is not expected to reduce the size of the hub-city population appreciably, nevertheless they can accommodate a certain further population growth in an orderly fashion, growth which might otherwise occur in the hub city itself.

The 1966 planning guidelines for Moscow stressed the development of 10 to 12 small cities in Moscow Province *outside* the suburban zone. This is in keeping with the policy of developing small cities generally regardless of their proximity to large urban hubs. The one difference is that major employers in such cases—notably research facilities—are those which can benefit from being within easy traveling distance of Moscow, for example to permit scientists to consult frequently with ministries in the capital. At present there are two much-publicized examples of this: One is Serpukhov, a picturesque old town astride main transportation routes 60 miles directly south of Moscow, where the world's most powerful research accelerator is presently being installed; the other is Dubna, on the Volga River 70 miles morth of Moscow, likewise a major nuclear research facility.

----

[52] *Vsesoyuznoye soveshchaniye po gradostroitel'stvu*, 1960, p. 23; Svetlichnyi, 1960, p. 51.

[53] Report of V. I. Korzh, *Vsesoyuznoye soveshchaniye po gradostroitel'stvu*, 1960, p. 479.

[54] Yevstratov interview, January 1964.

The question that emerged in the latter 1960's was whether or not the expansion of a city into its suburban zones could be contained in the neat packages of satellite cities, each planned for a carefully controlled level of population. The negative answer to this question by B. E. Svetlichnyi, a high *Gosstroi* official, is worth quoting at length:

Why does a giant city with a population of millions keep growing, though it already seems to have everything necessary for normal living? The point is that it cannot help growing. And not only because of the economic laws that influenced it at the outset, but also because of those that emerged as a chain reaction from the process of its development. The city's growth is accompanied, in particular, not only by a growth in production, but also by the enormous scale of its growing internal consumption. The city begins to work "for itself" to a considerable degree. After all, a population of five to six million people is equal to the population of many a country. Yet this does not mean that a giant city must keep growing indefinitely. At a certain stage of its development the nature of its growth changes sharply. If it is not to choke within its own stone confines, it spreads beyond its limits to surrounding spaces, forming variegated clusters of inhabited areas known as urban agglomerations. In principle, this is a profoundly positive, perhaps even salutory process. The agglomerations could draw off a considerable part of the populations of very large cities and at the same time create for them conditions of suburban comfort. The trouble is that it is even harder to direct the development of an agglomeration than to cope with the stubborn habits of the giant city. In the U.S.A., for example, as a result of the uninterrupted and haphazard development of such agglomerations, one continuous city has emerged all the way from Boston to Washington—a distance of almost 1,000 kilometers.

Quite a few agglomerations are springing up in our coutnry as well. We must learn to control their growth and, among other things, to apply the methods of regional planning.[55]

Svetlichnyi's reasoning echoes to some extent the arguments of the economist Oleg S. Pchelintsev of the Academy of Science's Institute of Economics. The latter concluded that cities within the various population ranges which urban planners have called "optimal," whether under 250,000 or under 400,000, are often precisely those which need growth in order to fulfill their economic potential. Even the one clear doctrine of the optimal-size theorists, namely, halting the establishment of new city-forming employers, will limit the rate of growth but not stop growth; these same theorists, Pchelintsev wrote, are at a loss to know how to project the

---

[55] Svetlichnyi, 1966, pp. 3-4. Trans. in *CDSP* XVIII: 48, p. 12.

development of their optimal cities beyond the optimum. They fail to see that medium-sized cities which are in the process of growing into big cities have the potential for transcending the compact jumble of uses which is the traditional urban form. Large cities are not just a multiplication of the characteristics of medium-sized cities, but represent a different type of economic and spatial organization. For one thing, they are capable of providing the skilled labor force which mans the "clean" industries and occupations, notably research facilities; it is the medium-sized cities that attract primarily the type of industry that presents environmental hazards. But more important, large cities are able to grow by vast spatial extension into their suburban areas. Here uses may be articulated on a large scale, yet integrated so as to permit agricultural and industrial-urban uses to coexist. Industries with large territorial requirements will be drawn to the expanding suburban areas, which Pchelintsev termed the "urbanized zones" or "broad zones of intensive use." Agriculture in these zones will become more specialized and more intensive, and the agricultural population will share fully in the benefits of urban life. Satellite cities will have their place in the "zones," but large-scale urban development tends to overleap and spread beyond anything that represents an obstacle, including these same satellite cities.[56]

The City as a Social Magnet.   For the unexpectedly rapid growth of the larger cities, and for the number of master plans which have been scrapped because of unexpected new industries and people, it is not short-term industrial needs or short-sighted industrial location decisions which are alone to blame. There is also the conviction on the part of those who choose industrial locations that large cities assure a labor force which is more plentiful, more stable, and more skilled than labor forces elsewhere. In other words, the preferences of the workers themselves count heavily, and economic plans ultimately must take these preferences into account.

While Soviet sociology of the 1960's has produced many studies on labor turnover and migration to and from Siberia, and has paid some attention to the question of why young people leave the farms and never return, so far nothing has come to the writer's attention which analyzes the apparent preference for the large cities on the part of those who have the choice between smaller and larger urban centers. This preference is only an apparent one, and cannot be demonstrated by reference to urban population statistics, which

---

[56]Pchelintsev, 1961. See also Perevedentsev, *op cit.*—he maintains that no one has produced a definition of "optimal size" or "excessive growth."

themselves are to a large extent a reflection of industrial location and expansion decisions. Measurement of the preference would involve in-depth studies of migration patterns, or of the preferences expressed by university and technicum graduates at the time they receive job assignments. The writer can offer only a collection of impressions based on conversations with university students ("Novosibirsk would be all right, but I don't want to get stuck in a small place") and casual contacts in small cities ("Our young people like Central Asia, but most of them try to get to Tashkent").

Among those migrants who are able to choose between big-city jobs and jobs elsewhere, doubtless the greatest single lure offered by the big cities is choice and variety. Among the types of choice that large cities offer, the most important would be likely to be job choices and advancement possibilities within one's specialty, jobs suitable for wives, choices involving further education and training, and choices of human association. In the Soviet Union especially, consumers' goods are decidedly more plentiful in the larger cities than elsewhere. There is a difference between what is "urban" and what is "provincial" in the levels of talent and general intelligence which one can expect among colleagues, fellow workers, and friends generally. Much harder to define is the human urge to be where there is motion and restlessness in society, and the conviction, right or wrong, that the quality of intrinsic interest in human association increases as numbers multiply. Added to all these feelings is the desire to have one's children grow up amid such benefits. If this description is even partially correct, as regards those migrants whose choice of residence has been open, then the efforts of *Gosstroi* to maintain standards that will make small cities as attractive as large cities is largely misdirected as a means of stemming the growth of large cities. Svetlichnyi, after expressing optimism with regard to the renewal of cities under 50,000 by locating industries in them, added that

. . . we must also reckon with a different set of factors and social phenomena. My point here is that the largest cities have a tremendous power of attraction. Practically speaking, everything is available in our big cities: every sort of work and schooling, and the entire store of mankind's cultural treasures. It is this inspiring atmosphere of the big city that attracts the people, particularly the young, who dream of wide horizons. We should not close our eyes to the fact that they will continue to rush into the big cities.[57]

---

[57]Svetlichnyi, "The City Awaits a Reply," 1966, p. 159. Trans. from *CDSP* XVIII: 48, p. 12.

ALLOCATING RESOURCES AMONG CITIES

During the 1960's, the world of the Soviet citizen as resident and consumer has made progress toward catching up, so to speak, with the world of the citizen as employee and producer. From the 1960's on, if present trends continue, the role of enterprises and industrial ministries in determining the quality of the urban environment around them will diminish, and the role of local governments and urban planners will grow. On the surface of things, this is an administrative transition, undertaken to help correct the investment imbalances and planning mistakes of the past. Actually, an important type of equality is involved, namely, the citizen's claim to equal treatment in the creation of the urban environment around him.

During the early five-year plans, the large industries and the ministries which governed them were favored not only in investment allocations, but also in the degree to which they were permitted to organize their physical environment. They determined not only the amount and type of housing, but also the level of services, the fate of urban planning and zoning, the level of cultural life, the ease of communication with the world outside their environment, and a good deal else. The Soviet railroad system, for example, long an investment-favored sector of the economy, was able to house a large portion of its employees in the vicinity of major railroad stations and equip these areas with services and facilities which were sorely lacking elsewhere. It was to help redress this balance that *Gosstroi* was organized in 1950 and its authority bolstered in 1962.[58] Svetlichnyi's summary of both the problem and the beginnings of a solution is eloquent:

We all remember well those recent years when ministries and plants literally tore cities into pieces, each one attempting by all means fair and foul to build "its own" housing right next to the plant, to create at any price "its own" private workers' community near the plant with "its own" water supply, sewerage, steam plant, club, and shop—in short, to do everything for itself and give nothing to the city.

This was primitive, expensive, and fundamentally in contradiction to the planning system of our government. During the seven-year plan just completed [1959-65] we have succeeded with great difficulty, though by no means

---

[58]*Izvestiya*, May 10, 1950; *Vedomosti SSSR* 1962, No. 49, Art. 497.

everywhere, in liquidating these "fiefdoms" and bringing them together into large areas of housing provided with the essential types of services and utilities. Cities have begun to develop in a more integrated and harmonious fashion, since local governments have begun to receive a larger proportion of the resources allocated to housing construction, whereas previously their share amounted to no more than 10 percent while the rest went to the economic ministries and agencies.[59]

The parallel between the behavior of early Soviet and early capitalist industries in this respect is too obvious to require comment.

The battle for local government control over investment in civil construction has been won in Moscow, Leningrad, and most of the large cities, but elsewhere it remains a serious problem. In the Russian Republic as a whole, for example, only half of all the funds allocated for housing construction go to local governments; the rest are transferred to industries and various organizations that build mainly to house their own employees.[60] *Izvestiya*, as the top government organ and spokesman for local governments, has waged a vigorous campaign since the 1950's for the transfer of all nonindustrial construction and operations to the jurisdiction of local governments, or, where formal jurisdiction already exists, for making such transfers administratively effective. A few recent examples will suffice. The head economic planner in Yerevan complained of the city's inability to build residential districts as integrated wholes, since housing investment funds were distributed among various industries and agencies, which in turn used two dozen different construction contractors. Enterprise-contracted housing there costs around 200 rubles per square meter as opposed to the city's 130-ruble cost; it was of inferior quality, and took more time to construct.[61] Two Moscow jurists investigated residential construction in Bryansk, and found 45 different civil construction organizations at work, most of them the creatures of local industries. Since the industries were interested first of all in rapid construction of housing space, construction of retail, service, and social facilities was being seriously neglected.[62] Rudnyi (pop. 84,000 as of 1966), a new iron-ore center in Kazakhstan, offers an example of a one-industry town whose

[59] Svetlichnyi, "Urban Construction and Economic Planning," March 1966, p. 32.

[60] I. Nomokonov and V. Perttsik, "A Single Complex," *Izvestiya*, January 30, 1969.

[61] G. Panosiyan, "Master of the City," *Izvestiya*, May 11, 1967.

[62] B. Gabrichidze and M. Shafir, "The Local Soviet and the Enterprise," *Izvestiya*, October 12, 1966.

welfare depends very much on whatever resources the Ministry of Ferrous Metallurgy is willing or able to devote to it. A recent account described the local government as functioning mainly in the role of petitioner before the Ministry and its several enterprises. Upon the decisions of these enterprises depend, for example, the construction of a polytechnical institute, sports facilities, a projected central park, a major hospital, daycare facilities, and a number of other projects.[63] The head of communal services in Zaporozh'ye wrote of the serious maintenance and operation problems posed by the circumstance that not only the city's housing and service structures, but its utilities and roads as well, were the property of a number of different enterprises, many of which devoted little attention to their holdings.[64]

The grievances of municipal governments in this respect may be summarized as their inability to (1) control industrial location and siting, (2) bring civil construction together under a unified plan, (3) correct the lag in construction of shops, services, and cultural facilities behind housing construction, (4) curb environmental pollution, and (5) coordinate management and maintenance of housing and service facilities. Part of these shortcomings can be attributed to pressures from industries and their ministries, part to the municipalities' small share of investment funds, and part to lack of initiative on the part of local administrators themselves, whose overall level of talent and experience is lower than that of administrators in the more important industries.

Until the 1950's there was hardly any remedy for these shortcomings in view of national investment priorities. New industries in new locations had to assure themselves of at least minimal housing and services in order to retain a labor force at all. If they had waited for urban planners and municipal administrators to settle on integrated development plans, then waited still more until permanent apartments, utilities, and all the rest were assured, one can well imagine the fate of production targets in the early five-year plans. High-priority industries got not only priorities in funds and material resources, but the best technical and managerial talent as well. Even

---

[63] N. Lisovenko, "The Enterprise and the City," *Izvestiya,* July 26, 1968.

[64] V. Kalanchin, "Whose Street Is This? Whose House Is This?" *Izvestiya*, August 26, 1966. See also the complaints of the mayor of Ufa in "Money Likes Management," *Izvestiya*, February 9, 1968. All these problems were summed up in the editorial "Our Soviet Power," *Izvestiya,* April 15, 1966, p. 1.

at the end of the 1950's, experienced architects and urban planners were still in very short supply, and a large number of cities and towns were without a qualified chief planner.[65] While all this did grievous damage to the urban planning of the future in view of the planning mistakes that were made, it could hardly have been otherwise. To this extent the Soviet Union's experience followed that of other industrial nations which experienced periods of rapid industrial growth.

There are two problems here: One is that of insuring proper distribution of housing and services in cities which, because of their industries' resources, have at least a potential local source of funds. The other problem is that of assuring an equal level of housing and services for the many smaller cities without major industries.

The first problem is probably easier to solve than the second, even though major Soviet industries even today are yielding their profits and prerogatives for the welfare of the communities in which they are located only under pressure. The mayor of Gor'kii recently proposed that enterprises not under urban jurisdiction be required by law to transfer a proportion of their profits to the cities in which they are located. Only by such means, he maintained, will the cities be assured of the resources they need to provide adequate housing and communal services, and to integrate planning and services.[66]

The control of industrial enterprises over housing construction and other civil construction has two sources. One is the proportion of profits which enterprises are permitted to use for building housing for their employees, and the other is the fact that a sizable portion of the nation's civil construction budget is simply assigned to the industrial ministries, whose structure commonly includes construction firms. There are no published comprehensive data showing how much of the civil construction budget is industry-administered, and how much is administered by local governments. As noted above, in 1968 half of all investment in housing in the Russian Republic was administered by local governments; nearly all of the remainder went to enterprises.

Until the 1965 economic reforms, enterprises used two categories of profits as sources of housing construction funds: (*a*) 40 percent or more of the "enterprise fund," which is formed from planned

---

[65]There were repeated references to this shortage at the 1960 urban planning conference. *Vsesoyuznoye soveshchaniye po gradostroitel'stvu*, 1960, *passim*.

[66]A. Sokolov, "The City's Autonomy," *Izvestiya*, November 3, 1968.

profits, above-plan profits, and above-plan savings; and (*b*) the housing construction fund, which was formed from above-plan profits alone, and could embrace as much as 30 percent of these profits. In 1965, just before enterprises began to convert to the new system for accumulating and measuring profits, housing built from enterprise profits accounted for roughly 10 percent of the total paid for by the state and enterprises together.[67] Consequently, it has not been the size of enterprise profits which accounts for most of the 50 percent share in housing construction enjoyed by industrial enterprises, but rather the assignment of state budgetary funds to the enterprises. Besides, the entire "enterprise fund" was held to an upper limit of 5 percent of an enterprise's total wage fund from 1955 on (5.5 percent from 1961). It remains to be seen whether the 1965 reforms will have the effect of allotting a larger share of profits (profitability itself having been redefined) to housing and related construction. During 1967, the more than 5,000 enterprises which had converted to the new profit system were setting aside an amount equal only to 3 percent of their wage funds for all social and cultural measures, including housing.[68]

The problem is not, therefore, that industrial enterprises do not spend their resources on housing and services. Rather, it appears that the ministries which have jurisdiction over them see little reason why they should assist the budgets of the larger cities. In new industrial areas, apparently, where housing and services have to be provided "from the ground up," both the ministries and *Gosplan* have found it more convenient to make the new industries themselves responsible for building their environment around them. In the old established industrial cities, whose budgetary funds are already considerable, and which are comparatively well provided with specialists and experienced administrators, the industries·prefer to let the municipality shoulder most of the burden for present construction. Mayor Sokolov complained specifically that of the total budgetary funds assigned by various ministries to their enterprises in Gor'kii for all types of investment, only one sixth to one tenth is earmarked for housing and services. When the city's enterprises do lay out money

---

[67]Estimated from data in *Narodnoye khozyaistvo SSSR*, 1965, pp. 610, 611, 775-76. No figures are given for the exact share of the state budget in the total, as distinguished from enterprises and cooperative organizations.

[68]*Sotsialisticheskii trud*, No. 8 (August, 1968), p. 28. A full explanation of the 1965 reforms is given in U. S. Department of Commerce, Bureau of the Census, *The Soviet Financial System: Structure, Operation and Statistics*, 1968, pp. 106-26.

for general community needs, they hedge this aid with conditions in the manner of a "rich relative" giving handouts to his kin.[69]

In large cities such as Gor'kii, the enterprises try to hang on to and operate what they have already built, which includes not only housing and shops, but in some cases transportation lines and utilities. It is the large industries in the high-priority branches which are best able to do this. The smaller factories and consumer-goods industries have often had a difficult time assembling an enterprise fund at all. Since the size of profits in any given type of enterprise can be manipulated from Moscow through central price-setting as well as through direct and indirect subsidies, this favoring of large industries must be regarded as a policy.

An *Izvestiya* editorial written two weeks after Mayor Sokolov's article, clearly in reply to this and similar proposals for increasing local financial resources, accused local governments of using their funds improperly. The solution to their financial problems, according to *Izvestiya*, is not any further largesse from the general state budget, but rather the pursuit of greater economy by municipal governments and an increase in the profitability of the small local industries whose profits (unlike those of the larger enterprises) are paid by law into local government treasuries. The editorial pointed out that these profits would grow as the economic reforms of September 1965 are extended to the local industries.[70] If this editorial is any indication of the policies of the newspaper's sponsor, the Soviet government, it appears that the industries have won the latest round against the local governments.

The second problem, that of the small cities, is a far more difficult one. In nonindustrial urban investment there are distinct rewards for rapidly growing cities, and no corresponding rewards for growth limitation. Data on housing investment from the state budget and other nonindustrial investment in cities is not broken down sufficiently to furnish a systematic picture of investment levels as among cities. However, comments by local officials, urban planners, and economists all indicate that this investment is directed heavily into growing industrial centers of over 100,000 (and into the very largest cities, of course, growing or not). The smaller cities are largely dependent on what their industries may be able to build with their profits; and those small cities without substantial industries receive

---

[69] A. Sokolov, *op. cit.*

[70] "The Local Soviet's Budget," *Izvestiya*, November 15, 1968.

less investment per capita than any other category. For the bulk of towns under 50,000, those which have no growing industrial base, the only practical hope for receiving major civil construction investment lies in their attracting industry. That is to say, old housing is not replaced by modern apartments only because it is old and overcrowded, and streets are not paved simply because there is mud; such improvements still go primarily to those cities which need to provide for a growing labor force, not to those which have no such influx to cope with. It is little wonder that local government and Party officials go in pursuit of new industries as assiduously as any small-town chamber of commerce in the United States.[71] The anecdotal literature on this problem in the Soviet press has been quite substantial during the 1960's.

The irony of the small towns' budgetary woes is that the Soviet planning and financial systems appear quite capable of dealing with them effectively. The tight central coordination of industrial investment, which has been such a stable feature of the Soviet system since the first five-year plan, should enable *Gosplan* and the Council of Ministers to locate new industries in the small towns even at some additional initial cost, if necessary. Since the central press has carried numerous items during the past decade stressing the need to do this, this policy has not been without its supporters in the Party and government. The 1961 Party Program, while it repeated the familiar formulae about the need to develop small towns industrially as the primary method for raising their welfare to the national urban average, did so only in passing and provided no further specific guidelines for realizing this policy.[72]

In 1966 the Russian Republic issued a decree according provincial governments the right to review plans worked out by both Republic-level and national-level ministries concerning investment on their territory. Objections and proposals concerning these plans can be submitted both to the appropriate ministry and to the *Gosplan* offices at the Republic level. An official of the Irkutsk Province government wrote that this at least offers a channel for affecting the decisions of the 427 industries not subject to its jurisdiction—and it

---

[71] Examples of the plight of economically static small towns are given in items such as the following: Inessa Burkova, "Kuzma," *Literaturnaya Rossiya,* May 6, 1966 (trans. in *CDSP* XVII: 19, pp. 16-19); V. Belyayev, "Away From the Main Road," *Pravda,* July 9, 1966; Konstantin Paustovskii, "The Fate of Small Towns," *Pravda,* July 16, 1965; and the follow-up to this in *Pravda,* September 7, 1965.

[72] *XXII S''yezd KPSS,* Vol. 3, pp. 281-82, 298-99.

does have jurisdiction only over 104. The problem is not only with industries, however, since the Russian Republic Ministry of Culture also is accustomed to building libraries, clubhouses, and other facilities without consulting with the provincial government as to what is needed where. The Province's ability to cope with these situations depends also on its own ability to plan and evaluate the plans of others, and at present it simply is not staffed to do this effectively.[73]

The Soviet national budget, because it encompasses local budgets and is used to determine the level of local receipts from taxes, could readily be employed in order to equalize investment in housing and in all forms of civil construction for cities. While only scattered data on local budgets are available, the impression one gets from both professional and journalistic discussions of local budgets is that they are used by Moscow and the republic governments to reinforce the pattern of investment in industries. That is to say, those cities which are already receiving additional investment in housing, utilities, shops, and so forth because their growing industries are spending money on these things, are also favored in the state budget so as to enable them to build yet more housing and facilities of their own. One might say that the Marxist principle governing the present socialist period, "to each according to his work," has been applied to communities as well as to individuals.

This preference in allocation is quite understandable on two counts: first, it is understandable as a consequence of the Soviet government's constant resolve since the late 1920's to place a rapidly growing industrial output before all else; and secondly, to equalize civil construction investment per capita of urban population would have meant dispersing it very thinly indeed. Where funds are short, some things must come before others.

Two major alternatives to the present policy on small cities have thus far been rejected by most Soviet policymakers who have expressed themselves on the subject: (1) declaring a number of small cities economically dead, and relocating their people; (2) giving cities and regions a degree of economic autonomy similar to that of local government in Yugoslavia.[74] The latter policy would mean that cities would have an independent tax base, the ability to borrow

---

[73] Nomokonov and Perttsik, *op. cit.*

[74] See the description of the Yugoslav approach in Jack C. Fisher, *Yugoslavia—A Multi-National State* (San Francisco: Chandler, 1966) pp. 166-77.

money for improvements, and the authority to set up a great variety of industries under their jurisdiction, rather than just the small assortment of enterprises serving local markets which Soviet cities control today. It would greatly diminish Moscow's capacity to allocate resources, which might or might not be economically advantageous for the nation, but which certainly might lead to a diminution in Moscow's political authority as well. Rejection of the first alternative is commonly supported with the economic argument that the small cities with an underemployed labor force are already equipped with housing, schools, and other facilities, which would have to be replaced were the population moved elsewhere. But so far there has been little professional or journalistic discussion of other kinds of costs: What does it cost the nation's economy to provide for the young people who, for want of local employment opportunities, do leave such cities in large numbers? What does the underuse of those who remain cost in terms of production?

Thus far, the debate among professional people over the allocation of investment among regions and cities has produced no major proposals for shifting responsibility for some of these decisions to the cities and provinces themselves. There is no lack of interest in regional economic planning among Soviet economists, however.[75] Systematic research in regional planning is carried on under the auspices of the Academy of Sciences and *Gosplan* jointly, as well as in the Academy's Institute for Economic-Mathematical Modeling. But thus far the one policy which carries political weight is that of bringing industries to economically static small cities, regardless whether this can be fully justified by estimates of overall costs and benefits as between a big-city location and a small-town location.

CONCLUSION

If Soviet political leaders and economic policymakers do not yet appear to be convinced that the present system of nonindustrial investment allocation is in need of revision, they do appear to be

---

[75] The U.S.S.R. Academy of Sciences and *Gosplan's* Council for Studying Productive Forces have jointly published *Bibliografiya po voprosam razmeshcheniya i raionirovaniya promyshlennosti SSSR* (Bibliography on Industrial Location and Regionalization in the U.S.S.R.) (Moscow: Nauka, 1964) and are currently issuing a series of regional studies that has begun with *Zapadno-sibirskii ekonomicheskii raion* (The Western Siberian Economic Region) (Moscow: Nauka, 1967) and *Severo-zapadnyi ekonomicheskii raion* (The Northwestern Economic Region) (Moscow: Nauka, 1967).

willing to experiment with new policies with which to cope with the problem of growth in the largest urban areas. In the design of residences, services, and urban amenities, the interest of some architects in something more than square meters, services, and convenience may during the 1970's result in a new concept of what the urban environment is. One of the fruits of this new sociological interest may well be to open the way for much more local experimentation in design, quite apart from what *Gosstroi's* norms may or may not be. It may also direct the efforts of the young and growing sociological profession more toward problems of human association unrelated to work. Clearly it is too early to say whether or not the Soviet Union is on the way to discovering policies for the urban environment which will succeed where the efforts of other nations to solve analogous problems have failed. The policies which have evolved so far appear today to be much less settled, and less clearly defined, than most of the policies described in the preceding chapters of this study. In any case, the 1970's promise a number of Soviet urban planning experiments that will be well worth the attention of the other industrialized and industrializing nations.

.7. *Communities in the City*

RESIDENTIAL ARRANGEMENTS AND SOCIAL RELATIONS

Can residence-based communities be successful in large cities? If so, does this depend to any great extent on the physical organization of residential units and services? Even if proper residential planning would promote geographically-based relationships, are they a desirable or even possible feature of modern urban society?

As a result of transferring a large number of everyday functions out of the apartment and into the communal sector [of the proposed new commune-type apartments], which will broaden the opportunities for social contact among the residents and for various common activities—cultural, educational, sports, and recreational—the time which people spend in their individual apartments will be reduced. The separated character of residential units and the population's closed-off manner of living will be overcome. — Georgii A. Gradov, Soviet design institute director and specialist in public buildings, 1968.[1]

. . . .

. . . Many architects and planners have tried to recreate the local primary group artificially, by means of the neighborhood idea. They have hoped that if people would only live in small physical groups, round modern village greens, the social groups would follow the same pattern; and that these artificial groups would once more provide the intimate contact which is in such short supply in urban areas today. But this idea of recreating primary groups by artificial means is unrealistic and reactionary: it fails to recognize the truth about the open society. The open society is no longer centered around place-based groups; and the very

---

[1]Gradov, 1968, p. 103.

slight acquaintances that do form round an artificial neighborhood are once again trivial: they are not based on genuine desire. — Christopher Alexander, "The City As a Mechanism for Sustaining Human Contact," 1967.[2]

The idea of residential complexes designed specifically to create and sustain social interaction among their residents can be traced far back into utopian thought. The best known of these dreams, designs, and actual projects not only provided a specific pattern of living in residences, but linked residential arrangements to places of work. Thus, in the conceptions of Robert Owen and Charles Fourier (1772-1837) productive work, life as residents, and recreational activities were to be shared among the same group of people.

Soviet architects have not, to the writer's knowledge, sought a self-contained work-and-dwelling complex as a goal. Naturally, the "company town" is just as familiar an arrangement in the Soviet Union as it is elsewhere. But even in the cities which have a variety of major employers, the assignment of both apartment buildings and whole residential complexes to the employees of a given enterprise is a common practice, especially where enterprises have put up their own housing; and it is not uncommon for this housing to be grouped near the enterprise, and for the residents to share the enterprises's service facilities. But such complexes were built first of all as a matter of convenience for employers and employees alike, without much thought to whatever social function they might serve. While even today one occasionally sees disapproving references to Soviet advocates of what are termed "production and service communes," the writer has not discovered any such communes.[3]

On the other hand, the idea of the residential complex as the framework for social interaction and shared services has a long history in the Soviet Union. The idea has loomed much larger than the reality, since the number of such apartment houses cannot have been more than several dozen during the entire half century of Soviet rule. In the 1960's, however, now that some of the nation's most urgent housing needs have been met with the mass-production of ordinary apartment buildings, the *dom-kommuna* or "commune-type apartment house" is enjoying a new burst of popularity among some Soviet architects and social scientists, to the extent that prototypes have been going up during the last few years in Moscow and

---

[2] William R. Ewald, Jr. (ed.), *Environment for Man: The Next Fifty Years* (Bloomington, Ind.: Indiana University Press, 1967), p. 65.

[3] Kharchev, 1964, pp. 319–20.

Leningrad. The term *dom-kommuna* might also be translated "communal apartment house" or "communal residence," but the term "communal" in connection with residential arrangements somehow evokes in Western minds the notion of barracks living, common soup pots, and the dissolution of family life. This, as will become clear, is not at all the present Soviet meaning.

The Communist Party's first postrevolutionary Program (1919) placed an official stamp of approval on the idea of the commune-type apartment house. Its justification was not the desirability of creating urban social groupings, but simply the need to free women for employment: "The Party, not limiting itself to formal legal equality for women, strives to free them from the material burdens of the outmoded household economy by replacing it with commune-type houses, public eating places, central laundries, nurseries, etc."[4] While it was a full decade before even the first clumsy architectural experiments in this direction were undertaken, the years of the Revolution and the decade of the 1920's saw a number of urban communes organized in the large cities which used existing housing. Unlike the Chinese urban communes which were organized during the latter 1950's, these were cooperative residential and service arrangements having no formal link to productive enterprises. Usually they were managed by elected committees, which not only looked after housing needs, but in some cases organized foodstores, bakeries, laundries, and recreational areas. Some of the communes were composed of students alone, who shared their slim resources in a manner familiar to students of other places and times.[5] For the time being, the Party treated these experiments with silence; it considered them the work of enthusiasts in pursuit of a very particular view of the communist future which was not necessarily shared by the Party's leaders.

During the 1920's there were some very vocal supporters of the idea that the family in socialist society would die a natural death, a process which could be hastened by communal dwelling arrangements. Alexandra M. Kolontai (1872-1952), the nation's first commissar for social welfare, prophesied the following:

Family households will inevitably die a natural death with the growth in number of communal houses of different types to suit different tastes; and as the individual household which is enclosed within the limits of a separate flat dies

---

[4] *KPSS v rezolyutsiyakh,* Vol. 1, p. 415.

[5] Wesson, 1963, p. 84.

out, the fundamental clamps of the contemporary bourgeois family will be wrenched looser. Once it has ceased to be a unit of consumption, the family will be unable to exist in its present form—it will fall assunder, be liquidated.[6]

Among Soviet architects, A. M. Sabsovich was the best known supporter of this "left tendency" in social relations. Common services and common facilities for recreation and leisure-time pursuits, he wrote, "will dispense with any need or reason for the separate life of separate families in isolated flats and little houses designed with an eye on the 'family hearth.' "[7] This point of view gained such popularity in the architectural world that Sabsovich and others pursuaded the Soviet Society of Modern Architects to adopt a resolution specifying the essential life processes or functions, for all of which the commune-type dwelling was to serve as the organizer. The vision of one architect (Kuz'min) would have made an Orwellian fantasy out of the commune in that he proposed regulating the performance of each function to the minute via central radio commands.[8]

Altogether only some ten commune-type apartment houses were actually built during the period before World War II, and these mainly in Moscow and Leningrad. Nevertheless, there was considerable interest in them among Soviet architects, who organized a number of design competitions to this end.[9] The first experimental building went up in 1929. While only part of its dwelling units were kitchenless and served by a common dining room, even this modest communal arrangement was abandoned after only two years, and the dining room and other common facilities subdivided to make further apartments.[10] A dormitory for university students built at about the same time suffered a similar fate, one of its principal flaws being that its dwelling units were tiny (65 square feet) cubicles with bunk beds, intended for nothing but sleeping.[11] Insofar as these were accommodations for young single people, their physical facilities hardly differed from those of a well-provided YMCA residential hotel.

Design and construction of commune-type dwellings was quickly

---

[6]Schlesinger, 1949, p. 51.

[7]*Ibid.,* p. 171. See also the articles by Gol'tsman, Sabsovich, and Miliutin in Lunin, 1930.

[8]Gradov, 1968, pp. 48-50.

[9]*Ibid.,* 1968, pp. 43-58.

[10]This was the project of G. Vol'fenzon and S. Leontovich on Khavsko-Shabolovskii Lane. Gradov, 1968, pp. 46-47.

[11]This was designed by I. S. Nikolayev, and built on Donskii Lane. Gradov, 1968, pp. 47-48.

abandoned as a result of Stalin's sharp attacks of 1930-31 against all those who were trying to build pieces of the communist future in the present, whether it be by organizing urban communes or by levelling earnings. A Party resolution of May 1930 condemned the more extreme experiments and proposals as "utterly unjustified, half-fantastic, and therefore extremely harmful." While this same resolution did call for attention to the practical problems of grouping services, its actual effect was to put a sudden end to further designing of the commune-type dwellings.[12] The June 1931 Party resolution on urban affairs delivered a rebuke, in passing, to those who would abolish the domestic kitchen in favor of communal dining facilities, or who would impose the new "dwelling communes" *(bytovye kommuny)* in an artificial manner.[13]

This condemnation was probably just as well, considering the economic needs and pressures of the 1930's. Most of the various designs for commune-type housing represented an increase in the costs of construction and operation. More important, the level of services and amenities which these designs called for would have run contrary to the low national priority for these items, had the designs been widely used. In view of the enormous pressure on urban housing space, it is not hard to imagine the nondwelling areas of the new communes being partitioned for additional rooms and apartments, as happened with the few that were actually built. The architects who came up with the most famous commune design of this period, a blueprint commissioned by the Russian Republic's State Construction Committee, omitted any calculation of what probably would have been enormous operating expenses. This would have been a giant cross-shaped structure, 70 percent of whose space was devoted to communal facilities.[14]

Twenty-five years passed. Soviet residential building during the 1930-55 period, woefully inadequate as it was in quantity, was in all too many cases designed first of all for external display. After a period of experimentation with the "constructivist" style then popular in Europe, the bizarre pseudoclassic facades of the Stalin era began to appear. Not only was this style heavily monumental and the building techniques consequently wasteful, but the microdistrict itself, the layouts which grouped apartment buildings very sensibly

[12]*Ibid.*, 1968, p. 56.

[13]*KPSS v rezolyutsiyakh,* Vol. 3, pp. 125-26.

[14]Gradov, 1968, pp. 50-53.

about services and recreational areas, was sacrificed to the construction of long "parade avenues." The years following World War II saw an accentuation of this trend rather than any kind of modification based on experience; in this same period (1946-52) there rose the ornate skyscrapers which today punctuate the Moscow skyline.

All this was condemned by the Party and the Union of Soviet Architects two years after Stalin's death,[15] and with Khrushchev's accession to power, the emphasis was on austere, mass-produced apartment complexes, mainly five-story walk-up apartments made of prefabricated panels. While the microdistrict idea received a powerful new impetus at this time, construction organizations reckoned their output largely in terms of square meters of housing space. Consequently, the comparatively meager funds for shops and services were often re-allocated to build yet more square meters. The prefabricated apartments which Khrushchev promoted were in turn criticized after his deposition from power (1964) for being too uniformly austere and wasteful of space in large cities.

The policies of the Khrushchev era, for all their one-sided emphasis on the quantity of housing space, did impel architects and social scientists to go to work on the problem of urban society and its relationship to the physical environment. From the early 1930's on, most of the social sciences had stagnated in the Soviet Union; social science became nothing more or less than the exegesis of Party doctrines. The extravagant monumentalism of architecture during this period was one significant reflection of the "Byzantine" character of social thought: symbolism was everything, content counted for little. Khrushchev personally reopened the debate about future social development in proclaiming that the transition from socialism to communism was under way. The Party Program of 1961 provided only the most general policy outlines for residential arrangements, while stressing the growth and equitable distribution of services. The highly optimistic statements of this period did serve to bring out into the open a variety of ideas about the future. Social scientists, urban planners, and architects were in effect invited to produce their own ideas of how the Soviet urban populace would live in the future.

A modern reincarnation of the commune-type apartment idea was offered in 1960 by the then 83-year-old Stanislav G. Strumilin, an

---

[15] *KPSS v rezolyutsiyakh,* Vol. 4, pp. 112-22.

economist of some note who had once served as head of the Central Statistical Administration and as vice-chairman of *Gosplan*.[16] His principle of organizing communes to act jointly as producers and as consumers harked back to the utopianism of the early 19th century. What his proposal boiled down to, though, was "palace communes" housing 2,000 or 2,500 residents each, each serving a single enterprise which is not necessarily adjacent to the commune. Strumilin's building layout would first of all provide apartment units of different sizes for different family sizes and situations, including a wing for the aged—all this, were it realized, a great improvement over the uniformity of most floor layouts then being built. More striking features of his layout included communal dining facilities plus social rooms on each floor, and a special wing for children, who were to sleep apart from their families. Strumilin stressed that there would be no compulsion about taking communal meals—ready meals could be served to individual apartments just as well. While palace communes would be grouped into microdistricts, Strumilin's "layering" of services placed many more services at the apartment house level than do *Gosstroi's* 1958 and 1966 regulations, or current residential design practice. Up to one fourth of the commune's 400,000 or more square feet of floor space would be devoted to common use.

Strumilin viewed the ideal society specifically as one made up of intensive group associations based on close proximity, everyday contact, and the sharing of both employment and leisure-time experiences within the same group. While he certainly did not advocate the breakup of families, he would reduce even the nuclear family to its husband-and-wife core by removing from it every kind of material burden and necessity, including care not only of the elderly, but of children as well. This meant separate accommodations for children from kindergarten age on, right through to the end of secondary school. Strumilin did not propose that they be removed geographically, for even a boarding school for 400 students could be built right into a palace commune for 2,000 residents. Family ties would be sustained through frequent contact between parents and children, but at the same time the basic task of raising children and preparing them for their role in society would be borne by professional staff.[17]

During the early 1960's, following the surge of official optimism

[16]Strumilin, 1961.

[17]Strumilin, 1964, pp. 144-63.

in 1958-61 about building a new communist way of life, it appeared that Strumilin's proposal was an attempt by an old idealist to revive a dead idea. The microdistricts springing up on the periphery of every large or growing city contained conventionally organized apartments served by small-scale shopping centers. Their guiding principles were—and are—uniform distribution of services, adequate housing space, convenience, and hygiene. Whatever might be called specifically socialist beyond these internationally accepted principles existed in the form of neighborhood organizations of different kinds, and even here the Soviet Union and the socialist countries have had no monopoly on the institution of volunteer work in neighborhoods.

At this time, the one major statement in support of the *dom-kommuna* came from Georgii A. Gradov, a noted architect specializing in public buildings who was then head of the Experimental Design Institute for Public Buildings, and later head of the corresponding design institute for educational buildings:

Together with measures for improving the system of cultural and everyday services for urban populations, the time has come to carry out research and experimental construction of new types of collective dwelling complexes, based on the maximum degree of sharing in cultural and everyday services. In this regard the concept expressed by N. S. Khrushchev in Kiev in 1959 for organizing an all-encompassing system of public services on the basis of community participation, from birth to advanced old age, has a great significance of principle. In essence this is a further development of V. I. Lenin's directives concerning the transformation of small-scale household management into large-scale socialist management. This is also the truly communist way of developing our urban environment. It is precisely collectivism, in conjunction with satisfying individual needs, which constitutes the difference between Soviet urban planning and that of capitalism, whose ideal is the principle "My home is my castle." The collective complex of housing and social facilities, situated on well-landscaped territory, should include primary residential groupings immediately connected with child-care facilities, a public catering unit, and facilities for cultural and everyday services. Besides these, there should be provision for a boarding school, a cooperative social center, and a park. An integrated system of services with maximum community participation with minimal expenditures for labor would permit a practical solution to the problem of freeing women from small-scale household operations, and of strengthening the communist way of life. ...[18]

Gradov considered the ideal number for good social interrelationship

[18] *Vsesoyuznoye soveshchaniye po gradostroitel'stvu*, 1960, pp. 359-60.

in the primary residential unit (the commune-type dwelling, in this case) to be between 1,000 and 1,500. True, he arrived at this figure by reckoning the smallest economically justifiable preschool and dining facilities—200 children for the former, 200 to 250 places for the latter.[19]

In architecture and urban planning as in the other areas of social policy dealt with here, the universal emphasis on central standards and mass-production of a small number of building designs has been giving way in places to the encouragement of variety and experimentation. This circumstance, together with the increasing availability of funds for civil construction, apparently opened the door for the fairly small group of architects which has become interested in planning something more than square meters and services. In 1964 there were two design competitions for apartment complexes with a large range of built-in facilities and services, one for a 2,000-person unit in the southwestern part of Moscow, the other an open national competition for a 2,000-person unit likewise, though one without preschool institutions. No first prize was awarded in the former competition, and none of the designs submitted was, to the writer's knowledge, actually built.[20] The next year the design was published for what was to become the much-publicized housing complex *(kvartal)* No. 10 in Moscow's Novye Cheryomushki district. Nathan S. Osterman's design office in the Moscow Institute for Standard and Experimental Designs (MITEP) called its 2,200-person complex the "House of the New Way of Life" *(Dom novogo byta)*. It is equipped for providing all meals to its residents on the same floors with their apartments, and supplies a variety of other services heretofore provided only in facilities shared by an entire microdistrict. Much of the manpower to operate these is meant to be voluntary, and this presumes a well-functioning system of self-government within the complex. Physically, the House consists of two 16-story residential towers, joined by a spacious two-story complex for communal use.[21] (See Diagram 3.) Occupancy took place at the end of 1969. In the summer of 1969 the writer was able to inspect a sample floor which had been both finished and furnished for display purposes, and to talk with some of the personnel involved in planning and designing the House.

[19]Gradov, 1968, pp. 137-38.

[20]*Ibid.*, 1968, pp. 82-85.

[21]Osterman and Petrushkova, 1965. Yurii Polukhin, "Not a Dream, But Reality." *Literaturnaya gazeta,* November 6, 1968. Trans. in *CDSP* XXI:3, pp. 16-18.

Diagram 3
SECOND-STORY FLOOR PLAN OF THE "HOUSE
OF THE NEW WAY OF LIFE," MOSCOW,
COMPLETED IN 1969

1 – dining-living room on each floor; 2 – meal-serving facilities plus kitchen for residents' use, on each floor; 3 – radio and television hobby room; 4 – photographic hobby room; 5 – reading room, lending library; 6 – buffet, bar, and billiard room; 7 – lounge on each floor.

The wings on the left and right, which contain apartments and dining facilities, are each 16 floors high; the connecting central portion, containing various community and service facilities, has 2 floors.

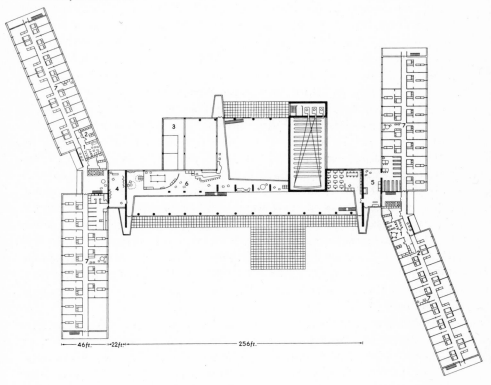

Source: *Arkhitektura SSSR* No. 7, 1965, p. 19.

This experiment is of considerable interest because Osterman and the group of architects who undertook it based their innovations directly on the relevant passages in the 1961 Party Program. In so doing they enlisted the advice not only of Strumilin and Trapeznikov, but of some 30 research institutes and other agencies in every conceivable specialty. Because Osterman and MITEP were planning for future rather than just present needs, the standards they chose were more generous in many respects than those of the 1958 or 1966 "Standards and Norms." The most striking component of the design stemming from this orientation to the future is the dining facilities. Other unique features are the widespread use of accordian-type folding partitions within apartments, and the lavish provision of recreational, social, and hobbyroom facilities. Dining facilities in the earlier variants of Osterman's design were centralized, but the final design reduced the size of the central dining room to 250 places, and instead provided for a dining hall on each floor with places for one third to one half of the floor's occupants, who number not more than 60. The designers assumed that in the normal course of things the residents would not all eat at the same time anyway. Dining facilities are run by a food service staff of 76 paid employees and 26 volunteers. On each floor, a well-paid cook will heat and serve the food that is sent up by dumbwaiter, and act as waiter and dishwasher as well; meanwhile, the central kitchen downstairs will take orders and supply meals to the 30 dining rooms by dumbwaiter. The kitchen has not been omitted from individual apartments altogether, but it is a cupboard-type facility which can be screened off with a sliding partition. It offers a two-burner electric stove, a small refrigerator, a sink, and shelf space. For those who want to prepare something more elaborate than the cupboard kitchen permits, there is a fully equipped do-it-yourself kitchen on each floor as well. The designers, by their own account, debated the economic and social wisdom of such a large number of kitchens and eating facilities, but concluded that individual choice in eating habits is important enough to justify it.

Full day-care facilities are provided, and are to be staffed entirely by volunteers. However, beyond this arrangement there is no segregation of children of any age into separate sleeping accommodations. The circumstance that the microdistrict of which the "House of the New Way of Life" became a component already had full school facilities (daytime, not boarding) made unnecessary any decision as to whether school-age children should be housed in dormitories. Physical culture is provided for by no less than five indoor gymnasium rooms of different kinds, plus a 25-meter indoor swimming pool, outdoor tennis and basketball courts, and two saunas. The microdistrict's school sports field is nearby. Indoor facilities for clubs, hobbies, meetings, and cultural events are no less generous in number and dimensions.

The designers did not ignore the problem of construction and operating costs, of course. While the writer has not seen the detailed estimates, Osterman's rough estimates per square meter of total space were just under those for apartments of comparable dimensions not fitted out with all the "extras," i.e., just under 130 rubles. The head of the U.S.S.R. Union of Architects stated that in his opinion the construction and operating costs of such complexes, if they are mass-produced, would not exceed the costs of ordinary apartment buildings.[22] Maintenance of a full-time staff of 115 (plus just over 100 full-time volunteers, or the equivalent in volunteer labor) must be measured somehow against two economic benefits: the guarantee that all working-age women are free to work, and the reduction in service personnel in neighborhood shops and services which a wide network of these apartments would make possible.

The apartments themselves are distinguished by their accordion panels and by the fact that they are furnished. As many furnishings as possible were built in so as to conserve space. Household appliances and extra furniture for guests may be borrowed from a common supply, so that they do not take up space either. The rooms are not large, reckoned as they are from 139 square feet of living space (182 square feet of total space, if one includes bathrooms, closets, etc.) per person in one-room units to 98 square feet (total 125 square feet) per person in three-room units. These norms do not include common hallways, lounges, or other shared space. There is as much mixing of one-room, two-room, and three-room units as is practicable within the layout, and apartments for families of four or more can be created by joining two apartments with an interior door. While there is some possibility of moving from apartment to apartment within the two residential towers with each significant change in family size, probably the full advantages of such moves will have to wait until there are many furnished apartment complexes throughout the country.

The scale of volunteer services which residents are expected to provide necessitates a "Union of the House of the New Way of Life" with its own legal existence. To begin with, it is the Union as a whole, not its members individually, which is to rent the entire premises from the state. Paid staff members will occupy an important position in the House's system of government. Osterman

---

[22] G. Orlov in *Pravda,* April 21, 1967.

and his team consider the House to be an important agent for ideological and political education as well as a school for social cooperation. Above all, it is to be much more than merely a network of conveniences. Beyond making these recommendations, however, the designers injected nothing into their project—and probably could not have, in any case—which would require the House's members to do more than maintain a sort of club of conveniences and services.

Further experiments with the *dom-kommuna* are in the making, and some of these are being built. Gradov's design organization, the Central Scientific Research and Design Organization for Educational Buildings, came forth in 1968 with the design of a 44-story dwelling complex for 6,000 persons, with adjoining low-rise structures for a social center, preschool care, and a full 10-year boarding school. Each floor of the tower is equipped, in addition, with a buffet, coffee shop, lounges, and clubrooms.[23] Designs produced by leading architects in Leningrad and Kiev have concentrated a much smaller range of services and amenities in the apartment houses themselves. Georgii D. Platonov's 1968 design for a Leningrad version of the "House of the New Way of Life" relied for many services on a nearby primary services bloc which serves several apartment buildings, and which is also open to the general public. Platonov believes that kitchenless apartments are suitable only for single people and couples without children, furthermore that greater emphasis should be placed on a well-isolated room for every person. N. V. Baranov's design for an apartment complex on the western portion of Vasil'yevskii Island (also in Leningrad) stresses a mixture of apartment unit sizes on each corridor, for the specific purpose of intermingling family units of different sizes. Nikolai P. Yevdokimov's design for a complex in Kiev is outwardly quite similar to the Moscow experiment, and like the Osterman design provides for both public dining rooms and precooked food to take to one's own apartment. But its apartments have full kitchens, or rather a combined kitchen and dining room, which can be joined with the living room by pushing back a partition. Its health center is designed to be at least as well staffed as that in Moscow, but its recreational, social, and hobby rooms are on a far more modest scale. Perhaps more important, Yevdokimov and his team of architects do not assume that the residents will have to be hand-picked, or that their incomes need to be somewhat above the average. Why, after all, should either the designers or the tenants regard the new apartment

[23]*Pravda,* November 13, 1968, p. 6.

complex as a risk? The Ukrainian branch of *Gosstroi* apparently does see some risk, though, since it decided in 1968 to wait until the Moscow experiment could be evaluated before allocating funds for realizing Yevdokimov's design. However, the head of the U.S.S.R. Union of Architects in 1967 expressed his approval of the experimental apartment complexes generally, and since that time the whole notion of the *dom-kommuna* has suddenly become respectable, if pursued with great caution for the present.[24]

But let it be noted that the "House" in Novye Cheryomushki had acquired foes even before it was completed and occupied. *Literaturnaya gazeta,* which had published an approving account of the experiment some months before its completion, subsequently carried a devastating critique by two academic figures under the title "House with Privileges?" They disputed the architects' operating cost estimates, especially because of the number of paid, full-time service personnel required. These together with their families will normally constitute 16 percent of the House's residents, and all of them must be supported by the remaining 84 percent. Meals will be over 10 percent more expensive than home-cooked meals, while other services and utilities will cost two or three times what they do in ordinary apartments. (Admittedly, the House's residents will get more for their money, beginning with the swimming pool, sauna, gymnasium, and clubrooms.) Construction costs too were greatly underestimated. But the greatest single objection made by these two critics had to do with the privileged status of the House's residents. Whatever the excellent personal qualities of its hand-picked residents, is it just that they enjoy a larger share of the social wage than their fellow citizens? If the swimming pool and all the rest are restricted to residents, such will be the case. If they are to be open for neighborhood use, why put them in this one apartment complex? All in all, they called the "House" an unwise leap into the distant future, which will create problems and animosity in the present.[25]

While there seems little present likelihood that Strumilin's basic ideas will be embodied in the bulk of Soviet housing construction during the 1970's, at least, he did have the effect of setting architects, urban planners, and social scientists to thinking about

---

[24]"The House of the New Way of Life," *Literaturnaya gazeta,* December 25, 1968; *Zvezda,* No. 10 (October, 1966), p. 155; G. Orlov, "Architecture and Man," *Pravda,* April 21, 1967. See also Gradov's designs for microdistricts and entire cities built around the *dom-kommuna* idea. Gradov, 1968, pp. 154-88.

[25]Ya. Zhuchok and B. Zuikova, "House with Privileges?" *Literaturnaya gazeta,* January 8, 1969, p. 11.

what kinds of urban association ought to be promoted. To the extent that the *dom-kommuna* is intended to foster intensive social interaction among the same people, it points in a direction opposite to that sought by most of the people who prefer big-city life. While Strumilin abjured any compulsion in connection with participation in his palace communes, and certainly had no intention of discouraging association outside the *dom-kommuna,* still his idea of the commune was one of multiplying substantially the time and energy expended by the individual in interaction with the same group of immediate geographical neighbors. Indeed, the circle of neighbors which he proposes is smaller than the smallest planned microdistrict populations in Soviet cities, and smaller by tenfold than the populations of the largest microdistricts, which can reach 20,000 or more.

Such a reconstitution of patterns of urban association might be appropriate where these patterns have taken root in some form by themselves. We know that in our American experience, the reasons for neighborhood-based association are various: ethnic ties, poverty, peculiarities of the geographical setting, a low level of awareness of the opportunities for association offered by the city as a whole, or preoccupation with local problems and crises. At the same time, the influence of these factors is an unstable one. The urge to escape this influence is widespread among those who find themselves in a position to do so. Those who do "escape" discover that cities offer the possibility of doing different things with different groups in different kinds of communities. Many of these "communities" are geographically unlimited except by the possibilities for mobility within the larger urban area itself. Those who choose nonpartici- pation, or a low level of participation, are not subject to any kind of social pressure from their neighbors, since the smaller geographical neighborhood is one possible kind of association among a great many, and often a quite unimportant one. Getting *away* from one's immediate geographical community to do things which are no concern of one's close neighbors is important to the city dweller. While rather little sociological research has yet been done on patterns of association among Soviet city dwellers[26] it is hard to imagine that these same advantages of choice are not a large part of the social attractiveness of large cities in the Soviet Union also.

---

[26]Yanitskii, 1967, summarizes what has been done so far.

Svetlichnyi made an interesting comment on the desirability of making urban districts self-contained:

The city dweller who never sees anything but his own courtyard and the route to his place of work will turn into a provincial even if he lives in the capital. Constant communion with the city is imperative. It breeds in man a sense of unity with the collective, awareness of the obligation to be useful to others, for others are constantly doing something for him in the process of the social division of labor. Herein lies the enormous social significance of cities in general and of socialist cities in particular.[27]

All this is not to say that present-day patterns of association must be left as they are, for better or for worse, or that planning cannot to some extent alter them. One of the most disquieting features about American urban behavior is the extent to which habits of non-involvement prevail over other impulses even in the situations where the city dweller most needs the help of neighbors and passers-by. Problems like this may lie beyond the province even of sociologically aware urban planners. A builder who plans the kind of physical layout which brings neighbors more into contact with one another, equipped with facilities which must be used through voluntary cooperation if they are to be used at all, may have no way of telling whether he is simply organizing a higher level of friction and dissatisfaction. If, instead, the planning of neighborhood units emphasizes the availability of services and conveniences, the actual effect may be to give residents more time for activities away from the neighborhood.

The question of the influence of spatial planning on social relations contains at least three parts: the extent to which planning is able to influence social relations, the desirability of increasing this influence in any given setting, and the quality of relations which are sought at any given level of influence. The American sociologist Herbert J. Gans, in dealing with suburban planning (i.e., single-family dwellings) in the United States, concluded that the planner's influence is not very great and that there is no reason to increase it. As for the quality of relations to be sought, Gans prefers to facilitate a maximum choice of relationships on the part of the resident. This means, for example, neither tight clustering nor very great separation of houses. It also means different types of layouts which enable prospective residents to choose the degree of neighborhood inter-

---

[27]Svetlichnyi, 'The City Awaits a Reply," 1966, p. 160.

action and/or privacy which best suits them.[28] Irving Rosow, in a 1961 survey of studies on patterns of urban association, called attention to the lack of evidence that planned communities work any kind of change that would make their residents behave differently from groups of similar social composition in unplanned communities. If anything stands out in our knowledge of the subject, he said, it is the persistence from setting to setting of given social patterns among groups of similar composition.[29]

Have the designers of the new commune-type apartments had thoughts about their possible effect on family life? In Soviet Marxist ideology, the family of the future will be one built on affection and personal affinity alone, and not at all on economic necessity, or on the need to provide those elements of childrearing which can be performed better by institutions. This view is strongly supported by Anatolii G. Kharchev, the nation's leading specialist in family relations.[30] While there is no disagreement on the need to reduce to a bare minimum the work of housewives, or on the desirability of extensive (if not necessarily universal) day care for preschool children, no consensus has yet emerged on the subject of boarding schools as part of future family living patterns. From the vantage point of the latter 1960's, it now appears that the drastic cutting back of plans for a universal boarding school system, a system proposed in 1958 by Khrushchev, was due not only to its tremendous expense (see Chapter 3), but also to the serious questions that were raised by specialists concerning the whole purpose of boarding schools. Just how different are they supposed to be from the regular day schools? Is the boarding facility merely a dormitory next to a school? Is it intended to be first of all a convenience for parents? This is hardly justifiable as a goal. What are boarding-school children supposed to do during after-school hours? Is there any good reason for providing a setting which encourages them to lead lives separate from those of their parents?[31] From Soviet professional people, teachers, and university students, those for whom progressive ideas of childrearing should have the most

[28]Herbert J. Gans, "Planning and Social Life: Friendship and Neighbor Relations in Suburban Communities," *Journal of the American Institute of Planners,* XXVII:2 (May, 1961), pp. 139-40.

[29]Irving Rosow, "The Social Effects of the Physical Environment," *Journal of the American Institute of Planners,* XXVII:2 (May, 1961), p. 132.

[30]Kharchev, 1964, pp. 318-19.

[31]Svetlichnyi, 1964, pp. 168-69.

appeal, the writer has heard mainly negative opinions on the desirability of a universal boarding-school system. As to the urban working class, perhaps an opinion survey will soon furnish the answer.

Some of the architects and planners who advocate full-time care for children outside of their parental homes have produced designs for housing units intended primarily for couples living alone. At one point Gradov drew up a plan for a housing district for 40,000 Muscovites based on this notion.[32] However, even if a larger number of small apartment units were built at the present time in Moscow or in many other large cities (except perhaps in Central Asia), the effect would be simply that of redressing the present imbalance in living unit sizes. As long as space allocation norms continue at the level of 9 to 10 square meters of living space per person, the prevalence of three-room and four-room units means that a childless couple is very likely to share such an apartment with at least one other family. One of the functions of Soviet sociologists in this respect has been to urge the study of family size patterns in each locality as a basis for planning apartment layouts. They point out, for example, how little attention has been given, in the process of designing apartments and assigning housing space, to the number of times the age and size composition of a typical family undergoes important changes.[33]

THE MICRODISTRICT AS CONVENIENCE AND COMMUNITY

The microdistrict *(mikroraion)* unlike the commune-type apartment, ceased being an experiment a dozen years ago, and became the universal planning system for new residential construction in cities both large and small. It is true that even today lack of funds often forces delay or cancellation of the construction of the central facilities which form much of the justification for the microdistrict concept. Still, urban planners think basically in terms of the microdistrict in designing residential layouts.

The microdistrict in its present Soviet and East European versions presents few characteristics that have not been at least experimented with elsewhere in the industrial world. The grouping of apartment housing around community facilities, the planning of shops, services,

---

[32] Kiselevich and Rabinovich, pp. 25-26.
[33] Yanitskii, 1967, p. 22.

and amenities, the provision of recreational space as part of the
ensemble, and the encouragement of self-help and voluntary administration among the residents—all these things are part of the
repertory of governmental and private builders throughout much of

Diagram 4
DESIGN FOR A MICRODISTRICT OF ABOUT 6,000 RESIDENTS

A—Location of service facilities for everyday use within groups of apartment houses with
2,000 residents each; B—A group of apartment houses with primary service facilities in the
center of the group.

1—Social and shopping center of the microdistrict; 2—School; 3—Kindergartens and
nurseries, 4—Primary service bloc; 5—Garages; 6—Park for the entire microdistrict; 7—Park
serving a group of apartment houses, and sports areas.

Source: N. Baranov *et al.*, *Osnovy sovetskogo gradostroitel'stva*, Vol. II (Moscow:
Stroiizdat, 1967), p. 102.

Europe, North America, and elsewhere. The Soviet microdistrict is not a unit of government or administration, except insofar as its boundaries may coincide with the jurisdiction of the local housing office, which looks after maintenance, checks residence permits, and performs other local functions. It does provide a setting for community organizations of various types, although these vary greatly from one microdistrict to the next in number and level of activity. If anything is unique about the Soviet experience with microdistricts, it is the sheer number of them that have been built, the central determination of design standards, and the way in which they have been promoted as the one best way of organizing residential areas in the city of the future. Noteworthy also is the way in which the microdistricts form the next-to-bottom "layer" of territorial units in the systematic allocation of services and facilities prescribed in the 1958 planning norms.

In the 1950's the microdistrict formed part of a systematic pyramid or "layering" of residential planning units, which now include the following, from the smallest to the largest:

(a) apartment house
(b) housing complex *(kvartal)*
(c) microdistrict *(mikroraion)* (roughly 5,000 to 20,000 residents)
(d) residential district *(zhiloi raion)* (30,000 to 50,000 residents, according to the 1958 planning directives).

However, the microdistrict as a term and a concept was dropped in a number of cities during the 1960's. In part it was that Soviet planners and others found the term somewhat too mechanical; in translating it into English they had always preferred to say "neighborhood." But more than this, the size of the planning units kept growing and changing until the distinctions among the "layers" became blurred. Moscow planners have long used the *kvartal* (housing complex) as the smallest spatial planning unit instead of the microdistrict. Today the *kvartal* is a somewhat indefinite concept even though the boundaries of specific *kvartaly* remain. The residential district *(zhiloi raion)* is still employed, but above it are two more layers of units: the "urban district" *(gorodskoi raion)* of 100,000 to 300,000 population, and the "urban zone" *(gorodskaya zona)* of 800,000 to 1 million population, Moscow now being divided into seven such zones. These large units were developed partly in an effort to find some kind of territorial framework within which employment will be available for the bulk of the population within a given area of Moscow; commuting time, according to the Moscow Master Plan Institute, should be limited to not over 30 minutes each way, or 40 minutes at the very maximum.[34]

This type of formal "layering" was developed only in the 1950's. Before World War II, the one territorial common denominator in Soviet planning had been the housing complex *(b),* made formal in 1925 in the first of what was to become a series of standard planning directives.[35] Actually, the housing complex of those years was simply a smaller version of the microdistrict of today. The microdistrict as such became formal under the 1958 standards issued by *Gosstroi,*[36] although the concept was already in wide use at this time.

A number of strands of social and planning philosophy have led up to the idea of the microdistrict. Of these, some have been abandoned and others greatly modified in the course of time. The most important of these are the following:

(1) The idea of re-creating a desired type and intensity of social interaction by grouping residences and drawing the residents into shared tasks. The many utopian variants of this idea were rejected by Soviet planners with the exceptions already described above; but the one basic idea of improving human relations by means of planned communities persists.

(2) The idea of radical environmental improvement for city dwellers. While the Ebenezer Howard variant of this idea was rejected after the 1920's, hygienic residential organization, particularly in space-conserving building arrangement and generous provision for recreational space, have been among the basic requirements of micro-district planning.

(3) The idea of systematic grouping of shops, services, and facilities of every kind within planned residential units. This may be done strictly from the point of view of convenience, to save time for residents (and for school children, if schools are included among the facilities) and to ease the burden on transportation of every kind

---

[34] Yevstratov and Matveyev, 1967, p. 69.

[35] Zile, 1963, p. 25.

[36] *Pravila i normy . . . ,* 1959.

by reducing the number of trips outside the residential grouping. It may also presume that residents will take a proprietary interest in the shops and facilities.

(4) The articulation of urban residential areas so as to distinguish neighborhood from neighborhood visually, to provide variety within large housing areas, and to give residents a sense of geographic identity.

What today has become the microdistrict was first embodied in Moscow's 1935 plan, and in the designs of the latter 1930's made according to the plan's specifications. The *kvartal* of those years, smaller than today's microdistrict, was fully equipped with schools, preschool facilities, shops, community centers, parks, and playgrounds. One design of 1936 even provided ample parking space for private automobiles, underground as well as above ground, surely an expression of optimism for the future![37] Population size was in the 3,000-to-7,000 range—and permissible densities were between 160 and 190 residents per acre with the housing unit itself, which is somewhat higher than postwar Soviet norms of 120 or so, but probably more suited to Moscow conditions. Physical layouts stressed "closed" rather than "open" systems; their inward-oriented structures lined the periphery of the housing complex's territory. The grouping of housing units into housing districts, the separation of district from district by park areas, and the "layering" of services at the level of the *kvartal,* residential district, and city were all just as accepted in the 1930's as they have been in the 1960's.[38] Actually, very few such *kvartal* designs were drawn up in the 1930's; emphasis was placed instead on rather standard apartment houses. The reader need only glance through the designs in any year's worth of issues of *Arkhitektura SSSR*—the leading architectural and planning journal—from the 1930's and compare them with designs in the 1960's in order to appreciate today's preoccupation with the microdistrict and residential district.

The norms drawn up by *Gosstroi* in 1958 defined the microdistrict according to these criteria: population size, residences consisting of apartment houses of at least five stories (except in the smaller cities), isolation from vehicular traffic, relation of building area to open space, and provision of given types of service with specified service radii. Under both the 1958 norms and the revised 1966 norms,

[37]Parkins, 1953, p. 39.
[38]*Ibid.,* pp. 36-41.

services provided at the level of the *kvartal* include day-care centers and playgrounds; these have a service radius of 1,000 feet. The microdistrict as a whole offers primary and secondary day schools, shops, and dining facilities, as well as garages for private cars, all with a service radius of 1,600 feet. The residential district, the next larger planning unit, is provided with a public center having a service radius of 5,000 feet. This center is equipped with a shopping complex of its own, a film theater, a library, polyclinic, club building, and other conveniences.[39] Both sets of norms specify in some detail how much of each facility (school places, restaurant seats, hospital beds, etc.) is to be provided per thousand population.

There has been considerable debate over these norms. Gradov, as the leading specialist on public buildings and service facilities, argued shortly after the 1958 "Standards and Norms" were issued that they are oriented toward a comparatively low level of services, a level set 30 years previously. What will happen, he asked, when land is no longer available in microdistricts now under construction for the facilities which will be necessary to meet the much higher norms of the future?[40] Svetlichnyi pointed out in 1964 that twice the investment would have to be made in nonresidential structures and facilities even to meet the 1958 norms, and at that point he saw no massive additional investment forthcoming.[41] In the late 1950's and 1960's, construction enterprises were permitted to devote to nonresidential service buildings and premises only 5 percent of the total funds allocated to build any given group of residences such as a microdistrict. Where some of the microdistrict buildings are cooperatively owned, as is now increasingly the case, the 5 percent is calculated only from the sums spent on the state-owned buildings, even though the co-op residents must use the shops and services too.[42]

In one sense, the geographical "layering" of service structures, especially the fact that these norms are supposedly obligatory for planners and builders, has been an administrative device for assuring a proper pace and distribution of service facility construction. To be sure, this has not prevented construction organizations from aban-

---

[39] *Pravila i normy* . . . , 1959, ch. 5; Shkvarikov and Luk'yanov, 1967, p. 26.

[40] *Trudy VI sessii Akademii stroitel'stva i arkhitektury* . . . ,1961, p. 139.

[41] Svetlichnyi, 1964, pp. 174–75.

[42] A. Aksomitas (Chairman of the Lithuanian Republic Gosstroi), "A Microdistrict Is Being Built," *Pravda*, September 12, 1968.

doning work on microdistrict projects before they have finished (or even started) building some of these facilities, nor has it always guaranteed that completed facilities will be occupied. In a number of microdistricts which the writer has visited in both large and medium-sized cities, shops and services were housed on the first floor of residential structures pending the construction of separate service buildings in the center of the complex. In many microdistricts, contrary to Gradov's observation, there is still the opportunity to catch up on this construction, since today there is generally no danger of the central building sites being used for further residential construction.[43]

Most of the debate over microdistrict facilities has concerned not their social effects, but rather the factor of convenience, specifically whether shops and services should be sited to serve the microdistrict alone, or to attract customers from outside it as well. In the terminology of Soviet planners, this is the difference between "closed" and "open" forms of service, and in the 1960's the advocates of the latter appear to be in the majority. Today, for example, Moscow planners criticize the skyscraper complex of Moscow University because it is far too self-contained, and in a way isolated from the city around it. The "open" form means facilities sited so as not to isolate them from streets and transportation routes. The notion of convenience, according to the proponents of "open" services, must extend beyond the convenience of specific residential groupings. From the point of view of liberating working wives and mothers from unnecessary inconvenience in shopping and errands, the "closed" forms of service may be beside the point, and could actually reduce convenience. A number of prominent architects and planners have felt obliged to speak out against the idea of the "closed" microdistrict.[44] The writer has a definite impression that in Moscow, at least, a large proportion of the shopping for food and household necessities is done en route home from work at shops around major transportation routes and transfer points. Meanwhile,

---

[43] See the criticism, for example, by N. N. Ullas, a senior planning official for Moscow, at the December 1964 conference on microdistricts. *Arkhitektura SSSR*, No. 2 (February, 1965), p. 4.

[44] These include Mikhail V. Posokhin, Chairman of the State Committee for Civil Construction within *Gosstroi*; K. I. Trapeznikov, head of the Institute for the Theory, History and Long-Range Problems of Soviet Architecture; N. V. Baranov, a noted architect and planning official; N. A. Orlov, director of the central design institute for retail structures; and others. Posokhin, 1964, pp. 2-3; *Nauchno-tekhnicheskoye soveshchaniye . . . ,* 1965, p. 3; Kiselev and Rabinovich, 1966. p. 26.

those stores which appear to be underused during the day are those situated amid the spacious central plazas of the new housing districts, and not immediately adjacent to transportation.[45] Often enough, the sparse daytime clientele of these stores consists mainly of elderly women, many of them shopping for their children's families.

In a society which encourages female employment perhaps to a greater extent than any other industrial society in the world, who will be left to do the shopping in residential areas? The increasing residential separation of the elderly from the working-age population and children, whether one regards this as a good thing socially or not, may accentuate this pattern. If the microdistrict of the future is fully equipped with preschool facilities, and if primary schools are provided with extended-day programs, young parents will ordinarily want to get their shopping done at the end of the day before picking up their children. These considerations argue not only against siting most local shopping facilities as part of a closed service network within the microdistrict, but also against distributing them by microdistricts at all. Locations along shopping streets adjoining main transportation routes would be preferable. It may take a further economic reform to demonstrate the usefulness of one or another type of siting, a reform placing the individual store completely "on its own" in planning its sales and disposing of its income.

N. V. Baranov, in an article written in anticipation of the 1964 conference on microdistricts, mentioned a current of opinion which opposed the microdistrict as the level at which the basic shops and services should be grouped. The critics found the retail and service centers too small to handle the volume of trade. Instead of more generous norms, they recommended the dispersal of these facilities by groups of apartments. But Baranov feared that this would lead right back to something resembling Moscow's earlier pattern of siting small establishments in the first floor of apartments facing main streets, obliging shoppers to cover a good deal of ground in going from store to store. He even cited the discussions of the United Nations symposium on new towns, held in Moscow in September 1964, to emphasize the near-universal acceptance of the microdistrict idea among the world's urban planners. Another target of Baranov's criticism were those planners who would leave out of microdistrict plans any substantial facilities for meetings and organizations, since,

---

[45]These very same observations were made by the architects E. Levina and E. Syrkina in *Zvezda* No. 10 (October, 1966), pp. 150-56. Summary in *CDSP* XIX:3, p. 35.

they maintained, political and educational activities for all except children and retired persons are carried on at places of employment.[46]

Among architects and urban planners, discussion of the convenience factor in designing microdistricts has understandably taken precedence over the much less definite topic of community, of social interaction. The latter topic is left to the press, which has long carried accounts of successful community organization and exhortations to citizens to participate in community work. Hopefully it will not be long before Soviet sociologists produce definitive, large-scale analyses of types and levels of community participation at the microdistrict level, together with correlations of factors which may promote or discourage this participation.

Experimental design organizations in Leningrad, Tashkent, and Kiev have in fact undertaken surveys on the problem of social interaction in residential areas, the factors which promote certain types of interaction, and especially the influence of different types of non-residential structures and community facilities.[47] Up to now, the results have not been published in systematic form. The Soviet Union is in a far better position to collect data of this type than are most of the other urbanized nations of the world, since the Housing Offices which serve all state and cooperative apartment buildings either have a good deal of community organization data, or have easy access to it. It would be interesting, for one thing, to know whether affluence has been reducing community participation, as it well might in view of the fact that one of the fruits of affluence is greater mobility and different ways of using leisure time.

A microdistrict which the writer visited in 1964 in Yaroslavl' has been upheld in the Soviet press as a model of community organization and a good example for other microdistricts.[48] It consisted of some 40 apartment buildings erected in the late 1950's, housing a population of 8,000. While its volunteers had indeed assumed responsibility for a wide variety of activities, it did employ a full-time staff of 77, which was shared with a neighboring microdistrict; and a militia (police) officer was on duty permanently within the area of the two microdistricts. The Residential Committee, the coordinator of many voluntary projects, functioned in

---

[46]Baranov, 1964, p. 4.

[47]Yanitskii, 1967, p. 23.

[48]This was Housing Administration No. 12 in Lenin Borough.

many ways as the Administration's auxiliary. Of the Committee's 25 members, 18 were pensioners. All of these whom the writer met seemed to derive great satisfaction from being useful and taking part in the kind of community interaction which their work entailed. Members of the Committee head commissions dealing with (1) physical improvements, (2) sanitation, (3) financial and management questions (including assistance in rent collections), (4) current capital repairs, and (5) cultural and social undertakings. Through the Committee's efforts, a volunteer-run lending library with 3,000 volumes had been established, and, somewhat more surprisingly, a polyclinic. The clinic was the result of persuading some 3 dozen local doctors of varying specialties to devote a minimum of two hours a week each to keeping the clinic open from 5:00 to 7:00 each evening. Some of them, according to the Committee's chairman, had given up private patients in order to volunteer their services. Three groups not under the Committee's direct supervision dealt with problems of public order: a Comrades' Court, a Social Council for Work With Children and Adolescents, and a People's Volunteer Detachment *(druzhina)* of over 100, mostly young people, who could be mustered for special occasions or emergencies. The Communist Party was present in the form of a Party group closely associated with the Housing Administration. A Group for Aid to Party-State Control had a representative in each house to keep track of matters of economy and administrative propriety in the use of state funds. Finally, deputies to the borough and city soviets had their reception hours posted at their residences, and stood ready to handle complaints and requests. Organization at the apartment-house level was rudimentary, which is understandable in view of their small size (they averaged 200 residents each). There were apartment house councils of about a dozen members each, and each council supplied a representative for sanitation matters plus a member of the Comrades' Court.

All told, some 500 residents, roughly 10 percent of the micro-district's adult population, had some kind of formal role in community organization; others participated for special occasions, cleanup campaigns, and the like. While those who took active part in one or another of these organizations derived satisfaction from their contact with neighbors and the performance of community tasks, it seemed to the writer that they regarded the microdistrict as a convenience to be maintained rather than as a social unit or a way of life. The pensioners, it appeared, were more neighborhood-oriented than the working-age population, while the young workers and adolescents directed their energies to borough-wide or city-wide organizations, among them sports organizations and an especially popular conservation society which sponsored numerous field trips.

OCCUPATIONAL AND ETHNIC INTEGRATION IN CITIES

Among the various planning goals that have been promoted by political leaders and urban planners, one would expect to find the goal of residential integration of various occupations, ethnic groups, and income levels. To the writer's knowledge, no major Soviet surveys of housing occupancy patterns have been carried out, although a survey would be no problem if residence permit data were made available to social scientists. The social scientists, for their part, have made scant reference to the whole matter, save in impressionistic historical surveys which recount the manner in which the pre-Revolutionary distinction between the workers' suburbs and the wealthy center city have been erased, or the distinction in non-Slavic areas between the "white" city inhabited by Russians and the "black" city of the local ethnic group or groups.[49]

The answers which the writer received from urban planners and laymen on the desirability of one or another kind of integration indicate (1) that it is not a topic of great concern, and (2) that integration in all its forms has already occurred in many of the large and newly built housing areas, and will continue to occur as cities are reconstructed.

While there seems to be neither a policy nor much of a potential policy problem as regards any form of integration, the following observations may be of interest: Enterprise-built and enterprise-controlled apartment houses, although they are presently diminishing as a proportion of total housing, cannot help but integrate income levels if they accommodate any substantial portion of an enterprise's employees. In such cases, however, one must ask (1) whether the managerial personnel of an enterprise live in better housing apart from the bulk of employees, and (2) whether some enterprise-controlled districts are better built and run than others. No systematic data is available on either question. But the writer has

---

[49] See, for example, Krupyanskaya and Rabinovich, 1964.

discovered examples of both segregation and integration, as well as great variations in quality among enterprise housing districts. The housing preserves of Soviet political leaders are too well known to require comment, beginning, for example, with the estates in the Kuntsevo region of Moscow. Just beyond Kuntsevo, interestingly, there has grown up during the 1960's a whole housing district for employees of the Party Central Committee, whose incomes are doubtless well above those of most other professional and white-collar people. On the other hand, the Moscow University skyscraper complex offers an example of highly-paid professors living virtually cheek-by-jowl with some of the University's cleaning women, albeit the former are assigned more living space. The writer's own impressions of integration versus segregation of income groups add up to a very mixed picture: aristocratic segregation in some cases, and a rather surprising degree of integration in others.

Cooperative housing accounted for about 8.5 percent of total housing construction in 1968.[50] It does tend to place the higher-income groups together in the same apartment buildings because of the cost involved. Beginning in 1962, housing cooperatives have been able to get loans from the State Construction Bank covering 60 percent of construction costs, repayable at .5 percent interest over 10 to 15 years. But the down payment still remains considerable: 900 to 1,000 rubles for a one-room apartment and around 1,700 rubles for two rooms.[51] In a large part of Siberia and Kazakhstan, a 70 percent loan is available. Svetlichnyi pointed out that under such circumstances cooperatives are not in keeping with the principle of providing housing for those who most need it. Accordingly, he advocated a reduction of the down payment to 20 percent, granting of credit on the down payment in the form of personal participation by members in constructing the apartments, and creation of privileges for low-income groups and persons still living in unsatisfactory housing: "It would be wrong if cooperative housing, for which the state provides credit, material resources, and services of construction organizations, were built for persons already living in good conditions simply because they have the money."[52] The fact is that the Soviet Union is far behind some of the countries of Eastern

[50]*Pravda,* January 26, 1969, p. 2; February 16, 1969, p. 1.

[51]*SP SSSR* 1962, No. 12, Art. 93. *Trud,* December 2, 1964 carried the text of the decree reducing the interest rate.

[52]Svetlichnyi, 1965, pp. 45-46.

Europe in providing easy financing for buying co-ops, and that there is some resentment in the Soviet Union about the advantages of those who have money for the down payment. One co-op resident whom the writer met in Kiev felt definitely that his building had been poorly constructed and was being poorly maintained, by comparison with rental housing in the same microdistrict, because the construction and maintenance workers resented the co-op system.

The co-op buildings may include what in Soviet circumstances have been luxury features, e.g., 8-foot ceilings, parquet floors, and built-in closets, for which the co-op members have paid extra. Co-op buildings, however, are not ordinarily grouped in special sites or given preferred locations. The co-op organization may choose the area of the city in which it wishes to build, but the completed structure is likely to be part of a microdistrict which consists otherwise of state housing. In fact, during the 1960's city administrations have made a practice of trying to sell ordinary state apartments already under construction to co-ops. Residential grouping of co-op members by enterprise or organization is not uncommon, simply because association at places of employment provides the initial contacts for forming many co-op membership lists. However, those cities which are actively promoting co-ops put together membership lists of anyone who is interested and can meet the down payment; furthermore, membership in co-ops organized at a given place of employment may be transferred to anyone else, regardless of employment status.[53]

Visitors to the cities of Central Asia who have explored the older residential sections naturally wonder to what extent the population of these cities is ethnically integrated as between Europeans and Asians. There is little doubt that the traditionally built structures of brick and mud are occupied almost exclusively by Asians—Uzbeks, Tadzhiks, Kirghiz, Turkmens, and a number of smaller ethnic groups. Such housing, where it still exists in cities, occupies areas of its own simply because of the way these cities evolved historically. Occupancy of modern housing varies. From visits to these cities and inquiries of local residents, the writer gathers that there is considerable ethnic residential mixing in Tashkent, but much less in Samarkand, for example. Central Asians everywhere in these cities

---

[53] See the comments by A. S. Boldyrev, chairman of *Gosstroi* for the RSFSR, *Izvestiya*, September 20, 1963, and the trade-union official, K. Guseinov, *Izvestiya*, July 6, 1966.

have been cautious about moving into structures which in some cases are not sufficiently adapted to the climate, and in which space for their often very large families may be reduced. Actually, the Russians with whom the writer discussed housing questions in Tashkent and elsewhere seemed indifferent as to whether there would be further residential mixing or not. At the same time they were quite concerned that the persistence in urban circumstances of the Central Asian tradition of very large families would continue to complicate the problem of housing space generally. Statistical data on the ethnic composition of individual cities is beginning to appear, and the recently published demographic analysis of Khar'kov is hopefully the first of a series of this kind.[54] But as yet the writer has discovered no data on ethnic composition by residential areas within cities.

THE FUTURE OF THE GEOGRAPHICAL COMMUNITY

A tentative conclusion which may be drawn from the developments of the 1960's is that organizing the physical layout of cities according to highly specific national norms may not serve to produce either the comforts or the structure of urban society which those who devised the norms had in mind. If, as the critics of the central norms charge, Soviet cities are currently being equipped for a level of services and amenities which is well below what is desired for the future, urban planners might do better to concentrate their resources on certain areas and clusters of services where the future norms can be achieved. Also, central norms issued in an attempt to alter actual construction priorities may simply lead to a frittering-away of some resources. The pressure on cities and construction firms has been pressure to produce residential floor space. The 1958 norms have simply invited cities to make a beginning on service facility construction which they may wait years in some areas to complete. Industries which put up the bulk of their own housing often behave similarly. Furthermore, the great stress on the *proximity* of a wide variety of facilities to residences may overlook emerging patterns by which these facilities are used. If more and more people are striving to be mobile within a metropolitan area so as to benefit from the best it has to offer, the quality of service which can be justified economically for a group of 10,000 to 20,000 people may hold little

---

[54]Kurman and Lebedinskii, 1968, Ch. 6.

attraction. At the very least, the time would seem ripe for launching a great variety of experiments with services.

As concerns the promotion of certain kinds of human association in cities, the assumption that a large proportion of these associations will be geographically based is a questionable one for urban planners to make. It is understandable that Soviet planners search for new forms of consumption which involve the sharing of facilities provided by the state, and that they look to urban neighborhoods as the framework within which a good deal of this sharing will take place. Certainly we Americans can only welcome the Soviet determination to organize new forms of consumption which require no expenditure choices by individuals and households. Let it be said here that "consumption" is meant broadly; it can include an evening stroll in the park or a pack trip in a wilderness preserve, just as long as someone—governments, organizations, or individuals—has decided to devote certain material resources to keeping these choices open to the stroller and the hiker. If Soviet experiments point the way to different types of consumption which might be adapted to our own society without doing violence to our American feelings about consumer choice, so much the better for us.

But at the same time, our experience with rising consumption levels, public and private, should have some kind of message for *Gosstroi* and its army of planners. Affluence means the expansion of individual consumption choices, regardless whether it is individuals or governments that are able to direct their resources toward opening up these choices. Increased mobility, whether in private automobiles or improved public transport, is among the basic choices that affluent industrial societies throughout the world have made, without exception. Intensive neighborhood association is not likely to be the choice of those who share in affluence. In the United States, at any rate, it certainly appears that whoever has the kind of income which will support a suburban home or apartment plus a car is not likely to prefer the kind of inner-city communities whose promotion is urged by some American planners.[55] The unanswered question here is, will a continued rise in Soviet personal incomes produce the same phenomenon? To be sure, mobility in choice of residential location may continue to be restricted in the Soviet Union

---

[55] Such is the emphatic conclusion of Herbert J. Gans, *People and Plans: Essays in Urban Problems and Solutions* (New York: Basic Books, 1968), pp. 28-30.

by shortage of space and governmental housing distribution systems even after personal incomes are a good deal higher than they are now. Such is the case, for example, in Sweden and other parts of Western Europe. Even without great freedom in the housing location choices of residents, is it possible that the Soviet microdistrict will become less important as a social unit when the work of volunteers is taken over by paid staff? To what extent can or should voluntary cooperation among neighbors be sustained as a "good" in itself past the point where the problems it arose to deal with have already been solved?

It is not the intention here to belittle the Soviet notion that intensive neighborhood association is desirable as a means of keeping society human, of supporting man as a growing social being rather than man as a devourer of goods and pleasures. America has long been in the midst of a smouldering spiritual crisis over just this issue. The point is simply that it may require greater effort than Soviet leaders and urban planners have yet put forth to sustain in the Soviet system a philosophy of consumption fundamentally different from our own.

.8. *Some Questions for the Future*

The reader may be tempted to end his perusal of this book with the notion that ideas and ideology have not been of great importance in shaping all these policies. There is good reason for such an impression: just look at the beginning of each policy development described here, the ideological justifications which accompanied it, and the way in which it was then dropped or else modified all out of shape with no corresponding change in ideological statements. Why, for example, should the regular 10-year schools still bear the adjective "polytechnical"? Or why should ideology still proclaim a transition to distribution according to need instead of according to labor, when so much of the debate about rewards is about improving their relationship to labor? It may be significant that while the massive restatement of Soviet ideology drawn up in the Khrushchev period remains in force, Khrushchev's successors have shown little inclination to elaborate on it, even where current policy problems suggest that this should be done.

Therefore, one might draw the following skeptical conclusion about the relation of Soviet policies described in this book to Soviet Marxist ideology: Basically they can be understood as a function of the continuing primacy of high investment levels, ongoing military preparedness, and the drive for a highly skilled and thoroughly efficient labor force to support these. Where innovation in the name of ideology promises not to consume sizable additional resources, or promises to yield benefits beyond its cost, it may be safely

265

encouraged or at least left to expert judgment. Such was the case with recent policy concerning urban communities and experimental dwelling complexes. The experiments in admissions to higher education fall in this category also, even though part of the reason for easing admission of the disadvantaged may be to fill places in the least desirable branches of higher learning. Where innovation promises no tangible economic gain commensurate with its costs, it is scrapped: such was the case with Khrushchev's proposal for universal boarding schools. Where ideological requirements and the needs of production are in harmony, there is no problem, and reform may be safely promoted in the name of ideology. This was the case in the decision to raise the income "floor" of both wages and pensions. Here the economic justification was the drastic reduction in the need for unskilled labor, and the ideological justification was a reduction of earnings differentials in preparation for the transition to distribution according to need. The drive for comprehensive child care and other measures for freeing women from their traditional constraints is even easier to bring under the double justification of equality for the sexes plus an increased labor force in a labor-hungry economy.

All this adds up to a situation in which the Soviet leadership of the Khrushchev and post-Khrushchev era has not really had to face the hard questions of what kind of society it desires to see after high investment, the size of the GNP, labor force size, and labor productivity have ceased to be the objects of great concern. Is it not rather the United States and several other noncommunist industrial nations which have had to face the questions: Wealth for what? Productivity for what?

In answer to this charge, several things may be said: first, there is the quotation from J. M. Keynes cited at the end of Chapter 1, which asserts that men in fact are ruled by ideas even when they may be little aware just what these ideas are; secondly, top political leaders, like most people, are moved by a great variety of ideas, often mutually contradictory ones; and finally, the workings of a modern industrial state demand that the job of drawing up a lot of policy decisions be left to nonpolitical circles, whose proposals may certainly be vetoed by Soviet political leaders, but who nevertheless carry authority because of their knowledge. The policies which have been described were certainly influenced by one or all of these factors, to the extent that it is impossible to write them down to a single set of motives on the part of the political leadership.

There is another dimension of the relationship between ideology and policy, which is that strict adherence to Soviet Marxism, in whatever form, is sometimes confused with adherence to long-established policies. The poet Yevgeny Yevtushenko's quarrel with the Soviet leadership in the early 1960's illuminated for the outside world the fact that Soviet ideology can be used by reformers as well as by supporters of the established order. For example, those Soviet leaders who have been conservative in the sense of supporting continued high industrial investment do not necessarily have ideology on their side. In fact, the debates on this subject that occurred first in 1953-54 and again in 1960-62 showed, if anything, that both the proponents of investment for consumers and the proponents of more heavy industry can cite both Lenin and more recent statements in their support. When foreign critics state that one or another policy is not in keeping with "ideology," usually they are stating in fact that the policy is not in keeping with the past policies of the Soviet leaders whom they themselves call conservative or Stalinist.

Each of the three broad areas covered in this study—welfare, equality in career and work choices and in the gaining of work rewards, and the job of creating an urban environment for the future—bears its own special relation to ideological pronouncements of the recent past. Urban planning has never received more than passing attention, and the experimental dwellings described in Chapter 7 were the product not of narrow ideological strictures, but of honest efforts by architects and others to extract concrete guidelines from the 1961 Party Program and other statements. Welfare measures fall under more definite ideological provisions about the responsibility of society for all its members, although Soviet ideology has left the specifics flexible. Work rewards are subject to the much-quoted prescription about the transition from rewards according to work under socialism to rewards according to need under communism. Yet ideological statements as such have said little about whether reward differentials should be great or small, as should be clear from Chapter 5. As to the concept of need, while Khrushchev attempted to define this as the need of "the normal cultured person" with rather temperate notions of his own needs, economists and others began only in the latter 1960's to investigate what normal needs ought to embrace. Furthermore, scholarly comment on the practice of labor rewards has been clear on the matter that rewards according to labor have been intermingled with rewards according to need since the early years of the Soviet system.

As concerns research, experimentation, and creative legislation in these policy areas, their relation to Soviet Marxist ideology is far from simple. Certainly, there is little basis for assuming "the less ideology, the more creativity," even if Soviet ideology continues even today to block some areas of inquiry which the Soviet regime might find useful from a practical point of view, and to retard many other areas. The types of relationship to ideology which would open the way for creative inquiry and experimentation include the following situations:

(1) Areas in which ideology promotes inquiry, with or without inhibiting certain types of findings (e.g., work motivations);
(2) areas which have been "de-ideologized," or in which ideological guidelines are permissive (e.g., urban planning);
(3) areas in which the Soviet government has promoted enquiry and experimentation regardless of ideological guidelines in order to find the solution to a concrete problem (e.g., high labor turnover).

Clearly ideology has not been an insuperable roadblock to the evolution of policy in any of the cases described here.

A much more formidable obstacle for the next few decades may be the official Soviet addiction to national legislative uniformity and the central setting of norms. Here is a system which would profit enormously from a certain amount of local and institutional diversity, yet which has denied itself this tool of social inquiry in most areas during most of the half century of its existence.

Are there any signs that the Soviet Union is on the way to promoting diversity of policies, or granting the administrative autonomy which would permit this? Perhaps there are, but the evidence is equivocal.

In the wake of Khrushchev's massive effort to recentralize and regularize policy in all the areas this book has dealt with, a countermovement may be under way which would enlarge local options and local consultative procedures in administering national policies. To those who think of the Stalin regime as the epitome of bureaucratic centralism, it may come as a shock to see Khrushchev and his administration described as the centralizers. Was it not Khrushchev who in 1957, with a majority against him in the Politburo, staked his career on a plan for dismantling all but a few of the central industrial ministries and distributing their functions to regional bodies? That the intent and the structure of Stalin's various administrative pyramids were highly centralist, there is no arguing. But the chaotic stream of central decrees and directives offered lower-level administrators greater latitude than as if they had been governed by a much smaller number of well-coordinated directives. Once lower-level administrators and managers understood what kind of excesses they might indulge in, curbing them subsequently proved to be difficult. The Khrushchev administration offers numerous examples of efforts to apply curbs to these excesses, to balance and coordinate the policy areas whose administration had bred so many bureaucratic fiefdoms. Urban planning had been in the grip of a mania for display, for the concentration of resources on a small number of highly expensive projects, for placing residences along main boulevards to the detriment of both convenience and community. In residential construction, emphasis had been on housing space statistics to the detriment of good residential layouts and the provision of services and amenities. In social security, the old-style centralism had meant high pensions for a privileged stratum of workers in key industries, and a pittance for the rest. In education, it meant the favoring of higher education and the preparatory track in secondary schools, to the detriment of good motivation for training in technology and vocations. In investment priorities, Stalin's style of centralism meant that the favored industries could shape their environments to suit themselves, as long as they turned out the planned volume of physical output. The list could go on and on.

By the mid-1950's, the Soviet Union also stood in need of a decisive rearrangement of substantive policy priorities. Khrushchev even made an effort to modify somewhat the two resource allocation priorities which in a sense had determined the rest: the proportion of the nation's annual output which was devoted to military expenditures, and the proportion invested in heavy industry. While his success in making these changes was limited, still the nation had recovered from the destruction of World War II and was beginning to produce the kind of wealth which could now be used to start shaping the society of the future. If this wealth was to be used rationally, the many administrative "fiefdoms" had to be forced to change their ways, or else be dismantled. Consequently, most of the policies described here were the product of central norms. In some cases this meant reducing the incentives and privileges in resource allocation which had been enjoyed by certain administrative structures, geographical areas, and occupational strata, and raising the incentives for others. The administrative bodies to which the new policies were entrusted had to be strengthened in order to do this; *Gosstroi* was the most notable example.

During the 1960's, two new kinds of problems came to the fore. Both of them may require further changes in the way the Soviet Union organizes its citizens' welfare. One is the way in which achievement of truly national standards places limits on those organizations and governmental units which have the resources to achieve standards above the national norm. To what extent may a school system set norms higher than the national norms, in a city whose industries have decided to pour their profits into local education? What of a similarly favored city which has the resources to raise its housing and service norms well above the national average? In both of these areas, but particularly in urban construction, present norms impose limits whose consequences for the future may be difficult to change. The foreign visitor who is repelled by the monotony and bleakness of the massive new housing districts should reflect that this is in part the consequence of norms set in 1958. These norms, even if some of them have been raised in the 1960's, are well below what the nation's leaders think desirable for the 1980's and 1990's. It is encouraging that in certain small ways, urban planners and educators have been allotted the resources with which to exceed present norms and build pieces of the future society in the present. The reluctance of Soviet economic policymakers to permit more of this is understandable: it simply exposes their country to more charges that it is favoring an elite of one sort or another.

The second problem is that the success of programs which affect the public welfare depends more and more on better local coordination. This is notably true in the areas of urban planning, career guidance, and employment choices. It is not true, of course, of most income maintenance programs (pensions, disability payments, and the rest), whose effectiveness depends on sound national policies and central coordination. In the area of work compensation, while agencies in Moscow retain firm control over wage rates and the wage bill for each enterprise, the capacity of enterprises to set their own labor force qualifications, to reduce the size of the labor force by introducing automation, and to set labor performance norms has probably been growing since the 1965 reforms—"probably" because the information now available consists of scattered case histories. The solution to one enormous problem not dealt with here, that of environmental pollution, depends very heavily on the success or failure of local coordination. (It would help, of course, if the ministries in Moscow offered better incentives to enterprises for constructing antipollution facilities.) In fact, even before the national controversy arose over the construction of a pulp mill which threatened to upset the ecology of Lake Baikal, the Soviet press was full of case histories and exhortations on the problem of air and water pollution. This was done mainly in order to put pressure on local industrial and government officials who hitherto had shown little willingness to cooperate.

One of the main tasks of the Communist Party is to harmonize the work of many different industries, government agencies, and other organizations locally. At the level of the city, the district, and the province, the first secretary of the local Party organization has a sizable staff to help him keep close watch over every major activity within his territory, be it a giant industrial plant, the public school system, local transportation, the supply of consumers' goods, or whatever. Conflicts among local agencies, as well as conflicts between local agencies and the industries which are controlled by a ministry in Moscow, invariably land on his desk. Where local government in the United States commonly relies on an informal coalition of local interests to resolve analogous disputes, a coalition which is usually dominated by business interests, the communist world has institutionalized the "inner circle" of power in the form of the Party.

Judging from the flow of anecdotal material in the Soviet press concerning the resolution of local disputes, the Party as a mediator and policy leader has functioned well but in many cases not well enough. All too often, the first secretary measures his success as local leader by standards which do not reflect a good balance of local interests and needs. A first secretary whose overriding goal is assisting the large industries in his territory to overfulfill their production targets is not likely to be enthusiastic about diverting the industries' resources to combat air and water pollution. A secretary who measures his contribution to local welfare in terms of highly advertisable statistics on increases in housing space may be inclined to encourage construction organizations to skimp on putting up shops and service facilities. Furthermore, the Party's full-time staff of approximately one-quarter million is full of specialists in one or another area of economic life who are organized into Party structures which parallel the structures of state economic administration. Inevitably, administrative disputes among enterprises and local governments are reflected to some extent within the Party itself.

The Party secretaries, whatever their professional training, are intended to be "generalists"; as such they are given further training in the Party's own educational system. They are moved from post to post, as well as from area to area, to round out their abilities as generalists. The idea of putting an experienced generalist at the core of each local power structure is in fact a very logical one. Given the Soviet preference for the centralized administration of most of the nation's important business, it is hard to imagine how the administrative system could have worked at all up to now were it not for the presence of local Party officials capable of mediating between one hierarchy and the next. The problem has been that in certain types of problems, for example, in the control of air and water pollution, their work has been the labor of Sisyphus. Certain of Moscow's priorities are nearly impossible to fight, and the only solution lies in a top-level decision to alter these priorities, which sometimes has to be done over the foot-dragging opposition of the state hierarchies whose operations are affected.

These are not insuperable problems, and the initiative of local Party leaders could be an important factor in resolving them. One of the possible developments which bear watching during the 1970's is the role of the most ethnically conscious of the non-Russian republics in promoting diversity: Georgia, Armenia, the three Baltic republics, and perhaps others. Will diversity among localities, whether among national republics or simply among local governments, eventually lead the Soviet political system in the direction of "convergence" with political systems outside the communist world? The idea is even more intriguing than the idea of convergence in the fields of public welfare, work motivations, and the rest. Was it not the issue of Slovak autonomy which, together with certain economic difficulties, launched Czechoslovakia on a course which, until the Soviet invasion seemed likely to produce a limited sort of multiparty system?

The writer must confess his skepticism that the same could happen in the Soviet Union. In Czechoslovakia, the pressures for tolerance of diversity in many areas of political and economic life have been rooted in a political culture far different from the political culture on which the Soviet system is built. The same can be said of Yugoslavia, and of most of the nations of Eastern Europe. The fact that Czechoslovakia had a reasonably good experience with parliamentary democracy between the two World Wars set it apart from the other Eastern European nations, whose democratic constitutions had been supplanted all too easily by authoritarian regimes during this same period.

Pressures for diversity of local institutions can be resolved within a one-party system provided the system is flexible enough, and its leaders perspicacious enough, to see the advantages of promoting diversity. Yugoslavia has already "come over the hump" in this regard, even if the future consequences of this diversity still leave some disturbing question marks. Czechoslovakia, had it been permitted to go its own way, might very well have surmounted this same "hump" even without developing a multiparty system. The Soviet Union, a nation of enormous ethnic and regional diversity, is only now cautiously approaching the "hump."

It is not inconceivable, in the writer's view, that the 1970's will see a considerable growth of local policy diversity in various areas of Soviet public welfare. If so, the permission to use local norms will be negotiated within the sprawling apparatus of the Party, without any movement toward basic changes in the political system. Tolerance of local demands might strengthen rather than weaken the rule of the Communist Party.

Whether the Party's full-time staff is flexible enough in its outlook to permit this is another question. The decade of the 1960's saw an increase in the average age of the top Party leadership and bureaucracy, and a slowing down of turnover of the upper Party strata both in Moscow and in the provinces. The men at the top are used to pulling many central levers of control, and are disposed to maintain uniform standards and uniform administration. The fact that the Yugoslav leaders have had such a long struggle to persuade their own higher bureaucracy of the League of Communists to accept diversity and autonomy in the nation's economy can hardly have been lost on the Soviet leadership. The slowness of Soviet Party officials to adjust even to the very limited economic reforms of the 1960's hardly augers well in this regard.

Therefore, both in its fund of ideas for social policies, and in its capacity to experiment with these ideas and to promote the best of them on a national scale, the Soviet Union is coping with its own special "mix" of pluses and minuses. The "mix" is a specific product of Soviet political and social evolution, and of its pre-revolutionary Russian background. It would be useless to try to show that the solutions which Moscow has so far brought to the problems of its own industrializing and urbanizing society are themselves some kind of inexorable product of industrialization and urbanization. Instead, there is every evidence that the ideas which the Soviet leadership has brought to bear have had a specific history of their own. True, the practical measures which have resulted from these ideas often resemble the things that noncommunist governments have promoted also. Maybe there are some constants in the nature of man, in his response to the drastically new environment of the 20th century, which have produced these. But it would be a mistake to assume that even if this is so, the social policies of modern governments will somehow converge; or at least, this remains to be shown.

On the other hand, one must not underestimate the process of learning across national boundaries which has been made possible by 20th-century communications. The very history of the Soviet Union is punctuated by the importation and adaptation of idea after idea, beginning with Marxism itself, but including, as has been shown, such items as modern sociology and urban design. Even where these imports are put to uses which are specifically Soviet and determined by the larger Soviet political context, it is very important for the future that there will be more and more Soviet specialists in social questions who can test their work against their opposite members outside the socialist bloc.

What of the solutions which these specialists, Soviet and foreign, are going to find to problems which look increasingly similar? And regardless what the specialists may propose, are political leaders inside and outside the socialist bloc going to favor the increasingly similar solutions? This book has presented a number of Soviet policy problems which may tempt the unwary reader to answer generally "yes" to both these questions. It adds to this temptation to reflect that for many problems which will be crucial in industrial nations during the remainder of the present century, there just are no specifically communist and noncommunist answers. For example, has Moscow produced any proposals to deal with environmental pollution which can be called specifically communist or socialist, or specifically Soviet? Or is it likely to do so?

To ask whether there can be anything specifically communist about an antipollution program (to continue with this example) is beside the point if the reference is to Soviet Marxism, which can embrace almost any kind of commonsense social or economic measure under its broad categories. But there is good reason to ask whether or not two nations can differ greatly in terms of their philosophy of resource use. A system which is dedicated to controlling pollution through comprehensive ongoing programs, and which has reordered its values and priorities in order to devote a large part of its resources to this task, certainly differs in one significant way from a system which deals with pollution only as crises occur. But what has happened in fact, as the 1960's showed, was that neither the United States nor the Soviet Union have proceeded much beyond dealing with crises. The point, of course, is not that this regrettable state of affairs is inherent in all mature industrial societies regardless of their ideological and political differences. What is important, rather, is that there exists and will continue to exist the possibility of very different responses to outwardly similar problems.

The reader has probably gained the impression from these studies that Soviet policymakers have in general shunned the more radical and more distinctive policy choices among the many choices which confronted them, and the writer shares this impression also. But there is no basis for using this impression to draw the conclusion that the remaining decades of this century are going to see any definite convergence in these policy areas. While the Brezhnev-Kosygin administration has been conservative in its choices, there is no guarantee at all that they and their kind will not be succeeded by some future Khrushchev who will renew the drive for some of the more radical choices. The fund of Soviet Marxist ideas is still present as a basis for these radical choices, and whether they are put to use depends very much on the temper of the men who assume responsibility for upholding and promoting them.

Transliteration of Russian Words

The system used here is based largely on that of the Library of Congress, but it has been modified somewhat at the expense of logic in order to convey the sound of names and titles more adequately to readers who have no knowledge of Russian. Thus, the Russian я is represented by *ya,* the Russian ё by *yo,* and the Russian ю by *yu,* even though *y* is also used to represent the Russian ы . The Russian e is transliterated with a Latin *e* except where it begins a word or is preceded by a vowel, a soft sign, or a hard sign, in which case *ye* is used. The Russian и and й are both represented by *i.* The Russian soft sign ь is rendered by an apostrophe ('), and the Russian hard sign ъ by a quotation mark ("). Names whose Russian and English sounds are roughly similar are given in the English spelling, e.g., Alexander instead of *Aleksandr,* Maria for *Mariya,* Lydia for *Lidiya,* etc.

Abbreviations and Special Expressions

CDSP   *Current Digest of the Soviet Press*
CPSU   Communist Party of the Soviet Union
CSA   Central Statistical Administration
ETP   Engineering and Technical Personnel
Gosplan   State Planning Committee
Gosstroi   State Construction Committee
GNP   Gross National Product
Komsomol   Young Communist League
KPSS   Communist Party of the Soviet Union (Russian initials)
Orgnabor   Organized Labor Recruiting Service
SP SSSR   see Bibliography: *Sobraniye postanovlenii . . .*
SU SSSR   see Bibliography: *Sobraniye uzakonenii . . .*
SZ SSSR   see Bibliography: *Sobraniye zakonov . . .*
Trans. in   Translated in
Vedomosti RSFSR   see Bibliography: *Vedomosti Verkhovnogo soveta Rossiiskoi . . .*
Vedomosti SSSR   see Bibliography: *Vedomosti Verkhovnogo soveta Soyuza . . .*
WSR   Western Siberian Region

Bibliography

BOOKS AND ARTICLES

Acharkan, V.A. *Pensii za vyslugu let rabotnikam prosveshcheniya i zdravookhraneniya* (Years-of-Service Pensions for Employees in Education and Public Health). Moscow: Gosyurizdat, 1960.

Akademiya nauk SSSR. Gosplan SSSR. Sovet po izucheniyu proizvoditel'nykh sil. *Zapadno-sibirskii ekonomicheskii raion* (The Western Siberian Economic Region). Moscow: Mysl', 1967.

Angell, Robert C. "Social Values of Soviet and American Elites: Content Analysis of Elite Media," *Journal of Conflict Resolution,* VIII:4 (December, 1964), pp. 330-85.

Baranov, N.V. *Sovremennoye gradostroitel'stvo; glavnye problemy* (Contemporary Urban Construction; Main Problems). Moscow: Gosstroiizdat, 1962.

———. "Zhiloi raion i mikroraion" ("The Residential District and the Microdistrict"), *Arkhitektura SSSR,* No. 11 (November, 1964), pp. 1-17.

Basov, V.I. *Obshchestvennyye fondy potrebleniya i byudzhet* (The Social Wage and the Budget). Moscow: Finansy, 1967.

Batkayev, R.A., and Markov, V.I. *Differentsiatsiya zarabotnoi platy v promyshlennosti SSSR* (Industrial Wage Differentials in the U.S.S.R.). Moscow: Ekonomika, 1964.

Bauer, Raymond A. *The New Man in Soviet Psychology.* Cambridge, Mass.: Harvard University Press, 1952.

Bereday, George Z.F., and Pennar, Jaan. *The Politics of Soviet Education.* New York: Praeger, 1960.

Bergson, Abram. *The Economics of Soviet Planning.* New Haven: Yale University Press, 1964.

278

_____. *The Real National Income of Soviet Russia Since 1928.* Cambridge, Mass.: Harvard University Press, 1961.

_____. *The Structure of Soviet Wages.* Cambridge, Mass.: Harvard University Press, 1944.

Bergson, Abram, and Kuzents, Simon (eds.). *Economic Trends in the Soviet Union.* Cambridge, Mass.: Harvard University Press, 1963.

Björk, Leif. *Wages, Prices and Social Legislation in the Soviet Union.* London: Dobson, 1953.

Brown, Emily Clark. *Soviet Trade Unions and Labor Relations.* Cambridge, Mass.: Harvard University Press, 1966.

Buzlyakov, N.I. *Obshchestvennyye fondy potrebleniya* (The Social Wage). Moscow: Ekonomika, 1964.

Bykov, V. "Sotsial'noye znacheniye domov-kompleksov v stanovlenii kommunisticheskikh form byta" ("The Social Significance of Dwelling Complexes in the Emergence of Communist Forms of Everyday Life"), *Arkhitektura SSSR,* No. 7 (July, 1965), pp. 8-12.

Cantril, Hadley. *Soviet Leaders and Mastery Over Man.* New Brunswick, N.J.: Rutgers University Press, 1960.

Chukhno, A. "Raspredeleniye po trudu i obshchestvennyye fondy potrebleniya" ("Distribution According to Work and the Social Wage"), *Voprosy ekonomiki,* No. 3 (March, 1963), pp. 49-54.

Conquest, Robert (ed.). *Industrial Workers in the U.S.S.R.* New York: Praeger, 1967.

Davidovich, V.G. *Rasseleniye v promyshlennykh uzlakh* (Population Distribution in Industrial Complexes). Moscow: Gosstroiizdat, 1960.

DeWitt, Nicholas. *Education and Professional Employment in the U.S.S.R.* Washington, D.C.: National Science Foundation, 1961.

Dodge, Norton T. *Women in the Soviet Economy; Their Role in Economic, Scientific, and Technical Development.* Baltimore: Johns Hopkins Press, 1966.

Dol'skaya, A.A. *Sotsialisticheskii zakon narodonaseleniya* (The Socialist Law of Population Development). Moscow: Sotsekgiz, 1959.

Fakiolas, R. "Problems of Labour Mobility in the U.S.S.R.," *Soviet Studies,* XIV:1 (July, 1962), pp. 16-35.

Feuer, Lewis S. "Problems and Unproblems in Soviet Social Theory," *Slavic Review* XXIII:1 (March, 1964), pp. 117-28.

Field, Mark G. *Soviet Socialized Medicine; An Introduction.* New York: The Free Press, 1967.

Figurnov, S.P. *Stroitel'stvo kommunizma i rost blagosostoyaniya naroda.* (The Building of Communism and the Growth of Public Welfare). Moscow: Sotsekgiz, 1962.

Fischer, George. *Science and Politics; The New Sociology in the Soviet Union.* Ithaca, N.Y.: Center for International Studies, Cornell University, 1964.

Galenson, Walter. "Wage Structure and Administration in Soviet Industry," in J.L. Meij (ed.), *Internal Wage Structure* (Amsterdam: North-Holland Publishing Company, 1963), pp. 300-334.

Geiger, H. Kent. *The Family in Soviet Russia.* Cambridge, Mass.: Harvard University Press, 1968.

Goodman, Ann S., and **Feshbach, Murray**. *Estimates and Projections of Educational Attainment in the U.S.S.R.: 1950-1985.* U.S. Bureau of the Census, International Population Reports, Series P-91, No. 16. Washington, D.C., 1967.

Gordeyeva, Z.P. "Nekotoryye voprosy analizirovaniya potrebleniya produktov pitaniya v zapadnoi Sibiri," ("Certain Questions of Analyzing Foodstuff Consumption in Western Siberia"), *Izvestiya Sibirskogo otdeleniya Akademii nauk SSSR; seriya obshchestvennykh nauk,* No. 5, vyp. 2, 1964, pp. 83-90.

Goroda-sputniki (Satellite Cities). Moscow: Geografgiz, 1961.

Gosudarstvennoye sotsial'noye strakhovaniye; sbornik ofitsial'nykh materialov (State Social Insurance; Collection of Official Documents). Moscow: Profizdat, 1963.

Gradov, G.A. *Gorod i byt* (The City and Everyday Life). Moscow: Izdatel'stvo literatury po stroitel'stvu, 1968.

Harris, Mary. "Social Aspects of Labour Turnover in the U.S.S.R.," *British Journal of Industrial Relations,* II:3 (November, 1964), pp. 398-417.

Heer, David M., and **Bryden, Judith G**. "Family Allowances and Population Policy in the U.S.S.R.," *Journal of Marriage and the Family,* XXVIII:4 (November, 1966), pp. 514-19.

Herzberg, Frederick. "Job Attitudes in the Soviet Union," *Personnel Psychology,* XVIII (1965), pp. 245-52.

———. *Work and the Nature of Man.* New York: World Publishing Co., 1966.

Holesovski, Vaclav. "Consumption and Welfare," *Problems of Communism,* XIII:6 (November-December, 1964); pp. 60-63.

Juviler, Peter H., and **Morton, Henry W. (eds.)**. *Soviet Policy-Making.* New York: Praeger, 1967.

Kamenskii, V.A., *et al. Prigorodnyye zony krupnykh gorodov* (The Suburban Zones of the Largest Cities). Leningrad: Stroiizdat, 1963.

Kapustin, E.I. *Kachestvo truda i zarabotnaya plata* (Wages and the Character of Labor). Moscow: Mysl', 1964.

———. *Obshchestvennyye fondy i rost blagosostoyaniya naroda v SSSR* (The Social Wage and the Growth of Public Welfare in the U.S.S.R.). Moscow: Sotsekgiz, 1962.

Kaser, Michael. "Soviet Boarding Schools," *Soviet Studies* XX:1 (July, 1968), pp. 94-105.

_____. "Welfare Criteria in Soviet Planning," in Degras, Jane, and Nove, Alec (eds.), *Soviet Planning: Essays in Honor of Naum Jasny* (Oxford: Blackwell, 1964), pp. 144-72.

Kharchev, A.G. *Brak i sem ya v SSSR* (Marriage and the Family in the U.S.S.R.). Moscow: Mysl', 1964.

_____. *Sem'ya i kommunizm* (The Family and Communism). Moscow: Mysl', 1964.

Khauke, M.O. "Ogranicheniye rosta krupnykh gorodov" ("Growth Limitation of the Largest Cities"), in *Planirovka i zastroika bol'shikh gorodov* (Planning and Construction of Large Cities) (Moscow: Gosstroiizdat, 1961), pp. 5-27.

_____. *Prigorodnaya zona bol'shogo goroda* (The Suburban Zone of Large Cities). Moscow: Gosstroiizdat, 1960.

Kiselevich, L., and Rabinovich, I. "Ob osnovakh formirovaniya perspektivnykh tipov zhilykh domov" ("On the Principles of Designing Future Types of Housing"), *Arkhitektura SSSR,* No. 11 (November, 1966), pp. 25-29.

Korzh, V. "Ogranicheniye rosta krupnykh gorodov putyom kompleksnoi raionnoi planirovki" ("Growth Limitation of the Largest Cities by means of Coordinated Regional Planning"), *Ekonomicheskaya gazeta,* October 10, 1964, pp. 8-9.

KPSS o rabote sovetov (The CPSU on the Work of the Soviets). Moscow: Gospolitizdat, 1959.

KPSS v rezolyutsiyakh (The CPSU in Resolutions). 7th ed. 4 vols. Moscow: Gospolitizdat, 1954 and 1960.

Krupyanskaya, V. Yu., and M.G. Rabinovich. "The Ethnography of the City and the Industrial Settlement," *Soviet Sociology,* III:2 (Fall, 1964), pp. 13-19.

Kurman, M.V., and Lebedinskii, I.V. *Naseleniye bol'shogo sotsialitsticheskogo goroda* (The Population of a Large Socialist City). Moscow: Statistika, 1968.

Kuypers, G. "Social Insurance in the Soviet Union," in Z. Szirmai (ed.), *Law in Eastern Europe,* No. 1 (Leyden: A.W. Sijthoff, 1958), pp. 27-69.

Lappo, G.M. "Sovremennoye rasseleniye i puti razvitiya gorodov v Moskovskom prigorodnom raione" ("Contemporary Population Distribution and Paths of Development for Towns in Moscow's Suburban Zone"), in *Planirovka i zastroika bol'shikh gorodov* (Planning and Construction of Large Cities) (Moscow: Gosstroiizdat, 1961), pp. 89-104.

Lunin, B. (ed.). *Goroda sotsializma i sotsialisticheskaya rekonstruktsiya byta; sbornik statei* (The Cities of Socialism and the Socialist Reconstruction of Everyday Life). Moscow: Rabotnik prosveshcheniya, 1930.

Madison, Bernice Q. *Social Welfare in the Soviet Union.* Stanford, Calif.: Stanford University Press, 1968.

Maier, V.F. *Zarabotnaya plata v period perekhoda k kommunizmu* (Wages in the Period of Transition to Communism). Moscow: Izdatel'stvo ekono-micheskoi literatury, 1963.

Manevich, Ye. "Ekonomicheskoye stimulirovaniye truda i formy perekhoda k kommunisticheskomu raspredeleniyu" ("The Economic Motivation of Labor and Forms of Transition to a Communist System of Distribution"), *Voprosy ekonomiki,* No. 5 (May, 1961), pp. 76-85.

_____. "The Management of Soviet Manpower," *Foreign Affairs* XLVII:1 (October, 1968), pp. 176-84.

Martens, M. "Providing for the Soviet Officer," *Bulletin of the Institute for the Study of the U.S.S.R.* III:2 (February, 1956), pp. 26-32.

Medved'yev, R.A. "On Selecting an Occupation in Secondary School," *Soviet Education* (February, 1963), pp. 35-41.

Musatov, I.M. *Sotsial'nyye problemy trudovykh resursov v SSSR* (Social Problems of Labor Resources in the U.S.S.R.). Moscow: Mysl', 1967.

Naleszkiewicz, Wladimir. "Financing and Coverage under Social Insurance in Soviet Russia," *Industrial and Labor Relations Review* XVII:2 (January, 1964), pp. 289-301.

"Nauchno-teknicheskoye soveshchaniye po planirovke i zastroike zhilykh raionov i mikroraionov" ("Scientific and Technical Conference on Planning and Building Residential Districts and Microdistricts"), *Arkhitektura SSSR,* No. 2 (February, 1965), pp. 1-9.

Noah, Harold J. *Financing Soviet Schools.* New York: Teachers College Press, Columbia University, 1966.

Osborn, Robert J., and **Reiner, Thomas A.** "Soviet City Planning: Current Issues and Future Perspectives," *Journal of the American Institute of Planners* XXVIII:4 (November, 1962), pp. 239-50.

Osipov, G.V. (ed.). *Industry and Labour in the U.S.S.R.* London: Tavistock, 1966.

Osterman, N. "O zhilishche budushchego" ("Concerning the Dwelling of the Future"), *Arkhitektura SSSR,* No. 6 (June, 1967), pp. 30-42.

Osterman, N., and **Petrushka, L.** "Zhiloi dom-kompleks s obshchestvennym obsluzhivaniyem" ("A Housing Complex with Communal-Type Services"), *Arkhitektura SSSR,* No. 7 (July, 1965), pp. 13-37.

Parkins, Maurice Frank. *City Planning in Soviet Russia.* Chicago: University of Chicago Press, 1953.

Pchelintsev, O.S. "Ratsional'noye razmeshcheniye proizvodstva i problema bol'shikh gorodov" ("Rational Industrial Location and the Problem of Large Cities"), *Voprosy filosofii,* No. 2 (February, 1961), pp. 90-102.

Pensionnoye obespecheniye v SSSR; sbornik ofitsial'nykh materialov (Pensions in the U.S.S.R.; Collection of Official Documents). 2d ed. rev. Moscow: Gosyurizdat, 1960.

Perevedentsev, V.I. "Nekotoryye voprosy mezhraionnogo pereraspredeleniya trudovykh resursov" ("Certain Questions Concerning the Interregional Redistribution of Labor Resources"), *Izvestiya Sibirskogo otdeleniya Akademii nauk SSSR; seriya obshchestvennykh nauk* No. 9, *vyp.* 3, 1964, pp. 77-83.

————. *Sovremennaya migratsiya naseleniya zapadnoi Sibiri* (Contemporary Migration of the Population of Western Siberia). Novosibirsk: Zapadnosibirskoye Knizhonye Izdatel'stvo, 1965.

————. "Voprosy teritorial'nogo pereraspredeleniya trudovykh resursov" ("Questions of the Territorial Redistribution of Labor Resources"), *Voprosy ekonomiki,* No. 5 (May, 1962), pp. 48-56. Trans. in *CDSP* XIV:26, pp. 3-6.

Pisarev, I. Yu. *Naseleniye i trud v SSSR* (Population and Labor in the U.S.S.R.). Moscow: Ekonomika, 1966.

Planirovka i zastroika bol'shikh gorodov (Planning and Construction of Large Cities). Moscow: Gosstroiizdat, 1961.

Posokhin, M.V. "Gorod budushchego sozidayetsya segodnya" ("The City of the Future is Being Created Today");·*Arkhitektura SSSR,* No. 10 (October, 1964), pp. 1-9.

Pravila i normy planirovki i zastroiki gorodov (Standards and Norms for Urban Planning and Construction). Moscow: Gosstroiizdat, 1959.

Prociuk, S.G. "The Manpower Problem in Siberia," *Soviet Studies,* XIX:2 (October, 1967), pp. 190-210.

Prokof'yev, M.A., *et al.* **(eds.).** *Narodnoye obrazovaniye v SSSR 1917-1967* (Public Education in the U.S.S.R. 1917-1967). Moscow: Prosveshcheniye, 1967.

Pryor, Frederic L. *Public Expenditures in Communist and Capitalist Nations.* Homewood, Ill.: Richard D. Irwin, Inc., 1968.

Rakitskii, B.V. *Obshchestvennyye fondy potrebleniya* (The Social Wage). Moscow: Ekonomika, 1963.

————. *Obshchestvennyye fondy potrebleniya kak ekonomicheskaya kategoriya* (The Social Wage as an Economic Category). Moscow: Mysl', 1966.

Raskhody na sotsial'no-kul'turnyye meropriyatiya po gosudarstvennomu byudzhetu SSSR; statisticheskii sbornik (Expenditures on Social and Cultural Programs from the U.S.S.R. State Budget; Statistical Handbook). Moscow: Gosfinizdat, 1958.

A Report on Social Security Programs in the Soviet Union. Prepared by the U.S. Team that Visited the U.S.S.R. under the East-West Exchange Program in August-September, 1958. Washington, D.C.: U.S. Government Printing Office, 1960.

Rutkevich, M.N. "Sotsial'nyye istochniki popolneniya Sovetskoi intelligentsii" ("Social Sources of the Replenishment of the Soviet Intelligentsia"), *Voprosy* *filosofii,* No. 6 (June, 1967), pp. 15-23. Condensed trans. in *CDSP* XIX:35, pp. 14-17.

Sbornik zakonodatel'nykh aktov o trude (Collected Legislative Enactments on Labor). 3d ed. rev. Moscow: Gosyurizdat, 1960.

Sbornik zakonov SSSR i ukazov Prezidiuma Verkhovnogo soveta SSSR 1936-1967 (Collected Laws of the U.S.S.R. and Decrees of the Presidium of the U.S.S.R. Supreme Soviet). 2 vols. Moscow: Izvestiya, 1968.

Schlesinger, Rudolf (ed.). *Changing Attitudes in Soviet Russia: The Family in the U.S.S.R.; Documents and Readings.* London: Routledge and Kegan Paul, 1949.

Schroeder, Gertrude. "Industrial Wage Differentials in the U.S.S.R.," *Soviet Studies,* XVII:3 (January, 1966), pp. 303-17.

Schwartz, Joel J., and **Keech, William R.** "Group Influence and the Policy Process in the Soviet Union," *American Political Science Review,* LXII:3 (September, 1968), pp. 840-51.

Shkurko, A.S. "The Industrial Wage System in the U.S.S.R.," *International Labor Review,* XC:4 (October, 1964), pp. 352-64.

Shkvarikov, V., and **Luk'yanov, V.** "Novyye normy i pravila po gradostroi-tel'stvu" ("New Standards and Norms for Urban Construction"), *Arkhitektura SSSR,* No. 2 (February, 1967), pp. 25-28.

Shubkin, V.N. "Molodyozh' vstupayet v zhizn'" ("Youth Enters Life"), *Voprosy filosofii,* No. 5 (May, 1965), pp. 57-70. Trans. in *CDSP* XVII:30, pp. 3-9.

_____. "Vybor professii v usloviyakh kommunistichekogo stroitel'stva" ("Choosing a Profession Under Circumstances of the Building of Communism"), *Voprosy filosofii,* No. 8 (August, 1964), pp. 18-28.

"Social Security in the U.S.S.R.," *Bulletin of the International Social Security Association,* XVII:8-9 (August-September, 1964), pp. 217-71.

Sonin, M. Ya. *Aktual'nyye problemy ispol'zovaniya rabochei sily v SSSR* (Current Problems of Manpower Use in the U.S.S.R.). Moscow: Mysl', 1965.

_____. *Vosproizvodstvo rabochei sily v SSSR i balans truda* (Reproduction of the U.S.S.R. Labor Force and the Balance of Labor). Moscow: Gosplanizdat, 1959.

Sotsiologiya v SSSR (Sociology in the U.S.S.R.). 2 vols. Moscow: Mysl', 1965.

Sovetskoye pensionnoye obespecheniye (Soviet Pensions). Moscow: Yuridicheskaya literatura, 1966.

Spravochnik po nalogam i sboram s naseleniya (Handbook of Public Taxation). Moscow: Finansy, 1968.

Stalin, I. *Voprosy Leninizma* (Questions of Leninism). 11th ed. Moscow: Gospolitizdat, 1953.

Strumilin, S. "Family and Community in the Society of the Future," *Soviet Review* II:1 (January, 1961), pp. 3-29.

————. *Nash mir cherez 20 let* (Our World in 20 Years). Moscow: Sovetskaya Rossiya, 1964.

Svetlichnyi, B. "Chelovek i gorod" ("Man and the City"), *Oktyabr'*, No. 1 (January, 1964), pp. 163-75.

————. "Gorod zhdyot otveta" ("The City Awaits a Reply"), *Oktiabr'*, No. 10 (October, 1966), pp. 157-69. Trans. in *CDSP*, XVIII:48, pp. 11-17.

————. "Gradostroitel'stvo i planirovaniye" ("Urban Construction and Economic Planning"), *Arkhitektura SSSR*, No. 3 (March, 1966), pp. 28-32.

————. "Nekotoryye voprosy perspektivnogo razvitiya gorodov" ("Certain Questions of Long-Range Urban Development"), *Voprosy ekonomiki*, No. 3 (March, 1962), pp. 58-69.

————. "Sovetskim lyudyam-blagoustroyennyye zhilishcha" ("Give Soviet People Well-Equipped Dwellings"), *Kommunist*, No. 6 (April, 1965), pp. 41-51. Trans. in *CDSP*, XVII:22, pp. 10-14.

————. "Sovetskoye gradostroitel'stvo na sovremennom etape" ("Soviet Urban Construction at the Present Time"), *Voprosy ekonomiki*, No. 7 (July, 1960), pp. 48-59.

Trapeznikov, K. "Sotsial'no-ekonomicheskiye predposylki planirovki i zastroiki zhilykh raionov" ("Social and Economic Bases of Planning and Building Residential Districts"), *Arkhitektura SSSR*, No. 11 (November, 1964), pp. 18-22.

Trudovoye pravo; entsiklopedicheskii slovar' (Labor Law; An Encyclopaedic Dictionary). Moscow: Sovetskaya Entsiklopediya, 1963.

Trudy VI sessi Akademii stroitel'stva i arkhitektury po voprosam gradostroitel'stva (Reports Made at the VI Session of the Academy of Construction and Architecture on Questions of Urban Construction). Moscow: Gosstroiizdat, 1961.

Tsentra'noye statisticheskoye upravleniye pri Sovete ministrov SSSR. *Itogi vsesoyuznoi perepisi naseleniya 1959 goda; SSSR* (Results of the All-Union Census of 1959; U.S.S.R.). Moscow: Gosstatizdat, 1962.

————. *SSSR v tsifrakh v 1966 godu* (The U.S.S.R. in Figures in 1966). Moscow: Statistika, 1967.

————. *Strana sovetov za 50 let; sbornik statisticheskikh materialov* (The Land of the Soviets for 50 Years; Collection of Statistical Materials). Moscow: Statistika, 1967.

————. *Zhenshchiny i deti v SSSR; statisticheskii sbornik* (Women and Children in the U.S.S.R.; Collected Statistics). Moscow: Gosstatizdat, 1963.

Urzhinskii, K.P. *Trudoustroistvo grazhdan v SSSR* (Channels of Employment for Soviet Citizens). Moscow: Yuridicheskaya literatura, 1967.

U.S. Congress. Joint Economic Committee. *Dimensions of Soviet Economic Power.* Washington: U.S. Government Printing Office, 1962.

_____. *New Directions in the Soviet Economy.* 4 parts, 5 vols. Washington, D.C.: U.S. Government Printing Office, 1966.

_____. *Soviet Economic Performance, 1966-67.* Washington, D.C.: U.S. Government Printing Office, 1968.

U.S. Department of Commerce. Bureau of the Census. *Estimates and Projections of Educational Attainment in the U.S.S.R.: 1950-1985.* By Ann S. Goodman and Murray Feshbach. International Population Reports, Series P-91, No. 16. Washington, D.C.: U.S. Government Printing Office, 1967.

_____. *The Soviet Financial System: Structure, Operation and Statistics.* International Population Statistics Reports, Series P-90, No. 23. Washington, D.C.: U.S. Government Printing Office, 1968.

Vneocherednoi XXI s"yezd KPSS (Extraordinary XXI Congress of the CPSU). 2 vols. Moscow: Gospolitizdat, 1959.

Vsesoyuznoye soveshchaniye po gradostroitel'stvu, 7-10 iunya 1960 g.; sokrash-chyonnyi stenograficheskii otchyot (All-Union Conference on Urban Construction, June 7-10, 1960; Condensed Record). Moscow: Gosstroiizdat, 1960.

Vsesoiuznoye soveshchaniye po gradostroitel'stvu. Sektsiya raionnoi planirovki, planirovki i zastroiki gorodov i posyolkov. *Planirovka i zastroika goroda Kryukovo* (Planning and Construction of the Town of Kryukovo). Moscow: Stroiizdat, 1960.

Wesson, Robert G. *Soviet Communes.* New Brunswick, N.J.: Rutgers University Press, 1963.

Yadov, V.A. "Davaite smotret' faktam v litso" ("Let's Look Facts in the Face"), *Voprosy filosofii,* No. 5, 1965, pp. 107-15.

Yagodkin, V.N. (ed.). *Puti likvidatsii tekuchesti kadrov v promyshlennosti SSSR* (Ways of Ending Excessive Labor Turnover in Soviet Industry). Moscow: Mysl', 1965.

Yanitskii, O. "Konkretnyye sotsiologicheskiye issledovaniya v gradostroitel'stve" ("Empirical Sociological Research in Urban Construction"), *Arkhitektura SSSR,* No. 2 (February, 1967). pp. 18-24.

Yanowitch, Murray. "The Soviet Income Revolution," *Slavic Review* XXII:4 (December, 1963), pp. 683-97.

_____. "Trends in Soviet Occupational Wage Differentials," *Industrial and Labor Relations Review,* XIII:2 (January, 1960), pp. 166-91.

Yargina, Z. "Zadachi sotsiologii v gradostroitel'noi nauke i proyektirovanii" ("The Tasks of Sociology in the Science of Urban Construction and Design"), *Arkhitektura SSSR,* No. 2 (February, 1967). pp. 13-18.

Yevstratov, N.F., and **Matveyev, S.M.** "Razvitiye i rekonstruktsiya Moskvy v perspektive" ("The Long-Range Development and Reconstruction of Moscow"), *Izvestiya Akademii nauk SSSR; seriya geograficheskaya,* No. 5, 1967, pp. 63-73.

Young, Michael. *The Rise of the Meritocracy.* Baltimore: Penguin Books, 1961.

Zdravomyslov, A.G., and **Yadov, V.A.** "Opyt konkretnogo issledovaniya otnosheniya k trudu" ("Results of an Empirical Study of Work Attitudes"), *Voprosy filosofii,* No. 4 (April, 1964), pp. 72-84. Trans. in *CDSP* XVI:24, pp. 12-17.

Zdravomyslov, A.G.; Rozhin, V.P.; and **Yadov, V.A.** *Chelovek i yego rabota.* (Man and His Work). Moscow: Mysl', 1967.

Zile, Zigurds L. "Programs and Problems of City Planning in the Soviet Union," *Washington University Law Quarterly,* No. 1 (February, 1963), pp. 19-59.

Zykov, S.S. "Voprosy razvitiya gorodov Sibiri" ("Questions of the Development of Siberian Cities"), *Izvestiya Sibirskogo otdeleniya Akademii nauk SSSR; seriya obshchestvennykh nauk,* No. 1, *vyp.* 1, 1964, pp. 63-69.

XX S"yezd KPSS (XX Congress of the CPSU). 2 vols. Moscow: Gospolitizdat, 1956.

XXII S"yezd KPSS (XXII Congress of the CPSU). 3 vols. Moscow: Gospolitizdat, 1962.

XXIII S"yezd KPSS (XXIII Congress of the CPSU). 2 vols. Moscow: Gospolitizdat, 1966.

PERIODICALS CONSULTED

Arkhitektura SSSR (Architecture of the U.S.S.R.)

Byulleten' Ministerstva vysshego i srednego spetsial'nogo obrazovaniya SSSR (Bulletin of the U.S.S.R. Ministry of Higher and Specialized Secondary Education)

Current Digest of the Soviet Press (cited as *CDSP*)

Doshkol'noye vospitaniye (Preschool Education)

Ekonomicheskaya gazeta (Economic Journal)

Geografiya i khozyaistvo (Geography and the Economy)

Gosudarstvennyi komitet Soveta ministrov SSSR po voprosam truda i zarabotnoi platy. Byulleten' (Bulletin of the U.S.S.R. State Committee for Labor and Wages)

Izvestiya

Izvestiya Akademii nauk SSSR; seriya ekonomicheskaya (Journals of the U.S.S.R. Academy of Sciences; Economic Series)

Izvestiya Akademii nauk SSSR; seriya geograficheskaya (Journals of the U.S.S.R. Academy of Sciences; Geographical Series)

Izvestiya Akademii stroitel'stva i arkhitektury SSSR (Journals of the U.S.S.R. Academy of Construction and Architecture)

Izvestiya Sibirskogo otdeleniya Akademii nauk SSSR; seriya obshchestvennykh nauk (Journals of the Siberian Division of the U.S.S.R. Academy of Sciences; Social Science Series)

Komsomol'skaya pravda

Literaturnaya gazeta

Narodnoye khozyaistvo SSSR v 19– g. (Economy of the U.S.S.R. in 19–) (annual)

Narodnoye obrazovaniye (Public Education)

Novyi mir (New World)

Planovoye khozyaistvo (Planned Economy)

Pravda

Problems of Communism

Problems of Economics

Professional'no-tekhnicheskoye obrazovaniye (Vocational Education)

Sem'ya i shkola (Family and School)

Skhola i proizvodstvo (School and Production Work)

Sobraniye postanovlenii i rasporyazhenii Pravitel'stva Soyuza sovetskikh sotsialisticheskikh respublik (Collected Resolutions and Decrees of the Government of the Union of Soviet Socialist Republics) (cited as *SP SSSR*)

Sobraniye uzakonenii i rasporyazhenii Rabochego i krest'yanskogo pravitel'stva Rossiiskoi sovetskoi federativnoi sotsialisticheskoi respubliki (Collected Laws and Decrees of the Workers' and Peasants' Government of the Russian Soviet Federated Socialist Republic) (cited as *SU RSFSR*)

Sobraniye zakonov i rasporyazhenii Raboche-krest'yanskogo pravitel'stva Soyuza sovetskikh sotsialisticheskikh respublik (Collected Laws and Decrees of the Workers' and Peasants' Government of the Union of Soviet Socialist Republics) (cited as *SZ SSSR*)

Sotsialisticheskii trud (Socialist Labor)

Sotsial'noye obespecheniye (Social Security)

Sotsial'nyye issledovaniya (Social Research)

Sovetskaya etnografiya (Soviet Ethnography)

Sovetskaya Rossiya

Soviet Education

Soviet Sociology

Soviet Studies

Trud

Trud i zarabotnaya plata (Labor and Wages)

Uchitel'skaya gazeta (Teachers Journal)

Vedomosti Verkhovnogo soveta Rossiiskoi sovetskoi federativnoi sotsialisticheskoi respubliki (Bulletin of the Supreme Soviet of the Russian Soviet Federated Socialist Republic) (cited as *Vedomosti RSFSR*)

Vedomosti Verkhovnogo soveta Soyuza sovetskikh sotsialisticheskikh respublik (Bulletin of the Supreme Soviet of the Union of Soviet Socialist Republics (cited as *Vedomosti SSSR*)

Vestnik statistiki (Bulletin of Statistics)

Vestnik vysshei shkoly (Bulletin of Higher Education)

Voprosy ekonomiki (Problems of Economics)

Voprosy filosofii (Problems of Philosophy)

Voprosy geografii (Problems of Geography)

Index of Names

291

Index of Subjects

293

This book has been set in 11 point and 10 point
Press Roman, leaded 2 points. Chapter numbers
are in 36 point and chapter titles are in 18 point
Univers Medium 689. The size of the type page is
27 by 45 picas.

All He Needs

Rhonda McKnight

ISBN 9798715530868

About the Book

The deal was to marry his best friend, get his inheritance, so he could make the investment of a lifetime, but this fake marriage might cost more than they ever expected to give.

Rachel Ingram

Rachel didn't know when her feelings for Zeke shifted from friendship to love, but she was here, loving him hard and willing to risk everything to have him. In a game that begins with lies and manipulation, Rachel must fight hard for love. Will she chase it down?

Zeke Bennett

Zeke thought his inheritance was a sure thing, until he finds out his deceased great-grandmother's will stipulates he be married to get it. Zeke doesn't want anything more than to invest in the Carolina United Soccer franchise, or at least he didn't think so until he opened his eyes and saw his best friend in ways he can't unsee. Has the woman closest to him caught the playboy bachelor?

Dedication

For those who encourage me.
You know who you are.
xoxo

All He Needs

Table of Contents

Chapter 1

"I'm in love with my best friend." A cloak of shame pushed Rachel Ingram's shoulders down. She climbed off her stationary bike and dropped into a nearby chair. She was glad she and her sisters were the only people in the gym's cycling class because she didn't think she could hold her emotions in for another minute.

"So, does that mean you're a lesbian?" Lauren, the oldest of the six Ingram sisters, used a towel to wipe the sweat off her forehead. She dropped into a chair next to Rachel.

Harper, the only sister who insisted on keeping sibling rivalry among them alive, deadpanned Lauren from her perch on her bike. "If you weren't so busy jumping on planes and going from place to place taking pictures of the world, you would know she's not talking about a woman."

Lauren frowned. "That little taking pictures thing I do is my career. A very successful one that put five of you chicks through college."

Everyone was quiet on that point, especially Rachel who had managed to get a full tuition ride to Spelman University, but still needed more than fifteen thousand a year for room, board, and expenses. She'd graduated without a single loan payment and appreciated her sister for making that happen.

After their parents died in a car accident, there was only enough money to pay off the family homes, the one in Forest Hills, Georgia where Sienna and Zoe continued to live and then the second, a vacation cabin in the Georgia mountains that they visited a few times a year. At twenty-three, Lauren had been the oldest, Harper at twenty-one had been behind her, then Rachel had just turned eighteen, but the youngest, Addison, Sienna, and Zoe had been difficult to keep out of the hands of the child-welfare workers.

Their grandmother's advanced age and failing health did not convince the social worker the Ingram girls had a safe home with her, so Lauren fought for her sisters. She'd been tenacious, temporarily giving up her dream of being a photojournalist to take a job editing film for Bennett Television, even though she greatly disliked the job. She'd been freed of it when she took an award-winning photograph in Ethiopia the year Zoe turned seventeen. That photo paid a small fortune, launched her career, and secured the Ingram sister's financial future. It also gave her permission to leave the reins of sister rearing to the more than capable and responsible Harper. Now Lauren traveled extensively; it seemed to make up for the lost years in her chosen field.

Lauren pursed her lips and raised a water bottle to them. After taking a long sip she said, "I know you aren't talking about that Zachary Bennett." At this point, all the Ingram sisters climbed off their equipment and gathered around the chairs where Rachel and Lauren were sitting.

"Yes, I am talking about Zeke. I can't take this anymore. He's working at home right now. I have to see him every day."

"You saw him every day anyway. You guys live across the cul-de-sac from each other. Remember his master plan to make sure you continued to make mud pies together?" Lauren raised her hand and removed her sweatband.

"Lauren," shushed Harper. She'd been the go-to for the sisters over the past seven years. Harper squatted in front of Rachel. Taking her hand, she asked, "Honey, when did you catch feelings for him?"

"Catch feelings?" Lauren sneered. "Why do you talk like you're on some low budget reality TV show? I paid too much for your education for you to use such language. You can't catch feelings."

Harper rolled her eyes. "You didn't pay for my education. I was the one who got to go with insurance money."

Rachel raised her hands to stop what she knew would become a battle between her two older sisters. Lauren took credit for everything good that happened with the sisters and Harper was determined to not let her. "Separate corners. Please, I'm trying to talk. This is a serious problem."

Lauren patted her on the back. "I'm sorry to interrupt. Our father was an English professor. I feel obligated to keep English as our first language, and you can't catch feelings."

"Yes, you can," Rachel said. "They feel like an illness, so trust me they can be caught."

Sienna, the most sensitive and kindest of the group interjected. "It's okay. I mean Zeke isn't a horrible person to fall for. He's fine as he can be, smart, educated, well-mannered."

"Filthy rich," Addison interjected.

"And a playboy since he was five," Lauren added coolly. "Just like his brothers, cousins, and uncles."

Addison shrugged agreement. "They've had a few weddings over the past couple years."

Lauren raised an eyebrow. "You're kidding? A Bennett man got married?"

"The oldest cousin, what's his name..." Harper popped her fingers. "Donovan got married and then, Perry Bennett got married last summer."

"All the uncles are married I think," Sienna added. "And their cousin, Jacob, is getting married. I just booked the venue in St. John for him."

Lauren shrugged. "As old as they all are, they should be."

"Seems Ethan Bennett's not that old. He was young enough for you to get involved with," Harper teased.

Lauren rolled her eyes. "Must you bring up my sordid and troubled past?" She wiped her wet forehead again. "Ethan Bennett was a juvenile mistake."

Harper continued, "Maybe his wife was one for him as well. She's run off, left the three-year-old behind. He's getting a divorce."

Lauren shrugged nonchalance. "How very sad for him."

"He's an old friend, Lauren, you could check on him," Harper continued.

Lauren's chest rose and fell heavily. "I could also pull my fingernails out one by one, but I'll pass. Now, back to you Rachel. What are you going to do about this Zeke Bennett flu?"

Rachel bit her lip. "I don't know. I want to believe I'll eventually get over it, but it's not looking good."

The sisters were all quiet and then Harper spoke up. "Is telling him how you feel out of the question?"

"He doesn't feel the same way. He still wants to go to the games and watch Westerns with me," Rachel replied.

"Well, he wants to spend time with you," Sienna said.

"He thinks of me as a buddy."

"That's because you look like one." Addison, a former fashion buyer, turned fashion reporter, interjected.

Rachel rolled her eyes. "I don't want to lose my best friend. I don't even have any girlfriends. Zeke and I do everything together, hang out, read the same books, go on vacations…we even fish together."

"The makings of a great relationship," Lauren stated.

"No, it's the waste of a perfectly good rich man," Sienna interjected.

"No, the end to the perfect friendship," Rachel insisted.

Harper released Rachel's hand. "Honey, it's already over on your end. Zeke just doesn't know it. You can't keep the way you feel about him a secret forever, so you might as well figure out how to give him the feelings-flu too."

Rachel twisted her lips before she spoke. "That's nearly impossible. Have you seen the women Zeke dates?"

"Yeah, he was with Miss New Jersey a few weeks ago." Zoe who'd been quiet the entire time chimed in.

"And that gorgeous supermodel from the Lancôme ads last month," Addison said.

"You stop that!" Lauren barked. "All the Ingram women are beautiful. You just have to package what you have right. Start with some new clothes and a makeover. We'll teach you how to walk in something other than mules and in no time, Zeke will be head over heels in love."

"We?" Harper asked. "Don't you have a plane to catch in five minutes or something?"

"It was a few days, but I consider it my duty to help my sister get the love of her life, so I will postpone my trip to Dubai and hang around until we have Operation Catch Zeke Bennett wrapped up."

Five pairs of eyeballs rolled in Lauren's direction. She was delaying a trip. Lauren had never delayed a trip, not even after their grandmother's funeral. She attended the services and hopped on her plane later that night.

"Thank you, Lauren," Rachel exclaimed, reaching over and wrapping her arms around her sister. "I knew I could count on you to help me."

Lauren smiled warmly at her secret favorite of the Ingram clan. "Let's put our pretty little heads together. We know what Rachel needs to do, get a makeover, but what do we know about Zeke Bennett that we can use to take him down?"

Chapter 2

Zeke Bennett leapt out of his Lamborghini, tossed the keys to the valet, and rushed into the restaurant. He almost knocked down the maître 'd and two waitresses on the way to his table. He hadn't needed anyone's help and none of the staff attempted to stop him. The Bennetts were well known at Fontana's. The Bennetts, a family who owned a television network worth nearly a billion dollars, were known in a lot of places, but for sure in the small suburb of Atlanta, Forest Hills—as was their attorney, Oliver Tindall.

Zeke spotted Oliver and slid into the chair across from him, as if the man would not notice he'd just arrived—forty minutes late.

Oliver shoved his phone into the inside pocket of his suit jacket. "Do you ever plan to grow up?"

Humored, Zeke smiled. "If it's as boring as it looks, not anytime soon."

"Well then, we don't need this meeting. It's a conversation for grownups."

Zeke picked up the untouched, sweating water goblet in front of him and took a long drink. "Are you going to continue to torture me with all your secretiveness or tell me why you called me here?"

"It's about your great-grandmother's will."

Zeke nearly choked before asking, "What kind of weirdness are you about to tell me?"

Zeke knew his grandmother had set specific rules in her will for each of the Bennett great-grandchildren. There were eight of them equally splitting a billion-dollar trust of which Zeke's part was a 125 million dollars. He was inheriting his portion in exactly thirty days, on his thirtieth birthday.

"Do you remember I told you to get married?"

Zeke felt the oxygen leave his lungs. "I know you're not going to tell me what I think you're going to tell me."

"That was your hint." Oliver nonchalantly cut his steak and put a piece in his mouth. He started chewing like he didn't have a care in the world.

Zeke closed his eyes. When he was done lamenting that he hadn't picked up on the hint, he opened his eyes and swore. "Was I even sober when you told me that?"

"You were in complete control of your faculties, Zachary. I'm good at my job."

Zeke drummed his fingers on the table. Oliver and his father were the only two people who called him by his full name. He couldn't help clenching his teeth. "You needed to remind me."

"I have. I've reminded you at every family gathering you've attended for the past year."

Zeke shifted in his chair. The old man had been a little pushy on the topic of marriage. "I thought you were just making small talk."

"You knew your thirtieth birthday was approaching. You were supposed to be looking for clues."

Zeke sighed. "Well, I'm not going to get married in thirty days, so what now?"

"Now you'll only receive twenty-five percent of your inheritance. Another twenty-five will be donated to charity and the other fifty percent will earn interest until your fortieth birthday."

Zeke slammed his fist on the table just as the waitress approached. "I need all of my money."

"Were you planning to go shopping?" Oliver was amused. The situation wasn't funny.

The waitress cleared her throat. "May I take your order, sir?"

A napkin was in Oliver's empty plate. He'd already eaten. Zeke had no appetite. The waitress was pretty, about his age, nice figure, and she had a beautiful smile. "I'm not hungry, sweetheart, but I do need a wife. Would you marry me?"

Oliver snorted. "That's not the way this works."

The waitress squinted. She raised a hand and wiggled the occupied ring finger. "Too late, charming."

Zeke felt a tinge of embarrassment. "I'm sorry. That was rude. I just got really bad news. I don't think I could eat a bite, but I will take a Scotch on the rocks."

"Liquor and no food." Oliver shook his head. "You'll kill yourself in that expensive car of yours."

"I'll get a ride home if necessary."

"The only thing that's necessary is that you settle down and get married to one of the four hundred women you've dated. Surely, someone in the lot was to your liking."

"No one was to my liking and for the record, I have not dated four hundred women. It's more like three hundred or something." Zeke pointed a finger. "And that's over a sixteen-year period. I've been at this since sixth grade."

"They can't all be duds. You might want to recalibrate your measuring rod," Oliver said.

Zeke chuckled. "Why Uncle Oliver, I think you just made a dirty joke."

Oliver blushed. "Zachary Bennett, you are devilish." Zeke continued to laugh. "I couldn't resist, Uncle Oliver."

Oliver waved the joke away. He was not his biological uncle, but he was married to one of Zeke's older second cousins once removed or something like that in the family line. He'd been handling Bennett business for over forty years, and he was more important to Zeke than any of his uncles right now.

"So, do you mean to tell me you don't even have anyone who's close to becoming a girlfriend?"

Zeke frowned. "For what?"

"For days like this when you need one." Oliver rolled his eyes.

"Even if I had one, a girlfriend and a whole wife are two different things."

"Then find a whole wife in thirty days." Zeke raised a finger in protest, but Oliver continued, "And you have to be married to her and living with her for twelve months to get the last fifty percent. Faking it would be a horrible idea. There's a penalty for that."

Heat rose in Zeke's chest. "But I need my money. I've got a business opportunity. I'll double my money in three to five years."

"You'll either be getting one hundred twenty-five or thirty-one million dollars. That's up to you." Oliver looked at his watch and stood. "Neither is too shabby."

"The deal requires fifty million."

"I can't loan it to you. I'm just an attorney." Oliver almost looked empathetic, but Zeke knew he wasn't. Who could empathize with someone being upset about only getting thirty-one million dollars? He felt stupid for whining about it, but the deal was a once in a lifetime opportunity, or at least it felt that way. Oliver continued, "I have another meeting. Good luck with your business venture."

He walked away just as the waitress returned with his drink.

"Are you sure I can't get you something?" she asked. "Mr. Tindall has a tab."

Zeke raised his glass and finished it in one long gulp, then he put it on her drink tray. "I need a wife. If you don't have one of those in the kitchen, I'm done here."

He stood and walked out of the restaurant.

Chapter 3

"Ouch!" Rachel screamed. "Are you almost done?"

The woman threading her eyebrows stepped back and looked at her. "Isn't this what you came for?"

Rachel shot daggers at her with her eyes. "To be tortured. No. That's not what I came here for."

"Stop being such a ninny," Addison interjected. "You're hairy and it's not cute."

Rachel groaned. She was a little sensitive to pain, but this was ridiculous. "What happened to wax?"

"Wax doesn't last as long," Addison replied.

"But this hurts. I've seen some of the ancestors. I'm going to blackout."

The threader laughed.

Rachel rolled her neck in the woman's direction. "Why are you laughing, you executioner?"

Addison had been tapping on her phone. She slid it into her bag. "You know what else hurts? Heartache. Do you want this man or not?"

"I don't. Not if it takes this." Rachel sat up. She was getting out of this place.

The threader rolled her eyes like she could care less, but Addison grabbed Rachel's arm and pushed her back into the chair. "Rachel, you can't get up. You've only got one eyebrow done."

Rachel took a deep breath and dropped back against the chair again. She grit her teeth and endured it. Just when she thought she was finished, the woman started on her lip. She was never so happy to have a service complete.

"Wait until you get a Brazilian wax," Addison teased as they exited the shop.

Rachel stopped walking. She grabbed her sister by the arm. "I will never, ever, ever, get a Brazilian wax. I don't think it's natural. God gave us hair down there for a reason."

"Girl, it's not that bad."

"And why have you had a Brazilian? It's not like anyone knows you're smooth down there."

"It was a work gift. I tried it. I'll definitely do it again before my wedding night."

"The one you're never going to have because you don't date anyone?"

Addison popped a mint into her mouth. "Yes, that one."

Rachel extended a hand and waited for Addison to drop an unoffered mint in it. "I'm never doing that. My husband is going to have to accept me shaved or Naired down or he can get gone."

Addison laughed. "Come on, girl. We need to find you a few dresses."

Rachel followed her sister through the shopping plaza. She'd lived in Forest Hills her entire life, but had never shopped in any of the stores because it was the Buckhead of Southeast Atlanta, which meant the stores weren't in her budget. In fact, the only reason they even lived in the area was because her parents had purchased the house way before the area blew up and became the home to many of Atlanta's elite, including scores of successful businesspeople, athletes, and actors.

Her family and Zeke's family, the now billionaire Bennetts, were the only original homeowners in their subdivision. Most families sold when the market was hot and gained twenty times the value for their houses. Technically, they, the Ingrams were worth over a million dollars, but the money was tied up in jointly owned family real estate, which none of them was willing to sell.

Sienna and Zoe were the only ones who continued to live in the family home. Rachel was renting a townhouse in another part of Forest Hills. Her landlord was Zeke. She never could have afforded the luxury, 2-bedroom unit if he wasn't giving it to her for a steal. He'd purchased five units from his older brother, Ethan. Real estate had been

Ethan's business, but upon their father's retirement, he now ran Bennett Enterprises. Zeke lived in one, rented one to her, and leased the other three.

"You're my friend. You deserve the best. I like having you across the way from me, and I'm overcharging all the other tenants," Zeke said of the rental price.

Her heart warmed thinking about how he'd blessed her. But then fear struck in her heart. If their relationship changed, like went south because of this *Operation Zeke* situation, not only would she lose her friend, she'd lose her housing because there was no way she was going to keep living across the way from him after he rejected her.

Rachel's phone rang. If old wives' tales were true, Zeke was going to live forever. She answered, admitting, "I was just thinking about you."

"Good. I don't have to worry about dying anytime soon, at least not physically."

He didn't sound like his usual, upbeat self. "What's wrong? Have the plans for your birthday party gotten all wonky?"

"Rae, no one says wonky except you, but no, my party is in the hands of your very capable sister. Has Sienna said anything to suggest otherwise?"

"No, I was assuming since it's your next big thing."

"It's not the party," he said. "I'll tell you about it when I see you. Speaking of which, do you want to have dinner tonight?"

Addison was nodding for her to say yes. It was easy for Addison to eavesdrop. The volume on her phone was loud.

"Sure," Rachel said. Even if they weren't working this Operation Zeke plan, she would have said yes. She was a homebody. Zeke and her sisters dragged her out of the house. "I'm a little busy now. Text me the details."

"Will do." Zeke ended the call.

"What do you think of this?" Addison asked, snapping Rachel out of her thoughts.

Rachel eyed the striking red, back-out dress. It wasn't a bodycon, but it did look like it would hug her curves in all the places a man would admire. She squinted. "You don't think that's too—"

Addison cut her off like she read her mind. "It's not for church, girl."

"But I am a church girl."

Addison raised a finger to shush her. She pulled her into the store. One of the clerks greeted them. Before Rachel could protest, she was in the fitting room stripping out of her clothes and sliding her size ten frame into the dress. It was too sexy. Zeke would laugh. He was used to seeing her in jeans and t-shirts. Tees were her business. She designed and sold them online and locally. When she stepped out of the fitting room, the look on Addison's face conveyed approval. Her sister pulled her into her arms and said, "He's all yours."

Chapter 4

"I'm going to lose this deal." Zeke dropped onto the sofa in his brother's office.

Logan and Rachel's sister, Harper, were standing back from a wall, looking at the paint samples she'd taped against it.

"Do you like the spruce or slate?" Harper asked.

Logan was taking longer than he should to answer. He took a few steps closer and a few back. "It's hard to choose."

"Hey," Zeke interjected, pointing, "you know what? They look the same from over here. They're both gray."

Logan threw up his palm strong and hard which sent the message, "shut up."

Zeke shrugged. "I was just giving you the visitor's perspective."

Logan cocked his head in his direction. "But you aren't a visitor, are you? You're uninvited, so that makes you an intruder."

"I am desperate to talk to my favorite brother about the biggest problem I've ever had in my life."

Logan smirked. "We all know Ethan's your favorite brother."

"Yeah, pending divorce and all, he's a little salty on the subject of marriage."

Harper threw a glance over her shoulder. "Five more minutes, Zeke, and he's all yours."

Zeke mumbled inaudibly, "No, sweetheart. He's all yours and has been since he was ten."

Zeke listened as he and Harper continued to discuss trim colors and flooring. She was decorating the six-thousand-square-foot house Logan had just moved into. Zeke observed them. The chemistry between them was insane. As far as he'd known, Logan had been happy with the house he was in. He wondered if he'd purchased the new one just so he could spend time shoulder-to-shoulder with Harper like he was right now. How many more properties would he buy before he asked her out?

Zeke pulled his phone from his pocket. He opened his contacts and scrolled through the names. One by one, he deleted them. They were beautiful women, but they were useless to him. He needed a wife, not arm candy. It was too late to do a mail-order bride thingy. He'd heard about those. Men still ordered up wives from faraway places overseas, but that took time, and it was risky. He wondered if it was ungodly and pushed the thought from his mind.

"Zeke, did you hear me?"

He looked up. Harper was standing in front of him. It amazed him how little she looked like Rachel. Rachel was her father's twin and Harper her mother's. Her skin was a cinnamon brown which was a few shades lighter than Rachel's deep chestnut complexion.

"Congratulations on your possible marriage," Harper said.

He popped to his feet. "What makes you think that?"

"You made the comment about Ethan..."

"Oh, no. I...it's just a nothing. I'm not even dating anyone serious."

Harper nodded like she didn't believe him. "Anyway, good to see you as always. Tell my sister I said hello. I'm sure you'll talk to her before I will."

Zeke looked at his watch. "We're having dinner in a few hours."

"Let me see you out, Harp," Logan said. The two disappeared behind the door. Zeke dropped back onto the sofa and resumed his sulking.

A few minutes later, Logan reentered the room. "What's got you all whiney?"

"Our great-grandmother."

Logan claimed the chair behind his enormous desk. He chuckled. "What do you have to do?"

"Get married."

Logan laughed. Not a little, but a lot.

"You think that's funny? My entire inheritance is on the line here."

"You should have heeded that warning. I told you Oliver was trying to tell you something."

Zeke shook his head. "Seriously, who would think it would be something as ridiculous as marriage?"

"You know the will is crazy. We all do. If we want the money, we do her bidding. It's not that hard. That kind of money is worth yielding for."

"What did you have to do?"

Logan settled back on his luxurious, padded, swivel chair. "You know I can't tell you, and you can't tell Connor or the twins," Logan said referring to their younger siblings.

"It doesn't seem like you did anything as extreme as getting married."

"Maybe I forfeited." Logan laughed again. "You could take your twenty-five percent and turn it into seventy-five being smart."

"But I have this deal. I hadn't told you about it. Some buddies of mine and I are investing in a soccer team. The Sirens. It'll be North and South Carolina. Carolinas United."

"Really?" Logan looked impressed.

"Yes. But I have to have my part of the money or I'm out. I was counting on it."

"Can't you go in with what you're getting?"

"I wouldn't be vested enough, plus I'm not giving up part of my money because of a crazy penalty."

Logan twisted his lips and shrugged. "It would go to charity."

"I give more than enough to charity." Zeke stood and walked over to his brother's desk. "Seriously man. I need a wife. Where can I get one?"

"I'm guessing your phone contacts aren't working for you."

Zeke shook his head. "Not a single possible in there. I deleted most of them. I can't commit to a stranger. Looks can only go so far."

"And there's the matter of the divorce. She might want all your money and she might not be charitable about it." Logan stood and walked to the other side of the office. He retrieved a file from the conference table and reclaimed his seat at his desk.

"There's a prenup for that."

Logan wagged a finger. "Prenups don't always go the way you want them to go." Logan was a lawyer. He wasn't practicing anymore, but he had for a few years before he purchased a luxury hotel chain.

"I need to get married."

"Good luck with that."

"Any chance you want to invest in a soccer team?"

Logan steepled his fingers like he was considering it, but then shook his head. "I'm not liquid enough for that right now, plus it's risky. I'm already taking a chance with this Vegas hotel."

Zeke knew Logan was tied up. His brother talked about it all the time. "How could great-grandmother do this? We're supposed to get married for love."

"True, but I guess she assumed you would have found your love by your age. Remember, she drafted that will sixty years ago. She's from a different time."

Zeke heard his brother. He knew he was right, but still the entire thing was lunacy to him. Who holds an inheritance from someone because they aren't married by thirty? "I'm going to go. I need a plan."

Logan looked at his calendar. "You've got a month. You'll figure out the answer."

Zeke picked his phone up off the sofa and made his way to the door.

"Hey," Logan called to him, "you're having dinner with Rachel. Tell her I said hello."

Zeke nodded and left the office.

Chapter 5

Rachel was never late. Zeke had just checked the time on this phone when a vision in red glided into the restaurant. He and every other man would have sore necks tomorrow careening to see who she was. Her back was to him while she stood at coat check booth. She turned, and he almost fell over the back of his chair.

Rachel made runway model strides in the stilettos she was wearing. He'd seen her in them before—a rare wedding or business mixer here and there, but the dress—she'd never worn anything that clung to her hips like this one did.

He stood. "Where are you going?" fell out of his mouth before hello did.

"I'm going to this here table right now. Since you're standing, do you mind?" Rachel cocked her head toward her chair. Zeke rushed around and pulled it back.

"Thank you."

He took his seat. "I mean after this?"

She smiled teasingly. "Why? Are you trying to crash the party?"

He smirked. "I'm not dressed for it."

"You're about to be richer than you already are. I'm sure you can go home and find something to wear."

He drummed his fingers on the table. "I could. It would have been nice to have been told before."

Rachel let out a quiet laugh. "Oh wait, I can't invite you. I'm a plus one."

The waitress interrupted them and placed glasses of water on the table. She took Rachel's drink order and offered Zeke another, which he accepted.

"What's this thing you're going to?"

Rachel waved a hand. "Nothing you'd be interested in. So, what's up? Drink two before dinner?"

Technically it would be his third, but she didn't need to know that. Zeke was annoyed. What did she mean he wouldn't be interested? He'd asked. He was interested. He wanted to know where she was going. What was the secret? She always told him where she was going.

The waitress returned with his Scotch and Rachel's lemonade. He wanted to chug this one down too, but he knew Rachel would complain. She hated to see him drink like a college frat.

"I've got a big problem."

"What is it?" she asked, raising her straw to her lips. The red lipstick she was wearing was striking against her dark skin—really pretty around her heart-shaped lips.

"Zeke," Rachel said, shaking him out of his trance, "what's the problem?"

That lipstick had him messed up. Rachel didn't wear red lipstick. He'd never seen her wear a red dress. He chugged his drink. He needed to clear his head and focus. "I found out that if I'm not married in thirty days, I am only getting twenty-five percent of my inheritance."

Rachel's expression was curious. She took another sip of her lemonade. Zeke observed how her full-bodied, swoopy curls bounced as she lowered her head. She was wearing makeup. Rachel didn't do that often, but she'd done a good job. The lipstick was perfect against her deep skin and the gold eye makeup and long lashes made her look like royalty. It wasn't just the dress that was stunning. It was everything about her. He looked around at a few tables near them and noted men were staring. This loveliness was not his imagination.

He continued. "I know this is like a poor little rich boy thing, but you know I wanted to invest in the Sirens."

She nodded.

"This is my dream."

Rachel nodded again, but she looked confused. "I know."

"But I won't have enough money."

Rachel scrunched up her face. It was the first time since she arrived at the table that she looked like herself. She always made that face when she was figuring out something that made no sense to her. "Explain your great-grandmother's will thing again. I don't understand the marriage part."

"My eccentric, dare I say, controlling great-grandmother has requirements for our inheritance. On our twenty-ninth birthday, Oliver gives us a hint about something we have to accomplish in our lives in order to get our money. We have to figure it out and do it, or on the day after our thirtieth birthday, we only get twenty-five percent of our money. Another twenty-five goes to charity and we have to wait until our fortieth birthday to get the rest."

Rachel raised a hand to her red lips and chuckled behind it.

"You think this is funny?"

"I don't, but my goodness, this is such rich people drama. You can't make this up."

Zeke dropped his head. "And the messed up thing is, Oliver gave me the hint. I heard him, but I blocked it out. Like, I'm not getting married just to get some money."

Rachel shrugged. "It's a lot of money."

"Yeah, but it's marriage. I'm wondering if Ethan married Lucy for his money, you know? Look at him now. Getting divorced. Raising his daughter on his own. That's not cool."

Rachel nodded. "It's not." She raised a finger. "If that's what your brother did. He seemed to love her."

Zeke shrugged. "What is love, Rae?"

She got a faraway look in her eyes. He thought about the dress and the exclusive invite she had for tonight. Was there something he didn't know? Was Rachel digging some guy?

The waitress interrupted them with their meals. He'd taken the liberty to order the General Tso's Chicken for Rachel. It was her favorite item on the menu.

She smiled when the waitress placed it in front of her. Her perfect white teeth were framed in the red lipstick. Zeke's heart sped up and adrenaline rushed through his veins.

"Another drink for you, sir?"

He shook his head. He was feeling impaired already because he was staring at Rachel's lips. "Just a cola."

The waitress smiled. "Right away."

Rachel picked up her fork. "I was going to get the Hunan Shrimp."

He smirked. "Liar."

They began to eat. "So, what are you going to do about the Sirens?" The concern on her face was overwhelmingly supportive. He was glad she cared. Neither Oliver, nor Logan had.

"I don't know. I have thirty days. If I can find someone to split the deal with me, I won't be an equal partner, but I'll be in it."

"What about a loan?"

"I can't get a loan for a sports team. I've already tossed it around. It's risky."

"You'll work it out," she said. "You always do."

"You don't have twenty million dollars laying around, do you?"

She chuckled. "I barely have a six-month emergency fund." She stabbed her food and continued to eat.

Zeke thought about all the possibilities with the Sirens. One would be that Rachel was going to be the corporate art director. She would design their logos and uniforms. He was taking his bestie with him all the way. Sienna would plan the team events. Harper could do some interior design at the headquarters. The Ingram sisters were on his list of people to help. They were family, but he'd failed—failed to find someone to marry because he hadn't cared if he had all his money. Now he cared, because he needed fifty million to make his and Rachel's family's dreams come true.

Chapter 6

"So," Lauren plopped down on the sofa. "Was he mesmerized?"

Rachel removed both shoes and massaged her toes. "More like half drunk."

"Drunk?" Addison exclaimed. "At dinner?"

"He wasn't tore up, but he's depressed. I had to drive him home. It's not like him to drink Scotch at dinner. I'm a little concerned."

"I saw him at Logan's office today," Harper interjected. "He was surly. I was hoping you'd cheer him up."

Lauren threw up her hands. "What? You saw him and knew he was in a bad mood. Why didn't you tell us?"

Harper shrugged. "What was I supposed to say?"

"You, silly-no-concept-of-what-men-want-girl, we would have delayed the red dress. She needed him at his best to get his attention."

Harper shrugged. "Sorry. I don't know anything about this operation-chase-a-man-down stuff."

"That's obvious," Lauren said.

Harper waved her words away. "You're the expert, right? I don't see a ring on your finger."

Lauren burned her with a look. "That's because I don't want one."

Harper stood and walked into the kitchen.

Rachel dropped her head on Lauren's shoulder. "I got threaded for nothing."

Lauren wrapped an arm around her and gave her a tight hug. "There's always tomorrow."

"What was he upset about?" Sienna asked.

Rachel stood and slid out of the clingy dress. She walked into the next room, removed the offensive push-up bra, and pulled a t-shirt over her head. When she returned, she answered Sienna's question. "His great-grandmother's will."

Harper walked back into the room with a bottled water. "She was a strange one."

Lauren nodded. "No way should they have not made sure that woman was in her right mind before letting her file that silly will."

"Logan told me she put the will together when she was kind of young." Harper interjected. "Like right after her husband died. At that point, none of her great-grandchildren were born."

Lauren shook her head. "She was obviously strange for a long time. What did she say he had to do?"

Rachel hesitated before replying. "You can't tell anyone because they have this rule that it can't get back to the younger siblings."

"Our lips are sealed." Lauren grabbed Rachel's arm and pulled her down on the sofa.

"He has to be married by his birthday."

"Married," Addison exclaimed. "Are you serious?"

"No wonder," Sienna interjected. The eight other eyes in the room stared at her. "He asked one of my employees to marry him today."

Rachel's heart dropped. She jumped to her feet again. "What? Who is she?"

"You don't know her. She works at Fontana's. She also picks up parttime work at my events. She just signed on to serve at Zeke's birthday party."

Rachel whirled her hand around like she was winding Sienna up to continue.

Sienna shrugged. "He was having dinner with some guy."

"Oliver Tindall, his lawyer," Rachel said, filling in the details for everyone.

"She came to the table and he asked her to marry him. She said no, of course. It was a joke, but she said the old guy wasn't amused."

Harper's brows knit together. "Okay, that makes sense. He said something about not wanting to talk to Ethan today because Ethan was going through a divorce and wouldn't have anything positive to say about marriage."

Rachel stood, paced a minute, and claimed a wing chair. She dropped her head in her hands before raising her head again. "He didn't give me any indication that he was going to try to get married."

"She said he was joking," Sienna offered.

"But he wasn't joking about Ethan," Addison added.

"He really wants this money," Rachel said. She felt like her heart would crack into a hundred pieces.

"He could find someone," Addison said. "I'd marry him if he wasn't such a player."

Rachel pinned her with a look. "He's not a player. Everyone knows where they stand with him."

Instead of responding, Addison continued, "And if my sister wasn't in love with him."

Lauren stood. "Wait, that's it." Everyone stared at her. "You solve his problem. You solve both your problems. Forget chasing him. Catch him, girl. Tell Zeke you'll marry him."

Rachel thought her sister must be kidding. "I don't want to marry a man who's not in love with me. Come on. That's blasphemous. That's not what God intended for marriage."

Lauren shrugged. "Who says? Certainly not the Bible. People were betrothed to people all the time. The entire Bible is full of arranged marriages."

"How would you know that?" Harper asked, teasing Lauren. They all knew Lauren had issues with organized religion, but Rachel knew her sister was a Christian. She also loved the Bible and read it all the time.

"I'm ignoring you." Lauren turned to Rachel. "I say you should do it. If he marries someone else this month, you'll die. This is you shooting your shot. You just have to decide if you're willing to go all the way."

Chapter 7

"I have lost my mind."

Rachel couldn't believe she'd let Lauren talk her into this, but if she didn't do something, Zeke might, and then where would that leave her?

She realized she was risking it all. First and foremost, her friendship with Zeke and then her dignity. What if he laughed in her face? Her stomach was in knots.

"I can't do this," she whispered, turned on her heels and proceeded to go down the path away from his house.

"Rae!" Zeke's voice came from behind her.

She froze and turned around.

"What's up?" Wearing only jeans, he pulled a t-shirt over his head. "Come in." He left the door open and walked back in the house. She could see him padding his way to the kitchen.

As luck would have it, a light drizzle began, so she didn't have time to talk some sense into herself. "Just do it." Rachel put one foot in front of the other until she entered his house.

She found Zeke loading the espresso machine. Upon closer inspection, she noted he appeared to be a bit hungover. That didn't take away from his good looks. Stubble covered his square jaw. His impossibly dark brown eyes were highlighted by thick, brooding brows and enviously long eyelashes. The Bennetts had an unfair amount of quality DNA.

"How are you feeling?" She eased onto one of the stools at the island. Zeke's townhouse was twice the size of hers, but it was five times emptier. He'd occupied the place for three years and had yet to really do anything with most of the decor. Black and white tile flooring was installed during construction, so was a red and silver back splash. He had a techno theme through the kitchen and dining room, but they were the only two rooms he'd finished.

"I feel like crap." He moved away from the coffee machine and came to join her at the island, standing opposite her. "Coffee will fix it though."

Rachel's nostrils flared as she inhaled his familiar musky, cedarwood scent. She cleared her throat, nervously. "So, what are your plans?"

"Today? I'm going to sulk," he said. "Tomorrow, I'll figure out something I guess."

"You can place calls, try to find someone to go in with you?"

"I've done that."

"Really?"

"Yes, I only had a few people in mind. I called them this morning."

"Before coffee?"

He smiled. "Before I got out of bed."

"And so?"

"I got no and heck no, but I left a message for my cousin, Stone. He made some money recently on a project in Alaska. I'm hoping he's interested."

The espresso machine began to whir. Once the first cup was done, he slid it in front of her. She declined. "I've had some already, but I'll take water."

Zeke opened the near empty refrigerator and removed a bottle of overpriced water. "How was your party last night?" He twisted the top off and slid the bottle in front of her.

She raised the bottle to her lips and took a sip before putting it down. "I didn't go."

Zeke cocked an eyebrow. "Why not? You were all fancy."

"I know, but once I dropped you home, all I could think was my bed was across the cul-de-sac, so I just skipped it."

Zeke was reflective for a moment before he said, "Weren't you his plus one."

"It's okay." She raised the water bottle and took a longer sip. "Who said it was a he?"

"The dress did." He brought the mug to his lips, seemed to realize the coffee was too hot, and placed it on the island.

Rachel smiled inside. He had noticed, and he remembered.

"I don't think I've ever seen you in red like that."

"You have too, Zeke. I wore red to prom."

"Prom was over a decade ago," he drawled. "I also don't remember your prom dress being clingy like the dress from last night. It was a ball gown."

Rachel smiled at the memory that slipped into her mind. "A horrible one."

Zeke shook his head. "I don't remember it like that. You were pretty that night."

She blushed. "Before my date spilled punch on me."

Zeke raised the coffee cup to his lips again. This time he blew on the contents a few times before taking a sip. "What a loser. I wonder where that guy is."

"NASA. He's an astronaut."

"Apropos. He was out in space." He took another sip of coffee. "So, what are you doing today? You want to hang out?"

She hesitated. The answer to that question had been yes for more than half her life, but suddenly, now that she was aware of him, she wasn't sure. "I have some work on a new design."

"Oh, come on, it's Saturday."

"I don't have an inheritance like you do, sir."

"I'll buy a thousand shirts," he offered.

"What'll you do with them?"

"Donate them to the Boys Club or something. I'm sure they'll love me for it, and it's a tax write-off."

"You already do that, Zeke. Every year."

He squinted like he didn't remember. "Do I?"

"You've done it for the past five years."

"We'll find another charity," he offered. Rachel looked into his deep brown eyes. Even though they were tired, they still held the warm charm she loved in them.

She shook her head. "Don't you need to be on a budget for your new endeavor?"

Zeke laughed. "You got jokes? No, either I have it all or it's not happening. Buying ten thousand dollars in shirts from you isn't going to make or break me."

"I appreciate the business. Sometimes I wonder if I'd even be in business if you weren't helping me out."

He smiled and her heart lifted to her throat. "What are rich friends for?"

Rachel knew this was her opening. She heard Lauren's voice in her head. *Do it now!* "Speaking of helping out a friend..."

Zeke's phone rang. He raised a finger and answered it. "Hey, babe, no. I was drunk. Yeah, Oh, you what? I'm sober now. Yeah. Look I'm in the middle..."

He snatched back his head. "She hung up."

Rachel took another sip of water. "Who was that?"

"You remember that Serene person I dated last year?"

"For eighty entire days."

Zeke nodded. "Yeah, that was a long time, wasn't it?"

"The longest."

"Apparently, I asked her to marry me last night."

Rachel held her breath until he continued.

"I didn't mean it. She'd make a horrible wife. No way would she settle for the prenup terms." He chuckled.

"You can't marry a stranger."

"Or a strange person."

They both laughed. Their eyes caught and held for a moment. Rachel broke the stare by reaching for her water bottle again. She tipped it back and forth in front of her.

"You're asking an old booty call to marry you."

"That sounds so dirty coming out of your mouth." He winced. "I didn't mean it."

"You're not really going to try to find a wife, are you?"

Zeke drank more coffee. "Honestly, Rae, I don't know what I'm going to do. I don't want to lose this deal."

"But marriage is a serious thing."

He groaned like he hated hearing the truth. "It doesn't have to be a real marriage. I just have to live with her."

"And you think that'll be easy for someone? You can't live with a stranger, and you've notably dated a bunch of gold-diggers."

He sighed, but he didn't sound the least bit regretful. "I have done poorly in that department."

"So, I have an idea..." Rachel began. She spread her palms on the island.

The doorbell rang.

"Hold that," he said raising a finger to her and racing to the door. He reentered the room with his cousin, Stone, at his side.

Stone approached Rachel and gave her a hug. "You're looking beautiful today."

Stone always flirted with her. He flirted with everybody. "Do you still have this lovely woman in the friend zone?"

Zeke shot him a nasty look. "Do you want coffee?"

Amused, Stone smiled. "I'll have what the lady is having."

Rachel stood. "I should go."

"No, you don't have to," Zeke said. "You already know what I have to talk to him about." He reached into the frig and removed another water.

"Just call me later."

"I wanna hang out," Zeke insisted.

"Call me." Rachel backed out of the room. "Good to see you, Stone."

Stone's eyes swept her figure appreciatively. "Always a pleasure."

Rachel left the room. She could hear them arguing behind her. As always, Zeke was chastising him for flirting.

She left his house and closed the door behind her. She'd failed. She was supposed to march in and get right to the point. Lauren told her that was the only way she'd have the nerve to go through with it, but now maybe Stone would solve the problem. Zeke was only thinking about marriage because of the money. If Stone went in with him, his mind would be on soccer for at least a year. She'd have more time to figure out how to get out of the friend zone. That was a good thing.

A few hours later, Rachel stretched. She'd been bending over her drafting table for longer than was ergonomically recommended. She picked up her phone. Two missed calls from Lauren and one from Addison. If she didn't call her sisters back, they'd be at her doorstep soon. She'd let the calls go to voicemail, because she didn't want to be lectured about why she hadn't followed their instructions with respect to Zeke.

She went into the kitchen for a soft drink and chips, but came out with more water and a bowl of grapes. Chips and soda were her go-to snacks when depression was settling in. She was determined she was not going to let her feelings for Zeke spiral into something else. She would simply have to get over him. People recovered from broken hearts every day. Her phone rang again. This time she answered.

"Okay, you do know I was headed over there," Lauren said.

"I didn't do it."

"What?"

Rachel could hear the disappointment in her sister's voice. "I didn't have time. He got a phone call and then Stone showed up."

"I told you to do it as soon as he opened the door."

"How do I just blurt it out as soon as he opens the door?"

"The way I told you to. Just say, 'Zeke, I have a solution to your problem. You can marry me'."

"Lauren, do you know how ridiculous that sounds?"

"It's no dumber than him asking the waitress at Fontana's to marry him, and no dumber than his great-grandmother stipulating he had to be married by age thirty. The ridiculous started with her."

The doorbell rang.

"I bet that's him!" Lauren shrieked.

Rachel smirked. "That's Fed Ex. I'm expecting a package."

She made her way to the front door and pulled it open. Zeke was standing there.

"Oh, it's you."

"Yeah," he said, stepping in.

"How did things go with Stone?"

"He's a no." He scratched his head. Rachel could tell he didn't want to talk about it, and he confirmed it when he asked, "You want to grab some lunch? I'm starved."

*Rachel, Rachel...*Lauren's voice amplified from the phone.

She took it off speaker and raised it to her ear. "Yes."

"Do it right now." Rachel could tell Lauren was speaking through grit teeth.

"Okay," she whispered, observing Zeke as he stood there waiting for her answer about lunch.

"You were going to ask me something earlier?" he said, scratching his chin.

Rachel felt pressure all around her. Lauren on the phone and now him in person. She had to get rid of it. She pressed end on the phone. Getting rid of

Lauren helped, but Lauren's plan still made sense. Catchin' Zeke was better than Chasin' Zeke.

He frowned. "Rae, what's up?"

Rachel pulled courage from her belly. "Yeah. I know this is going to seem weird, but I was thinking, I'm not busy for the next year or so. I could marry you."

Zeke's frown deepened, and she wished she'd kept the words in her mouth.

Chapter 8

The wind left his lungs. For some reason, the image of Rachel in that red dress came back to him. He studied her creamy, cocoa-colored skin and the mass of curls that framed her face, but what held his breath was her eyes. It was as if he was seeing them for the first time. Rachel had gorgeous eyes. He forced himself to look away for a moment. It was then that he remembered what she'd said, but he feigned deafness. "What did you say?"

Rachel took a deep breath before pursing her lips. "You heard me. If you hadn't, you wouldn't be looking at me like that." She pushed the door closed and walked into the family room. He followed.

"But you didn't mean it."

Rachel dropped on the sofa. She picked up a mug he could tell was long forgotten. It looked cold. "Yes, I do."

Zeke joined her on the sofa. "Rae, I can't marry you."

"But you can marry the waitress at Fontana's?"

He grinned.

She laughed. "Yeah, I heard about that. Forest Hills is small." She put her mug down and cocked her head to the side. "Come on. This is a good solution to your problem. You don't have to marry some random stranger."

Zeke swallowed. He couldn't believe they were having such a silly conversation. This was dumb—wasn't it? "I could just let the deal go. I mean, there are other cities and other potential teams."

Rachel shook her head. "You love the southeast. You're already emotionally invested in this. You've been talking about it for months."

She was right about that. It was his last chance to own a team close to home. "But it would be weird though."

She nodded. "I agree, but we hang out all the time anyway. It's not a real marriage."

Zeke peered at her curiously. "What if you meet someone?"

"I haven't so far, so I doubt I will." She raised a finger. "And neither will you."

His eyes widened, waiting for her next words.

"I have terms."

Now it was getting interesting. "Go on."

"One, you give me a million dollars for my trouble. You know I want to expand my business."

"I told you I'd give that to you anyway."

"I don't want you giving me money," Rachel paused. "You've already been generous enough."

He nodded. "Okay. Done."

"And," she bit her lip before continuing, "no other women. Not a date. Not a phone call. Not a text. Not anything. You have to be faithful to your fake marriage. I won't be made a fool of."

"So, are we talking no dating for a year?"

She shrugged.

"Rae, that's a long time."

She rolled her neck a little. "How bad do you want the Sirens?"

Zeke blew out an exasperated breath. "I don't know."

Now it was Rachel whose eyes widened. "Let me know." She stood and took her mug into the kitchen. She returned with her handbag. "Where are we going for lunch?"

Chapter 9

"I've never been so nervous in my life." Rachel raised her head from the table. She'd banged her forehead on it repeatedly.

"But you played it cool right?" Addison asked.

"I channeled my inner KeKe Palmer."

Lauren looked unconvinced. "Good thing you had those acting lessons in high school."

Addison groaned. "Even with lessons, she wasn't that good."

Rachel cocked her head in her sister's direction. "I did a good enough job of convincing Zeke I was in it for the money and to help."

"But he's thinking about it." Addison looked doubtful.

"That's to be expected," Lauren said. "No sex for a year is a big commitment for a Bennett man-whore."

Addison rolled her eyes. "Could you be a little less bitter about Ethan?"

Lauren reached for the bowl of popcorn on the table and took a fist full. "I'm not bitter about Ethan. We're not even talking about Ethan."

"Can we focus on me right now?" Rachel pleaded. "I've put myself out there. What if he says no?"

"He won't," Lauren insisted.

"He might."

"Well, if he does, it'll be about the no dating clause," Addison said. "At least that's a good reason for him."

Lauren tossed popcorn in her mouth. "He has no other way of getting the money. He needs his inheritance. Trust me, you're as good as married to him."

Rachel was overwhelmed. This time yesterday, she was sliding into the red dress. She'd been hoping she wasn't going to make a fool of herself. Now she was waiting to see if she was going to be his wife. "I hope this doesn't affect our friendship. He was acting odd at lunch. I feel like I'm already losing him."

"He's overwhelmed." Lauren stood. She paced. "It's normal. He's a rich man. He's not used to making concessions. He's used to getting what he wants."

"And there's nothing he can negotiate here," Addison added. "He can't control the terms because he doesn't care about the million, and he knows you're being reasonable about the faithfulness thing. No woman wants to be humiliated publicly. Even a fake wife has her pride."

"Zeke is spoiled." Lauren shrugged. "His great-grandmother has thrown him an uppercut and you poured hydrogen peroxide on the split skin the punch left."

Rachel considered everything they were saying. She did know Zeke to be a bit spoiled. Not in a bad way, but he'd always been rich. He'd always gotten things he wanted. He wasn't really used to having to figure out a way to do anything. She thought about that for a moment.

"What's wrong?" Lauren asked. "You're frowning."

"I think you guys are right and if you are, do I want a man like that? Is this really God's best for me?"

Lauren sat. "Only you can answer that question. You said you love him. What do you love?"

Rachel considered the question and smiled when she felt the answers rise in her spirit. "We like the same things—movies and books. He's funny. He's generous. Criminally so. He gives money to every charity and cause he hears about. He has a good heart. He gets me. He thinks I'm funny. He likes being around me. He's like seen me at my worse and ugliest and he's never cared. He gives a good back and foot rub. He knows me. Like everything." She bit her lip. "He's fun to be around. And I know he's carnal, but he is saved."

Lauren and Addison's eyes locked on Rachel's last statement before Lauren shrugged. "That's a lot of positives."

"And he's fine," Addison said. "Sounds like he's worth loving."

Rachel looked to Lauren. She nodded. "Sounds like it's too late to try to figure it out. Like you said. You already love him."

Rachel stood. "God wouldn't put more on me than I can bear."

Addison shook her head. "What do you mean?"

"I mean what I just said."

"Rachel, that scripture is not about struggle love. It's about temptation," Addison said. "Do we need to crack open the Bible?"

Rachel sighed. "We don't. I know what the scripture means." She swept her hand behind her ear. Her heartbeat sped up a little. A nervous sensation filled her belly, but she pushed it down. Clearing her throat and her head of a lingering thought about what Addison said, she shrugged. "So, now I just wait."

Lauren raised a hand to inspect her fingernails. "It won't be long. He only has thirty days."

"He's down to twenty-nine," Rachel said.

"And counting." Lauren sat back. She picked up her cola bottle and drained it. "Just get prepared. You're about to have to live with Mr. Perfect."

"It'll be weird."

"You and Zeke have had this quazi-friendship for forever. I guarantee you he feels the same way about you," Addison offered.

"He treats me like a sister."

"No, he doesn't. He and that sister of his fight like cats and dogs," Addison said, referring to Avery Bennett.

"That's because she's the female version of him," Rachel said.

The door opened and Sienna entered. She walked to the sofa and dropped heavily into it. "I was counting on your friend to make me a household name."

Rachel, Lauren, and Addison gave her their full attention.

"Zeke," Sienna began, "He told me to hold off on anymore more planning for his birthday party."

Rachel frowned. "I just had lunch with him. He didn't mention it."

"He called me an hour ago."

"Well, what did he say about why?"

"He didn't. I asked, but he rushed me off the phone."

Rachel stood. "He's been looking forward to this for months. He'd only cancel it if he was planning to be out of town."

"Why would he do that?" Lauren asked like she was ever in town.

"He goes away when he's depressed. He's done it a few times before. Disappeared somewhere for a month and not come back until he feels better. If he's cancelling the party, it's because he doesn't want to be here when the Sirens deal falls through."

Lauren shook her head. "You're jumping to conclusions."

"I'm not. Remember I said he knows me. I know him too. He's not going to accept my deal. He's going to go away." Her heart sunk into her shoes. The thought of not seeing him engulfed her. She couldn't believe she'd let herself become this vulnerable to a man who wasn't thinking about her.

And then Lauren's words broke through her thoughts. "I have an idea."

Chapter 10

"It sounds like a good idea to me."

Zeke raised his eyes from his phone to focus on Logan's foolishness. "How is marrying Rachel a good idea?"

"You can trust her. You can probably live with her, and she's available."

"I like my relationship with Rachel just the way it is. This marriage thing could ruin it."

Logan sighed. "Look man, you have to decide what you're going to do. You're either giving up on the Sirens or you're finding a solution. I personally think you could do worse than calling a beautiful, intelligent woman your wife for a year."

"That includes no dating for a year."

"Be honest. It's not the dating part you're concerned about." Logan spoke the truth. It wasn't the actual dinners he'd be missing. "You need to get your flesh under control anyway."

"My flesh under control? You couldn't have said that in a less churchy way?"

"That's the Bible, brother. You might want to open it more often."

Zeke groaned. "Speak for yourself. A year will kill me."

"You can make the sacrifice. Think about deployed soldiers. The married ones don't see their wives for long stretches. Celibacy isn't easy, but it's a thing. I mean, it's been a minute for me."

"That's because you're saving yourself..." Zeke chuckled, "... for Harper."

Logan's Adam's apple bobbed. "You could do worse than an Ingram sister."

"Except she's literally my best friend. I always envisioned Rachel and I having the relationship we have right now forever. Like into our eighties."

"Even after you got a wife?" Logan looked amused by his foolishness. "Man, your wife should be your best friend."

"I know, but you know what I mean."

"No, I don't know what you mean. Look, Zeke it's time to grow up and accept the fact that you've had Rachel in a glass case for years. You call her your friend, but there's no way you're not attracted to her. She's beautiful and smart and funny as heck. What's not to want?"

Zeke sucked in a breath. His memory went back to her stroll from the coat check to his table yesterday. The red dress. The lipstick. That feeling in his stomach when she said she was some dude's plus one. "I haven't. I mean not until yesterday."

Logan's focus shifted from his phone. "What happened yesterday?"

Zeke sighed. "She was dressed different. I'm used to seeing her in t-shirts and jeans."

"She looks pretty good in jeans."

"I know that, but still a nice fitting pair of jeans doesn't compete with the right red dress."

Logan showed interest. "Red?"

"Nearly painted on. She got body and booty and…" he stopped his imagination from going wild. This was Rachel he was thinking about. "…suffice to say, she's curvy. I never noticed before."

"She's got a great body, man. You've seen her in a swimsuit. I've seen her in a swimsuit."

"I was apparently seriously in the friend zone."

"And you just snapped out of it yesterday?" Logan said, repeating Zeke's words like he needed to hear them again.

"I think so. That's why I feel so messed up right now. If we get married, I don't want to have these feelings. I want to walk out of that marriage with our relationship intact the way it was before."

"Before the red dress." Logan interrupted his thoughts and words.

"I was a little buzzed yesterday."

"Not buzzed enough to forget."

Zeke bit his lip. "I want the Sirens deal, but it's not worth all that I might lose. Rachel means the world to me."

Logan laughed.

"What are you laughing at?"

"Rachel means the world to you. Bro, you're already in love. You just don't know it."

Zeke's phone buzzed in a text message from Sienna. She wanted to know when he was going to decide about the party. He'd pretty much already decided he wasn't in the mood to celebrate. Not if he wasn't going to make the Siren's deal. He knew she'd put a lot of work into it, but if he was going to lose the business opportunity of a lifetime, he was not going to party.

The door opened. Stone walked in. "You're not going to believe who Atlanta just signed for goalie."

Zeke angled his head toward him. "Please tell me you care because you're interested in the Sirens."

Stone took a seat. "Nah, but I care about what you care about, so I ear hustle when I can."

Zeke shook his head. "Don't tell me if I'm going to be angry. I'd rather wait for the press conference."

Stone told him anyway. "That kid from University of Tennessee. Wright."

Zeke groaned inwardly. He and his group were hoping to sign Wright after they announced the formation of the league. "How do you know this?"

"I had lunch with Montgomery Robb."

Hairs raised on the back of Zeke's neck. "So he's home."

"For a while," Stone stretched his arms across the back of the sofa.

"Why are you lunching with him?"

"I heard through a mutual friend that he's been trying to find out what he can about Carolina United. He's looking to invest, but he can't get an in."

Zeke popped to his feet.

"That's why I had the lunch," Stone said. "I knew you'd want to know what he was up to."

Zeke felt heat rise from his belly. If he had an enemy, it was Montgomery Robb. Smug jerk. He'd beat Zeke to the punch on a few other investments. He didn't like the guy and it wasn't just because of business.

Zeke caught sight of Logan and Stone exchanging cautious glances. They knew he was a hot head, but he was trying not to be impulsive. He didn't want to make the wrong move here, but he'd weep for a year if Robb was sitting in the owner's box in his chair.

"Your problem has a solution."

Zeke looked in Logan's direction.

"Marry Rachel. Get your money."

Chapter 11

Rachel stood in the full-length mirror. She twisted her body back and forth in the black dress. She couldn't believe she'd wiggled into a bodycon.

"You look great," Lauren said. "The goal is to get him in his feelings."

"I know. I know." Rachel was filled with anxiety and annoyance. "I've got the plan down."

"Well, let's go before we're late."

Rachel and Lauren picked up their bags and got into Rachel's car. They drove to Shiloh's Grille. Shiloh's had a popular Thursday Happy Hour. Zeke was always there. Sometimes Rachel joined him.

They entered the crowded restaurant. Lauren had Rachel wait by the door while she peeked around the corner to scout out Zeke. His car was in the parking lot, so they knew he was there. Lauren wanted to make sure he wasn't occupied with another woman. She rejoined Rachel. She was breathless with excitement.

"Montgomery Robb is at the bar."

Rachel frowned. "So."

"So, go talk to him," Lauren said. "Zeke is sitting directly in his line of sight. In fact, he was looking at him a moment ago."

"What am I going to talk to Montgomery about?"

"Anything. You look gorgeous, and he's a hound. He'll say something to you. Trust me. It'll help the plan."

Rachel sighed. "How?"

"Men want a woman who they think someone else wants. That's why you've been in the friend zone with Zeke all these years. You've hardly dated. He knows he can cozy up to you anytime."

Rachel's sigh deepened. "I think you all are overestimating my value here, and I'm starting to think I'm making a huge mistake. I'm the one who's in love, not him."

Lauren shook her head. "If only you could see what I see. What his family must see. He feels the same way about you, but like I said, you've been too available to him for him to have to choose you. Trust me. This is the right bait. We are catching this fish tonight. Now go before Montgomery leaves or something."

Rachel conjured up the confidence to follow her sister's instructions. Just as she approached Montgomery, a space next to him opened. She slid into it.

"Montgomery?" Rachel added a hint of surprise and appreciation to her voice.

Montgomery looked her up and down like she was a tall glass of lemonade on a hot day. "Rachel Ingram. My favorite Ingram sister." He leaned in and gave her a kiss on the cheek. "It's been a while."

"You've been…" She frowned like she was trying to remember, "…Where have you been?"

Montgomery chuckled. "London."

Rachel snapped her fingers like he'd jogged her memory. "Making more millions I'm sure."

"Well, a few. Every dollar counts." He laughed and his arrogance reminded Rachel why she'd never cared for him. "So, are you still designing socks?"

"Shirts," Rachel sighed. *This was painful.* "T-shirts to be exact."

"That's a nice, little niche for you. I guess it'll keep you busy until you snag yourself a rich husband."

Rachel's smile was pained. "Montgomery, I plan to marry for love."

"Love and money. Same thing." He winked. "Let me get you a drink."

Her phone beeped in a text message. Montgomery was busy signaling the bartender when she peeked and saw it was Lauren telling her to join Zeke.

"Miss, what can I get you?" the bartender asked.

"What are you having, Rachel?"

Rachel looked over her shoulder and saw Zeke and Lauren at the table together. "I'm joining Zeke and my sister. I just wanted to say hello."

"I'll treat all of you. What does Lauren drink?"

Although she knew her sister would want wine, Rachel told him they'd have two glasses of ginger ale. Her stomach was in knots. She needed to settle it.

"Let me escort you to your table." Montgomery placed his hand in the small of Rachel's back, and they moved away from the bar toward Zeke and Lauren.

Zeke stood and held out the chair for Rachel. He was heated. She could practically see steam coming off the top of his head.

Rachel smiled. Zeke didn't smile back.

Words from Montgomery's velvety tongue were directed at her sister. "Lauren. It's a pleasure to see you." He took her hand, pulled it to his lips and kissed it. "It's been a long time."

"A few years," Lauren said.

"You look fantastic as always."

Lauren accepted the compliment with a wide smile. "And I see Europe was good to you. Have you lost some weight?"

Montgomery pushed out his chest. "London is a walkable city. I ate well, but I walked everywhere. Too bad we don't have it that way here in the states. I've gained weight already, and I've only been back in Forest Hills for a few weeks."

"You should make time for the gym," Zeke interjected.

Montgomery looked in his direction for a moment but didn't respond. Zeke made time for the gym every day and it paid off with muscular thighs, hulking biceps and the washboard stomach every man wanted.

Lauren cleared her throat. "The walking is great. It's the same in pretty much every country I visit."

"Which is why you keep that beautiful figure." He smiled again, but it was more like a leer. Then he turned to Zeke. "Bennett, how are you?"

Zeke tossed a few peanuts into his mouth and replied, "Not that glad to see you."

Montgomery laughed. "Are you still salty about that poker game?"

Zeke shook his head. He raised his glass. "You know better than that, Robb."

Montgomery laughed uncomfortably. The waitress arrived at the table. She placed glasses in front of Rachel and Lauren and a beer in front of Zeke. "Courtesy of Mr. Robb." She walked away.

Lauren thanked him. They made some more small chat and Montgomery said, "You all enjoy your dinner. Zeke, maybe we can have a rematch."

Before Zeke could reply, Montgomery walked away.

Lauren raised her glass. "What's the story with you two?"

Zeke shook his head and said, "Nothing worth talking about." He leaned back and inspected Rachel. "I'm more interested in finding out where your sister is going in this dress."

"South Africa. Namibia to be specific." Bubbling, Lauren sprung forward in her seat. "Not tonight, but soon."

Lauren and Rachel raised their glasses and clinked them together.

***

Zeke frowned. "What do you mean Namibia?"

"Lauren told me about a great art program in the capital city, Windhoek. Textile design."

Zeke swallowed the selfish protest that almost escaped his lips. "Really, I didn't know you wanted to study some more. You hadn't mentioned it."

Rachel shrugged. "It's always been in the back of my mind. We all want to be the best at what we do, don't we?"

Zeke couldn't argue with that, but there were great art schools in Georgia. One right here in Atlanta.

Lauren put down her glass and picked up her menu. "I suggested it this morning at breakfast."

"I've been looking at classes here in Atlanta, but I think I want a change of scenery." Rachel picked up the menu and opened it like she was talking about switching supermarkets.

Zeke groaned inwardly. He was wondering why she had to go so far to study what was available locally. And wasn't Lauren already supposed to be gone? She never hung around this long. Now her wandering spirit had become contagious. He wanted to be supportive, but he was selfish, so he asked, "What about Savannah? They have a good program."

Lauren directed a dismissive question to Rachel. "How's the fish?"

"You'd love the salmon, but the grouper is good too."

"I'm not sure I'm in the mood for bony fish," Lauren replied.

Zeke wanted to scream. Were they really just going back and forth about fish when Rachel was thinking about going to Namibia? This was an entire country—on the other side of the world.

He picked up the beer Montgomery ordered and finished half of it in one gulp. He cleared his throat. "How long is this class?"

Rachel closed her menu. "The first one is six months."

Lauren was quick to add, "The second one is three months, so it's nine months total."

Zeke's stomach clenched. "Nine months?"

The waitress came to the table to take their order. He wasn't sure he could eat. Nine months without Rachel. He'd never endured a separation that long. "What about your business?"

Lauren and Rachel ignored him again. They placed their orders like he wasn't sitting there, emotionally begging Rachel not to leave him.

"Sir," the waitress said turning her attention back to him.

"Give me a burger. Well done."

The waitress pointed at the menu. "We have a large selection—"

"Just pick one!" he barked.

"Zeke." Rachel's brows came together. She turned toward the waitress. "I apologize for my friend. We'll get him together before you come back. He'll have the mushroom swiss. Well done, extra cheese."

She thanked Rachel, rolled her eyes at Zeke, and walked away.

Rachel pinned him with a look. "What's wrong with you?"

You're going to Namibia, he thought, but said, "I'm stressed."

"Welcome to the real world." Lauren stood. "I'm running to the restroom."

Zeke turned to Rachel. "Namibia for nine months? You don't even speak the language."

"I already do pretty well with it." She chuckled. "There is some German, but the official language is English."

Zeke didn't find a thing funny. He was blown away by how quickly she'd settled on this idea. This wasn't like her. "What about your work?"

Rachel picked up her phone and tapped the screen a few times like he wasn't even talking to her. When she was finished, she put it down. "I work from my computer. I can do that from anywhere."

"But you were planning to invest in some equipment and expand."

She shrugged. "Eventually. I don't have the money for that right now and this trip to Namibia could be a once in a lifetime opportunity."

"For who?" he asked. "Lauren's always going somewhere. If I'd known you wanted to go to Namibia, I would have already taken you."

She rolled her eyes. "Zeke, how many times do I have to tell you I'm not interested in you funding my life?"

"I understand that, but come on. We can go for Christmas if you want. You never mentioned it was on your bucket list."

"I've never thought about Namibia until Lauren mentioned that she would be there for a stretch. I'll have a chance to learn some fabric techniques, and I miss my sister."

But I'll miss you.

"I can't think of anything holding me here."

Like me. He swallowed. "What about the work for the Sirens?"

"That's why I said it's tentative. If you make the Sirens deal, I'll stay, but if you don't." She shrugged like she'd already made up her mind. "And you'll be looking for something interesting to do, so maybe you'll be traveling as well."

Zeke hated this. Never in a million years had he imagined that he would have to spend a single day not having access to Rachel. He'd barely gotten over watching her have a conversation with Montgomery and then now they spring this on him. How could she possibly think about going to Namibia for months? She'd never thought about leaving the country before. Not for more than a vacation. Otherwise, why hadn't she already done it?

Lauren returned to the table.

Rachel smiled. "You can get on the family jet and pop over to visit me anytime."

He bit his lip. He was being a jerk. She was excited and he needed to not make this about himself, but he was selfish, so he failed with the next thing that came out of his mouth. "I suppose so, but it's so far. I'm used to having you here all the time. It'll be a big change."

"You'll adjust, Zeke," Lauren said, raising her glass again. "Stop being a baby."

"Easy for you to say. You've been running around for ten years. Some of us stay put. Your sister is a fixture in my daily life."

Rachel laughed. "You make it sound like we're twins. We didn't share the same uterus."

"No, but we do share our lives or at least I thought we did."

Rachel took his hand. She looked into his eyes—deeply. He felt his heart rate speed up. "My temporarily moving to Namibia is not going to change that." She released his hand. "You don't need to spend time worrying about what I'm going to do for the next six months. You need to be figuring out how to get this money for the Sirens deal. That should be your only focus."

Zeke picked up his drink and listened as the sisters fell into a conversation about the party they were attending after this dinner. His eyes slid in Rachel's direction. Her hourglass figure was made for the tight dress she was wearing. The red dress came back to his memory. She'd looked just as good in that one. He sighed. *Focus.* Rachel was right. He needed to find a business partner, or he was going to lose more than a business deal. Offering her work with the Sirens was a way to keep Rachel in town. Suddenly, that was more important than soccer.

Chapter 12

Zeke hopped into his car and pulled the door closed. The meeting with his old college buddy, a multi-millionaire tech guru, resulted in a solid no. He was tapped out. There was no one else to ask.

He barked an order for the Bluetooth to call Rachel. He'd reached out to her a couple of times over the weekend, and she hadn't called him back. This time, she answered the phone on the second ring.

"Hey, I'm sorry I know you been calling. What's up?"

What's up?

Since when did he need a reason to call her? He was already feeling like trash. Now Rachel was sounding funny. "What have you been doing?"

"I signed up for an online German course. It's a five-day intensive. There's lots of homework. I'm so impressed with how much German I remember from college."

So, she was still on this Namibia thing. "German," he groaned, "for Namibia."

"I think it's a cool opportunity. Don't you?"

"I think you've given up on me in my ability to secure money for the Sirens deal."

"I believe in you. The question is do you believe in yourself?"

He didn't get a chance to respond before she continued. "Sienna told me you've cancelled the party. That means you're thinking about skulking away."

He was stumped by how well she knew him, but he shouldn't have been because he thought he knew her just as well.

"So, tell me what's been going on. Why have you been calling me so frantically?"

He heard German in the background, and it aggravated his entire soul. "Rae, can you turn that off, whatever it is?"

"Hold on," she said. He heard her put the phone down, some clicks on the keyboard, and then she picked the phone up again. "Okay, sorry about that. What's been so urgent?"

"I haven't been calling you urgently or frantically." Zeke cleared his throat. "I always call you. You're the only person who will tolerate me daily."

"Okay, so what would you have said to me if I answered the phone yesterday?"

"I would've told you I had a meeting today."

"For the Sirens obviously…" she said in a tone that said she was waiting for him to share.

"Yes, for the Sirens."

"Do I have to drag it out of you?" Rachel chuckled. "How did it go?"

"He's not liquid enough. No one is liquid enough right now."

"You sound down. Scratch his name off the list and move on to the next person," Rachel said.

"Rae, there is no next person. I'm tapped out. And at this point, I have less than three weeks."

"Keep looking. There has to be somebody you missed."

"People with this kind of money sitting around are few. I've run through my list. There's not many people left that I can trust."

Rachel was silent for a moment and then she said, "Montgomery seems to be interested."

"The keyword I said was trust." He started the car and pulled out of the driveway and onto the main road. "And I couldn't go in with him. He's too arrogant. His style wouldn't mesh with the rest of us. We're all nice guys."

"You'll find someone, or you'll find a wife. That might be easier." She paused and said, "Look I've got to go. I am hanging out with Lauren today. We're shopping for Namibia."

Zeke spoke through grit teeth. "Shopping. You sound like you're giving up on me."

"Stop whining. I'm not giving up on you. Lauren is doing the shopping. I'm tagging along. If I happen to see something that'll be good, I'll know where to find it."

Zeke didn't like it. Lauren had pushed her way into their lives, and she was taking his Rachel away. He knew he was being silly. He'd always have Rachel, but he preferred her across the street than a day away by plane. "Enjoy your shopping. Tell Lauren I said she sucks for even mentioning this Namibia thing."

Rachel laughed. Lauren's voice came across the speaker. "I love you too, Bennett."

He chuckled, and the line went dead. Any lingering joy Zeke had in his body died with it.

He pulled into his driveway just as a text message came in from one of his buddies on the Sirens investment.

We need to finalize the corporation. We want to set a meeting early next month.

Zeke opened his calendar app. The date was a few days after his birthday. Either he was in or he wasn't. He had pretty much run out of time. He entered the house and crashed on the sofa. Hours later, he was awakened by a nightmare in which Montgomery traveled to Namibia to date Rachel. They got married.

He swore under his breath, stood, and went to the kitchen for a bottle of water. He realized it was late. It was dark outside, and he was starving. He opened the refrigerator. There was nothing there. He opened the freezer. His part-time cook and housekeeper had left a few dishes, but nothing he was in the mood for.

It wasn't the food. The real problem was he was in the mood for company. Rachel's company. He hadn't seen her in five days. Lauren had come to steal his friend away for nine months, that is if he failed in his mission. He couldn't let it happen. But he was out of options and time. He wasn't going to find the money. It wasn't out there. He needed to get married. He mentally went down a list of women he knew again. It was a waste of time, but he did it anyway. And then he realized he had the perfect woman waiting for him. He was just afraid to involve her in this scheme.

He finished the water before tossing the bottle in the trash.

"Rachel has something to gain," he said, and she did. There weren't many things you could do to earn a million dollars in a year. And he could trust her. The problem was he was starting to wonder if he could trust himself. Those sexy dresses had turned his head. He couldn't unsee her beauty. He wasn't sure what was happening between them, but he knew one thing, he wasn't letting her go to Namibia. Not seeing her for the last five days was hard enough. She was the only person that talked to him this much. He liked to talk, so maybe he needed to think about the possibility...his thoughts trailed off.

Zeke grabbed a few nuts and returned to the sofa. This time, he turned on the television and went to the 24-hour soccer channel. They were running a marathon of Atlanta United's soccer games from the prior season. He loved soccer. He loved Atlanta. But it was too late to build here. They already had a team. A winning team. Rachel was right. The Carolinas were the closest thing to Atlanta, and they were ripe for building a soccer team. He couldn't let this opportunity pass him by.

He reached for his phone, but found it had died. Just as he plugged it in and rebooted it, the doorbell rang. He jumped up and answered it. Rachel was standing on the other side of the door. She held a bag out to him.

"I brought you some Thai food. Lauren and I found this really cool place downtown."

Zeke took her by the arm and pulled her into the house. "I'm glad you're here. I was just about to call you."

"What's up?" Rachel asked, placing the bag on the foyer table and sliding her jacket off.

Zeke couldn't hesitate. He'd mess this up if he did. He began to pace as he mumbled, "I know you offered first and I said it was a really bad idea, but I'm realizing I was wrong, so now I need to fix that. I had a good reason for thinking it was a bad idea, but things aren't going the way I planned, and I need a new plan."

Rachel raised a hand to halt him. "Stop pacing," she insisted. He did. "What are you talking about?"

"I'm talking about the proposal." He pushed the rest of the words through his lips before he lost the courage. "Rachel, will you marry me?"

Chapter 13

"You look amazing."

Rachel stared in the mirror at her reflection. "Are you sure I'm not making a mistake?"

Lauren adjusted her veil. "How could marrying someone you love be a mistake?"

"He doesn't love me back."

"He fought to keep you here, didn't he? The thought of you going to Namibia had him peeing his pants. That's not friendship, sister. It's just not."

"He likes having me around." Rachel sighed. "That's not marriage kind of love."

"I can't imagine that a solid friendship wouldn't be the basis for a good marriage." Lauren tugged at the bodice of her dress. She stood there for a moment admiring Rachel. "If Zeke Bennett doesn't see you today, he's blind."

"Or I'm not his type."

"You're his type," Addison said from her perch on a stool in the corner. "You look like every woman he's ever taken seriously."

Rachel couldn't deny that. Zeke did seem to be attracted to browner-skinned black women with curly hair. But he went for the type that put all her goods on display, not a conservative woman who spent her days designing and living in t-shirts. She was not going to become the woman in red, not even for him.

Lauren placed a finger under Rachel's chin. "Just remember, you'll be the wife. He has to be faithful. You'll wear him down. The marital bed is a powerful thing."

"Sex is not how I want to get my man."

Lauren chuckled. "Don't be naive. Many a great relationship was solidified with sex."

"In movies," Rachel said. "This is real life, and I'm not consummating a fake marriage."

"The love will blossom once you two are under the same roof." Lauren stepped back, held up her phone and took a picture of Rachel.

"Look at it this way. If it doesn't work out, you'll have a million dollars to put into your business. Work helps with heartache," Addison added.

Addison's words weren't encouraging. If it didn't work out, Rachel wouldn't be able to bear it. She didn't want to live a life without Zeke in it. He'd been in it for too long. If it didn't work out, they'd no longer be friends. "I can't believe I let you talk me into this."

"Problems have solutions. A month ago, you were whining about being in love with him, and now you're about to become his wife. You should be glad I was here to help."

There was a knock and the wedding coordinator's assistant stuck her head around the door. "He's going to make the announcement. Then we'll start the procession."

Rachel took a deep breath and let it out slowly. "This is happening."

Addison smiled. "It's happening." She picked up the remote to the television against the wall and turned it on. The videographer was livestreaming for guests who couldn't attend. Even with the declines, they had three hundred people in the outside courtyard. Zeke accepted a microphone from Sienna and stepped up on a stage.

"I want to thank everyone for coming. I know you received an invitation to a birthday party, but I have a surprise for you. Although it is my thirtieth birthday, this is not a celebration of my birth..." He paused for a moment before saying, "This is my wedding."

A round of gasps and applause filled the courtyard.

"I hope you don't mind," Zeke teased, "but Rachel Ingram has agreed to be my wife and I didn't want to wait another day. She might change her mind." There was laughter and he continued, "If you'll enter the building, we'll get this wedding started."

The doors to the main building opened on both sides and the crowd began to move inside.

Ten minutes later, music came up through the speakers. Harper, Addison, Sienna, and Zoe lined up with Zeke's groomsmen which included his brothers Logan, his younger brother, and Connor, and his cousins Cole and Stone.

Lauren was giving her away. She hung back, dabbed tissues under Rachel's eyes to keep tears from ruining her mascara. "Mom and Dad would be proud of you."

"You think so?"

"Immeasurably. I know I am."

Rachel smiled and they hugged. The two of them moved into the hall and made their way to the main ballroom.

Chapter 14

Sienna transformed the venue into a vision of spring. There were flowers everywhere, a blue sky filled with puffy, white, cumulus clouds covered the ceiling, and a full garden including fake grass had been installed underfoot. The path to the gazebo was paved with metallic gold-faced brick. Rachel's only requirement for the ceremony was that it not be outside because she detested the humidity and high pollen count this time of year. Zeke told Sienna to spare no expense, and she hadn't.

Zeke's parents were on the front row. They'd been on one of those 200-day cruises around the world for the past couple of months. Even though his mother, Constance Bennett, had never worked, the trip was a retirement present for her from his father. Bernard Bennett had worked for much of their thirty-eight-year marriage. When he announced his retirement last year, Zeke's mother began planning what she considered to be her reward for not leaving the work-a-holic. They got off the ship in Ecuador to fly home for the wedding and would re-embark in Peru in a few days.

While his mother was thrilled that he was marrying Rachel—she loved her and always had—his father spent the entire time criticizing him for what he called a fool's prenup. The criticizing him part was nothing new. That had been the story of Zeke's life from the time his mother had to enroll him in speech therapy in first grade.

Zeke had tutors for language arts and math until his middle school years. That was when he'd finally been able to manage his lessons on his own. But even after he'd established educational independence, his father less-than-affectionately called him Zeke the Geek, and when he was angry with him, it became Zeke the Weak. Zeke graduated in the top ten percent of his class, a challenging feat at Forest Hill Preparatory Academy, but congratulations from his father were replaced with the words, "You'll be a waste of the Bennett name if you don't make something out of yourself."

Zeke almost wished he hadn't told his parents about the wedding. His father's pious sneer was ruining his day. He released a long sigh and changed his focus when violin music floated through the speakers.

One by one, his groomsmen came down the aisle with one of Rachel's sisters. The doors closed and then an overhead, motorized basket on a pulley moved down the center aisle, dropping thousands of multi-colored rose petals on the brick floor. When it was done, the doors opened and one of Rachel's favorite songs, "All My Life" by K-Ci & JoJo, began to play.

Rachel, escorted by Lauren, stood in the opening. They began a spirited walk toward him and Ethan, his best man. Rachel was a vision in the white gown she'd chosen. The silky fabric of the dress made her look like an angel floating down the aisle. It seemed impossible with all the guests, but it felt like he and she were the only two people in the room. Rachel's smile was real. He knew because he knew when she was happy.

This façade had turned into a special day for her. His stomach clenched. He hoped he hadn't stolen something from her. But he realized he had taken her chance to be a real bride for the first time. He wanted to care about that, but it was hard to care when her loveliness was closing the space between them and stealing his breath with each step.

Once Rachel reached the altar, she handed the bouquet to Harper and slid her hands into his. Zeke's heart raced. That feeling he'd been avoiding for weeks, the one where his heart felt like it was going to explode, returned. He'd hoped he'd dealt with it, suppressed the attraction and emotion, but it was obvious he had not.

Rachel was lovely. He had never seen her look so beautiful. His eyes got a little misty from the emotions that welled in him. "You're very tall," he said, noting she was eye level with him.

She smiled, suppressing a giggle. "I'm wearing four-inch heels."

He smiled back at her. "And well."

The minister cleared his throat. "Are we ready?"

Zeke heard the man, but he hadn't taken his eyes off his bride. "Are you sure?" he asked Rachel.

It was now her eyes that were wet. She whispered, "I am."

Zeke inhaled deeply and looked at the minister. He nodded for him to begin.

The ceremony was kind of a blur. They said traditional vows, exchanged rings, and when the minister gave him permission to kiss his bride, Zeke didn't know what to do. Well he did, but he was paralyzed by the thought. He closed the distance between them and said, "We did it."

Rachel smiled and nodded like she wasn't in the mood for small talk.

From behind him came Ethan's voice on a whisper. "Kiss her."

Zeke took a deep breath and flipped the veil off her face. Rachel's expectant eyes shimmered with unshed tears.

Kiss Rachel. On the lips?

The task seemed surreal at this moment. He wasn't supposed to be kissing Rachel. What had he done?

Kiss her.

He wished he didn't want to, but the truth was, he did. He raised his hands to the sides of her face and lowered his head, so his lips were just above hers. He took in her scent, the heady fragrance forced him to close his eyes right before his lips touched hers. It was supposed to be a peck. That's the way it played out in his head, but once his lips touched hers, he couldn't stop himself. He couldn't not enjoy the sweetness of her mouth.

He heard the crowd rousing. Ethan's finger tapped his shoulder, and more whispered words came from his brother. "You have the rest of your life, but we don't have all night."

The wedding party chuckled. Zeke opened his eyes. He got the joke, but he and Rachel weren't laughing. Rachel's eyes were filled with happiness. His heart was coming out of his chest. They'd been married less than a minute and everything had already changed.

Chapter 15

Rachel vomited. Doing so without making a mess of her wedding gown was an acrobatic feat.

She pulled paper off the roll, wiped her mouth, and tossed it in the toilet.

"If my kiss has had that effect on anyone else, I don't know about it." Zeke let go of the skirt of her dress. He'd swooped it back to make sure she didn't stain it. She pushed the button to flush the toilet.

"Why did you follow me in here?" she asked, turning on the faucet and rinsing her mouth.

"I'm your husband. You run. I follow."

Rachel and he locked eyes. Zeke's were warm and sympathetic to her retching.

Zeke pulled paper towel off the roll and handed it to her. "Lauren should be back with a seltzer or something. Are you okay?"

"I'd be better if you weren't in this tiny bathroom watching me throw up."

"Rae, I've seen you be sick before. I nursed you back from the stomach flu last year and the crud the year before that."

"You gave me both bugs. You owed me." She checked her reflection in the mirror.

"You ran out so fast, I had to make sure you were okay. Like I said, I'm your husband or at least the world thinks I am."

Rachel felt like she was coming out of her skin in this small space. "The world's not watching now. Would you let me brush my teeth in private?"

Zeke nodded. He went toward the open door and took a few steps to exit, but then did a half turn and asked, "Why are you throwing up exactly?"

"I haven't eaten anything. I think it's nerves."

He nodded again. "I wanted to make sure you didn't have something contagious. I just kissed you."

Rachel pursed her lips and threw the paper towel at him. "Get out."

Zeke chuckled. "I'll see you in a few." He disappeared through the door.

Rachel dropped her head back. She was so embarrassed. Nothing like a little vomit to kill the mood after an earth-shattering kiss. She raised her hands to her lips. Zeke had overwhelmed her. She'd kissed her share of men before. Not a lot, but enough to know what she'd just experienced was more than she was ready to deal with. No one had rocked her to her core the way he did. She turned to face the mirror and whispered, "Molly, you're in danger."

"Quoting Ghost at a time like this."

Lauren entered the room with Addison and Harper behind her.

"Are you okay?" they asked in unison.

"I'm fine. My stomach...it's been turning all day."

Lauren handed her a glass of ginger ale. Then she raised a hand to her forehead. "You're not running a fever."

Rachel drained the glass. "I'm not sick. I was nervous."

"Nervous about the wedding night?" Addison inquired.

"Do I need to have the talk with you?" Lauren asked.

"You swear you're her mother." Harper's annoyance was palpable. "You're only five years older. For all you know, she's had more lovers than you have."

"Shows how much you know," Lauren said. "She's closest to your age and you don't know she's a virgin."

Harper gasped and turned to Rachel. "Are you?"

Rachel shook her head. "Can we exit this restroom?"

The women shuffled out backward. Addison grabbed a hanger off a nearby clothing rack and zipped down the garment bag that covered it. "We need to get her out of this dress and into this one."

"Are you really a virgin?" Harper asked again.

Rachel sighed. "Yes, stop asking me like it's a disease or something."

"On purpose?" Harper asked.

"I am saved you know. I'm not supposed to be having sex."

Addison zipped down the back of Rachel's dress and replied, "Even if she wasn't saved, why should she be out here giving it up to any old guy? No woman needs to be used by a man who's not worthy of her, saved or not." Addison's voice was tinged with temper. Her romance with a man she refused to identify ended suddenly and badly last year.

Lauren crossed her arms over her chest. "Well, Zeke has enough experience for the both of them."

"Lauren, really?" Harper said. Rachel thought her sisters were going to fight if Lauren didn't get on a plane soon.

Lauren shrugged. "Am I lying?"

Harper was about to open her mouth to reply when Rachel yelled, "Stop! I'm stressed enough without you two doing this tonight." She stepped out of the dress, picked up her travel case and went back into the restroom to brush her teeth.

Lauren was right. Zeke did have a lot of experience. She was in way over her head, but it wasn't like they were consummating the marriage tonight. They weren't a real married couple. This was the last conversation she needed to be having right now.

"Your guests are waiting." Sienna's voice echoed off the halls in the corridor.

Shortly after hearing her, Rachel saw Sienna's face as she peeked into the restroom. "Feeling better? Zeke sent me to check on you. He said you kicked him out."

Rachel inhaled and fought the overwhelming desire to throw up again. "There's nothing sexy about watching your bride vomit."

Sienna rubbed her back. "It happens more than you think. We need to get you into your other dress."

Rachel reentered the dressing area. Addison helped her step into a shimmering white and gold, A-line gown for the reception.

Rachel inspected herself in the mirror. The dress was nearly as beautiful as her wedding gown, but less poofy and more manageable to move around in. "It's stunning."

"Let's hurry and get you dinner," Sienna said. "Zeke said he's hungry, and he's not eating a thing until you arrive."

Rachel stood still as Sienna powdered her face. Addison removed the white flower from her hair and inserted a gold one. Lauren and Harper just glowered at each other.

"What's wrong with you two?"

"They're disappointed. Lauren's mad because Harper didn't know and Harper's mad because Lauren did know," Addison said filling in the blanks.

Sienna snatched back her head. "What don't I know?"

"That Rachel—"

"Eh," Rachel threw up a hand to stop Lauren from speaking. "It's my truth. I'll tell it." She made Sienna wait through a pause. "I'm a virgin."

"Are we surprised by that?" Sienna asked. She rolled her eyes at her sisters. She reached for a can of hair spray and after shielding Rachel's face, she sprayed. "But does Zeke know?"

"Zeke doesn't know, and he doesn't care. This is a fake marriage you guys. He's no more interested in me tonight than he was when we were five."

"Lies, girl. He was digging for gold with his tongue," Harper said. "You've unleashed the man in him. Ain't no putting that Genie back in the bottle."

"I agree," Sienna said. "He's definitely going to want to hit it."

"Don't be so crass," Harper said. "You sound like a man."

Sienna giggled. "I'm teasing her."

Rachel closed her eyes. "This is not funny. You all are driving me crazy. Let's just go to the reception. I'll worry about Zeke hitting it—thank you Sienna for your romantic term—later. Okay?"

Rachel let her sisters lead the way down the corridor. They entered the main ballroom and Zeke stood as she approached the table. She watched his eyes as she got closer. He was sweeping her body from head to toe over and over again. His face turned red. She could see it even under his dark skin. He reached for his collar and tugged it like his tie was too tight.

"Better?" he whispered pulling her chair out.

"Much," Rachel replied as she slid onto the chair.

Zeke cleared his throat before speaking. "You look amazing. You're a lovely bride."

Rachel smiled. "Thank you."

"Yeah, really great," he continued. "I wasn't expecting..." He stopped speaking.

"Wasn't expecting what?" Rachel pressed, lifting an eyebrow.

Zeke's eyes locked with hers. He looked like he wanted to say something, but his lips were frozen. He pressed them together and shook his head.

"Zeke, tell me what you were going to say."

Zeke's eyes swept the room. "I was going to say Sienna did a great job making this sham of a wedding look real."

A little joy seeped from her pores. "It is a sham, isn't it?" She reached for her fork.

Zeke's eyes returned to hers. He slowed his words down. They came out like a question. "Of course it is?"

Rachel reached for a drink. She didn't want him to see her bottom lip tremble. "And Sienna did do a good job."

Zeke nodded. "She did." He was quiet for a minute before saying, "Rae, I was thinking…"

A crack of static from a microphone filled the room. The wedding coordinator silenced the crowd before she began to speak.

Not caring what the coordinator had to say, Rachel placed a hand on his. "You were going to say something."

He twisted his lips and mumbled, "It was…nothing." He gave the coordinator his full attention.

Rachel lost the opportunity to hear what he was going to say. She had a feeling it was a moment she wouldn't get back.

Chapter 16

Like the wedding, the reception was a blur. The only thing that wasn't a blur was Rachel. He could see her clearly, and he hated what his eyes were telling his brain. Rachel was gorgeous, and he wanted her badly. He wanted her more than he'd ever wanted anyone. He told himself the reason for that was because getting women had always been so easy for him. He turned women away daily, so he didn't really have to work for female attention. Rachel was different. She didn't want him. Never had. Now he wanted her, so the desire was heavy on the wanting. He was in trouble.

The limo ride home was quiet. Rachel made a few comments about the food and the music. She raved about the cake, but he struggled with showing enthusiasm for small talk. All he could think about was how her lips felt when he'd kissed her, and how his heart pounded all evening as he sat and stood next to her.

"Zeke, what did you think?"

Startled, his mouth gaped open before he closed it again. He hadn't heard her. "What did you say?"

"You didn't hear me? You're looking right at me."

I'm looking at your lips. He reached for a bottled water he'd been drinking and took a sip. "Sorry. I guess I'm already acting like a married man."

Rachel chuckled. "You don't have to you know. I'm a fraud of a wife."

Isn't that too bad, he thought, but said, "So, you won't be nagging me?"

"I don't expect to have to." The limo pulled into his driveway.

Rachel continued. "I said people were asking why we weren't going on a honeymoon."

"Yeah, I fielded that question a few times myself. I think my answer was sufficient. I told them I have a business deal to close."

The door opened, the driver stepped back, and Zeke stepped out. Rachel slipped her hand into his. Her dress got caught on something and she fell into him. He wrapped his arms around her to keep her from falling. Once again, they were face to face. Their lips inches from each other. Their eyes locked in an unfamiliar dance. Why was she looking at him like that? It was innocent and expectant and sexy at the same time. If he didn't know any better, he'd think she wanted him, but he knew better. Rachel was doing him a favor and earning a million dollars for her trouble. She didn't want him, and he wasn't supposed to be thinking about her this way.

The driver reached in and unhooked the tail of her dress from whatever it was stuck on and then she was able to stand upright. Zeke released the breath he'd been holding.

Rachel was the first to look away. His eyes followed hers across the street to her empty townhouse. They agreed she'd be working there in the day, but spending her nights in his home because they had to. He wondered how Oliver would know, but he wasn't going to risk finding out by not appearing to be married for the twelve months. Besides, he wasn't done with her yet. *Not nearly*, he thought. He took her hand. "Let's go inside."

They stood in the foyer like two kids who'd come in from prom. "We have champagne," he offered.

Rachel shook her head. "I've had enough. Haven't you?"

He shrugged. "I suppose."

"I'm sick of these stockings and everything else I have on under this dress."

Zeke's heart thudded. "So, you're taking it off?"

She smiled. "I'm not going to sleep in it, silly. Aren't you sick of the tux?"

Zeke thought he needed a suit of armor to keep his hands off her. "You know I'm used to this."

Rachel nodded. "True. Millionaire attire."

He swallowed. He was itching to dismiss the awkwardness between them. "What about coffee? We have cake."

"Coffee would be good. Decaf please," Rachel said, bunching up the hem of her dress. "I'm going to change."

Zeke nodded.

Rachel took a few steps toward the stairs but then did a half turn. She twisted her body and raised her arm a little. "Would you mind getting the zipper for me?"

Zeke swallowed hard. He was an expert at unzipping dresses, but suddenly he had lead in his shoes.

Rachel pointed over her shoulder. "Just the top. It has a strange latch."

He breathed and stepped to her. He placed his hands at her waist from behind and slid his hands up and across her back. That was unnecessary. He was surprised she hadn't squawked about his molesting her. He undid the tie at the back and then pulled the zipper down halfway. The temptation to kiss her shoulders and back was overwhelming. He stepped away from her and made quick steps into the kitchen. If he kissed her again, he'd be taking off the entire dress. He heard her feet on the stairs and a bedroom door close. This wasn't a real marriage, but he wanted her like she was really his wife.

He washed his hands and put pods in the coffee maker. God help him. He was in trouble.

Chapter 17

Zeke tapped a repetitive melody on the lip of Oliver's desk with a pen he'd taken from the man's pencil cup.

Oliver raised his eyes to meet his, chastising him without saying a word. "I know you've married this woman to get your money, but I hope you realize you are actually married to her."

Zeke yawned. He was bored with Oliver's incessant warnings. "You're telling me that because?"

"Because divorce can be ugly. She's been your friend for a long time and a temporary marriage is not in line with the spirit of your great-grandmother's will."

Zeke chuckled. "The spirit of her will. No disrespect to the great-grandmother I never knew, but how does forcing someone to get married have a spirited aspect?"

"Your great-grandmother believed marriage settles a man and forces him to think about other people," Oliver replied.

Zeke frowned. "Getting married is supposed to make me solid?"

"Yes."

"That might have been true sixty years ago, but marriage doesn't change a man's character."

"You could be the exception."

Zeke's frown deepened. "How much longer are we going to be?"

Oliver cocked an eyebrow. "You planning to spend all the money at the mall tonight?"

"No, I have a flight to catch. I'm going to scout out locations for the Sirens."

"Full speed ahead on that, huh?"

"It's been my dream for a few years."

"Leaving two days after your wedding," Oliver chided. "Is your bride joining you?"

Zeke swallowed. "No, she has some work to do of her own. I'll only be gone a few days."

Oliver's brow crinkled with annoyance. "While you're here, you can sign the paperwork for Rachel's gift."

Zeke remembered the million dollars Rachel was to be paid. "Let's break that up. Half a million now and half a million on our anniversary. Make the half mill a wedding gift. I didn't get her one. She'll be pleasantly surprised."

"Whatever you like, Zeke." Oliver's tone was condescending. The man knew. Of course, he did, but he couldn't prove a thing and that was all that mattered right now.

Oliver had Zeke sign a few more documents and called his secretary into the office. He handed her the stack of papers and gave her some instructions before she left.

Oliver smiled. "Well, it's time for the big moment."

"My money?"

"Your meeting with the tax attorney."

Zeke glanced at his watch. "Today?"

"I told you to be prepared to be here for a few hours."

"I need to reschedule this, Uncle Oliver."

"I'm not transferring a dime to you until you meet with him."

As if on cue, Oliver's secretary buzzed the phone and let him know "they" were waiting in the conference room for Zeke.

Zeke sighed and stood. "It's such a burden to be rich."

Oliver did not look pleased.

"I was totally joking." He extended a hand to Oliver for a shake. "The next time you see me, I'll be part owner of the Carolinas Unified Soccer team aka the Sirens."

"And I'll be proud of you. I hope it'll be worth the price."

Zeke figured Oliver meant money. He had no doubt he and his business associates could launch a successful team. Zeke was more concerned about the emotional tax on his relationship with Rachel. He hoped the team wasn't going to cost him more than money.

***

The meeting with the tax attorneys was a brief overview. They had a much lengthier session planned for him in a few weeks.

Instead of parking one of his vehicles at the airport, Zeke hired a driver for the day. He climbed into the back of the limo just as his phone rang. It was one of his business partners from the Sirens. He let Zeke know something had come up, and he couldn't make the trip to Charlotte.

There was no point in Zeke going now. He couldn't make a decision about a stadium without him.

He considered putting the trip off, but then he realized how much he was looking forward to going away for a few days. He wanted to get away from Rachel. He'd been married to her for two days and already, he needed to escape. He had no idea how he would last a year. Besides, if he didn't go away, people would be wondering why they weren't on their honeymoon. They'd had a huge wedding. Who has a wedding like theirs and doesn't have a honeymoon?

He swiped his phone screen and video called Rachel. When she answered, he said, "Hey there, wife."

Rachel laughed. "Are you done?"

"I am officially an eighth of the way to a billion dollars. I'm rich."

"Well, you were kind of rich at eighteen."

"I know, but I had to be frugal. Now I can be as excessive as I want."

Rachel chuckled. "Goals, eh?"

He laughed. "Look, I was thinking we should go to the cabin when I get back."

"Are you trying to take me on a cheap honeymoon?"

"A fake honeymoon."

"If I was to go on a fake honeymoon with you, you'd have to spring for Bora Bora or the Maldives, sir."

"Well, we can do that, but both sound a little sedentary. I'd prefer something with some action and adventure," he said, but he thought, we won't be lying around in bed recovering from honeymoon sex. He needed activity.

"I don't care what people think or expect. Besides, I have ten new designs to get ready for a conference and the expo," she said referring to the annual imprinted sportswear show she attended every year. "If some nosy person asks, we tell them we're planning a trip for later in the year when we're not so busy."

Zeke nodded. "Works for me."

"You headed to the airport?"

He looked out the window. "Crawling through traffic right now."

"Well, let me know when you land."

He pulled his head back from the video. "Am I checking in with the little woman?"

Rachel rolled her eyes. "I did just say that didn't I? But in my defense, you're usually in the habit of calling me when you land somewhere."

"That was because I was using you as my personal assistant—without pay might I add. If I disappeared from the earth, you would know where I was, where I was staying, and who I was meeting with."

"You could have kept that on a calendar. Admit it. You like for me to know, so don't start changing things now."

Zeke's heart leapt. She stopped drawing. Her huge brown eyes met his and tugged at something deep inside of him.

Things had changed.

"Zeke, I lost you there."

"I'm listening."

"I said don't change things."

"Not me. Not on purpose." He decided it was time to change the subject. "You should be getting a courier from my attorney. I decided to give you a half million today and the other half on our anniversary. No point in not giving you an advance. Who works for a year without pay?" He could see the objection rising from her tongue, so he stopped her. "It's already done."

"You've been trying to give me money since we were ten. Remember, the school candy store? You treated me every day."

Zeke didn't remember. He could count on Rachel to remember everything.

"If I had let you give me money every time you wanted to, I'd already have a million dollars," she added.

Zeke hadn't realized he'd been that way. He knew he was overprotective of her. She was a woman without a father or brothers, but he wondered, was there some subconscious desire to take care of her? He dismissed the thought. It was too much to think about. "Now you can do what you want to do for your business."

"What did you tell Oliver about the money?"

"I told him it was a wedding present. Technically, it is."

"I'm sure he fell for that one." Rachel picked up a lipstick container, removed the lid, and ran it across her lips. Zeke remembered the kiss at the altar. She had beautiful, kissable, sweet lips. He knew that now. He knew it well.

He cleared his throat. "You're getting luscious. Are you going out? Expecting someone?"

Rachel giggled like he was being silly. "It's a moisturizer. I wear it every day."

No wonder her lips were so sweet and moist. She hadn't answered all his questions. "Are you staying in?"

"I'll be working until you get back."

And then what would happen when he got back? They were friends. Was she going to stop and put a chicken in the oven for him like she was the little woman? This was complex. Was she as confused? She didn't seem to be. She was too focused on her work. That's why he was going away. He needed the distraction of being focused on his work too.

Zeke heard the doorbell chime in the distance.

"Are you expecting someone?" he asked. She'd never answered the question.

She stuck the tip of her pen between her teeth. "At your house?"

"Technically, it's your home now too."

She picked up her phone and entered the hall. He heard a voice in the background and then Sienna's face popped into view. She waved. "Hi, brother-in-law."

He let go of the breath he'd been holding. What the heck? Was he jealous? Who did he think was coming to see her? "Hey, Sienna."

They chatted for a few minutes about the wedding, and Zeke ended the call so they could do their sisterly-get-together stuff. Whatever that was. His thoughts drifted back to his emotions. His stomach was tight at the thought of her having a visitor—other than her sisters of course. Things had definitely changed between them. If he was going to last a year, Zeke had to figure out how to change them back.

Chapter 18

Zeke stayed in North Carolina longer than she'd expected and then when he left, he went to Florida to fish. His story was that he'd be so busy working on the Sirens, he wouldn't have time for his normal leisure activities. Rachel kind of accepted that, but it was the next trip that made her realize there was a problem. After he left Florida, he went back to Carolina for a few weeks and then he went to New York. When he came home, he left again. He had to go on the road to scout talent for the team. He was traveling all over the US. They'd been married for three months, and she'd barely seen him.

Rachel stirred the straw in her water and finished it in one drink. She put her glass down. "I saw him more when we lived apart."

"Well, the team is a big undertaking, and it's not an in-state job," Harper offered in Zeke's defense.

Rachel rolled her eyes. "I don't know. Why doesn't he ask me to go with him? We've hung out on his business trips before."

"Why do you think he's not asking?"

"Maybe he's taking someone else."

Harper sighed. "I don't think so, honey. I don't think he'd do that to you."

"He's not doing anything to me. That's the problem."

"Are you Rachel Bennett?" A voice came from behind Rachel and she turned to see what Barbie Doll was speaking; and a real live Barbie it was. The woman was tall, in her heels, she was well over six feet, and seriously thin. She had a mane of wavy, thick hair that most women would give a kidney to have.

"Who's asking?"

"Sorry, I thought you'd recognize me. My name is Serene." She held out her hand for Rachel to shake.

Rachel looked up and down from the woman's face to her hands. She wasn't shaking it. "What can I do for you?"

"You're Zeke's new wife, right? I'm sorry I missed the wedding. I was in Paris for a fashion show."

Rachel nodded.

"Zeke texted me a month or so before your wedding asking me to marry him, so imagine my surprise when I found out he was having an actual wedding."

"A real one," Harper interjected, smartly. "With a whole wife."

Serene smiled tightly before saying, "Well, tell the rascal I said hello. If I'd known he was serious, I would have told him yes and beat you to the punch." She turned and strolled away.

"Who is she? Why does she have one name?" Rachel asked.

"She's a model. You've never seen her? She does all the Chaguall fashion campaign stuff." Harper cleared her throat. "She also dated Zeke for a while."

Rachel looked back at the woman. She'd joined a group of other model-types at the bar.

"Serene," Rachel said. "I remember, he told me about her—briefly. He dated her for almost four months. That was a long time for Zeke." Rachel looked around and waved the waitress to the table. "I need a Coke. Add a lemon."

"She's graduated from water to soda. Oh, oh, it's bad," Harper teased.

Rachel stuck her tongue out at her. She looked back over at Serene.

Harper reached for her hand. "Stop staring at her. She's an ex."

"He asked her to marry him."

"She said it was a text. Who proposes by text? And you know he asked that waitress. I'm sure it was a joke."

"He would have married anyone to get this money." Rachel dropped her head back. "I wanted him to get the money and now it's keeping us apart."

"So, don't let it," Harper said. "When is he going back to North Carolina?"

Rachel reached for her glass. "Probably next week as soon as he comes back from Chicago."

"Go to North Carolina. Find a work thing you can attend and tell him you decided to stop in to see him while you were in town."

"I can't do that. It'll be obvious."

"Look over your shoulder." Harper cocked her head in Serene's direction.

Rachel did. Serene and her friend were being seated behind them. "Zeke likes obvious. You're going to have to try harder, sister."

Rachel groaned. She pulled her glass closer and moved her straw around in it. "You know I was reading the story of Abraham and Sarah last night."

Harper sat back and crossed her arms over her chest. "What about it?"

"Abraham told Sarah God promised them a child. Sarah saw it as an impossibility, but she wanted the child. She came up with a plan..."

"To have Hagar, her maid, go in and have sex with her husband."

Rachel nodded. "So she could get what she believed God promised them—what she believed they deserved."

Harper frowned, uncrossed her arms, and leaned forward. "What's so curious about it?"

"I was thinking. What if Zeke was the promise for me, but instead of waiting for him, I did what Sarah did?"

Harper hesitated as if giving it some thought. "This is not the same kind of thing."

"Why not? The night before I told you all how I felt about him, I prayed that Zeke would see me. Really see me as a woman and not a friend. I asked God to spark a flame in his heart for me, and then the first opportunity I had to manipulate the situation, I did." Rachel sighed. "How is that different from what Sarah did?"

Harper reached for Rachel's hand and squeezed it. "If you believe that, now you have a different prayer. Ask God to do what He does and fix it. Ask Him to bless your marriage—anyway. No matter what, it represents Christ and the church."

"Are you sure, Harper?" Rachel asked. She was hoping her sister had more wisdom than she did, that she would say something that made this anxiousness within her all better. "All marriages are not ordained by God."

Harper was thoughtful again. "I don't know. I'm not a theology student. But God is good. He's not trying to punish us for being human."

"I suppose." Rachel paused. "You know I've been thinking about what Addison said about God not putting more on us than we can bear...you know about it not being about struggle, but temptation."

"From first Corinthians chapter ten."

"Yes. What if my desire for Zeke was a temptation? The scripture says, 'He gives us a way of escape.' What if I didn't take the escape?"

Harper shook her head. "I think your focus is on the wrong thing. You're all over the Word on this. You're looking for everything but God's grace."

Rachel shook her head. "I'm so scared."

"Fear is not of God, baby. Stop worrying and pray for your marriage."

Rachel twisted her lips. She thought about how much she loved Zeke and about how much this huge space between them was hurting their relationship. She had no control. She couldn't undo what she'd done. "Ask God to bless my hot mess?" Rachel felt her eyes fill with tears. Did she have the right to do that? Was it even Biblical? She bit her lip. She'd never been so confused in her life.

Harper's smile was sympathetic. "It's going to be okay."

Rachel closed her eyes and whispered, "God, if I've operated out of your will, please fix this mess." She opened her eyes and met her sister's again.

Harper released Rachel's hand. "I'm going to run to the restroom." She stood and left the table.

Rachel sat there with her thoughts and fears and all the pieces of the Bible she'd mixed to make a cocktail of fear. Her sister was right. This was not how God wanted her to feel, but she couldn't help thinking she'd made a hard bed with Zeke and now she was going to lie in it—alone.

Chapter 19

Rachel stood in his doorway as he took clothes from his suitcase and replaced them with other ones. He'd used the hotel laundry. Everything was removing was nicely pressed and folded. She wondered why he didn't just use the same clothes, but then she realized he was going to a colder climate. He needed warmer things.

Rachel folded her arms across her chest. "Maybe I could go with you."

Zeke grinned before crushing her hopes. "No need for that."

"I know it's not needed, but I've never been to Ohio. It might be nice to visit Chicago."

Zeke's smile tightened. "Maybe another time." He opened his closet, exchanged two suits and returned to the luggage.

"Why not now?"

"Rae, I'm working." His frustration with her enunciated every word he said. "I told you I was going to be busy."

"I understand you're working, but I mean how many times have I tagged along with you on business trips? We always hang out." She felt herself pleading, and she hated it. "Besides, I'd like to cash in my honeymoon chip."

"Except we're not honeymooners," he said matter-of-factly.

Rachel's heart sank. She knew that, but it didn't stop her from hoping he'd want her to join him.

He closed his suitcase, zipped his garment bag, and rolled both to the door. He placed a hand on her shoulder and asked, "Are you okay? You've been kind of unhappy. That's not like you."

Kind of unhappy? It was more like disappointment.

She moved from under his hand. "I'm fine. I just wanted to get out of the house. Your house."

Frustrated, Zeke rubbed a hand across his face. "I have an idea. Get Harper over here and decorate the place. It's long overdue anyway. You can bring some of your things in and make it our home."

She smiled a little. *Our home.* That had a nice ring to it. Not as fun as going to Chicago, but she did have her own money and her own freedom to come and go as she wanted. She could go somewhere without Zeke Bennett. But living separate from him was not a part of the plan. She only had a year to get him to fall in love with her or she'd lose him forever. She was down by more than three months.

"Rae, how does that sound?"

She shook off her deep thought. Unfolding her arms, she said, "Fine. I'll reach out to her."

"Good. I'm going to take a shower and hit the sack. I have an early flight."

Rachel nodded and turned to leave the room.

"Rae," Zeke called over her shoulder. "You can bring anything you want except that print hanging over your fireplace."

She turned and swatted at him. They'd had many discussions about the painting. "Stop talking about my Geneva Boseman."

"It's like Mona Lisa. Creepy. I don't want to see it every day." He smiled. Her heart did a little pitter-patter. She missed that smile.

She pursed her lips. "I'll keep it in my private collection."

There was a beat of silence between them. It quickly went from light-hearted to thick with atmosphere. Rachel's breaths came stronger and Zeke's eyes did a dance between hers and her lips.

"Well, take your shower. Catch your early flight. I'll decorate while you're gone."

"Have fun." He took a step backward. "Bill me."

She smiled. "I will." She turned and left his bedroom. If it wasn't beating so hard, her heart would have fallen into her stomach. He was avoiding her. She was chasing Zeke harder than she was before the wedding. She hadn't caught him at all.

Chapter 20

"I'm going insane."

"You need to give yourself some time. You've never lived with anyone."

"That's not it. Living with her isn't really a problem. I'm used to being around Rachel, and I haven't exactly been home," Zeke said. "It's the no sex thing."

"Knowing you, I'm sure you're counting the days," Logan chuckled.

"As a matter of fact, I am. It's been over a hundred days. That's more than a quarter of the year. I should have never agreed to her terms. I should have negotiated."

"All smart businessmen negotiate," Ethan said. "But that's not really the problem is it? It's not the no sex. It's that you haven't had sex with her."

"Another woman would take my mind off Rachel."

"Temporarily, like for fifteen or twenty minutes." Ethan laughed.

Zeke smirked. "Fifteen or twenty? Speak for yourself."

Logan and Ethan both laughed now.

"What's so funny?"

"Casanova, you are sprung." Logan raised a leg and perched his foot on the opposite knee. "Is that what they call it, E?"

"I don't know. I'm not current on the term," Ethan replied.

"I came over here to get this stuff off my mind, but you two are making it worse."

"The first step in dealing with a problem is admitting you have one," Logan handed him a beer.

Ethan interjected, "Meaning, this is not just about sex. You have to be honest with yourself, dude. It's not. You're in love with her. You have been for years."

"I'm not."

"I've been there myself. I know what it looks like," Ethan said. "You're lucky. At least you're married to a woman you love, and she loves you back." He groaned a little. "There's hope for you."

"Speaking of your past love…" Logan interjected, "where's Lauren these days?"

Ethan gave Logan a nasty look to which Logan merely shrugged. "I'm just curious man. I mean, you are getting a divorce."

"Rachel told me she's in Namibia," Zeke said, "She'll be leaving there for Kenya soon."

No one said anything for a minute. Ethan always had to process his emotions about Lauren, and Logan and Zeke knew that, so they waited. When he had, Ethan offered, "Look man, be a grown up about this. Take your wife out to dinner."

"Cook her dinner," Logan said. "That's more romantic."

"Yeah, cook for her, do the whole thing—candles, music, lighting. Tell her things have changed for you. You have feelings and you want to explore them since you're hitched together anyway and then you know...put those twenty minutes on her." Ethan laughed at his own joke. Logan joined him and then the two clicked their beer bottles together.

"You guys are not listening to me." Zeke's voice was shrill with emotion. "I'm not willing to risk our friendship like that. Once this year passes, I need my bestie. I can't blow this."

"Dude, we're listening. You're the one that's not getting it." Ethan chuckled. "You've already risked your friendship. You risked it when you opened your eyes and discovered how hot she was. I've told you there's no going back. Once you see a woman sexually, she's out of the friend zone."

"You're saying men and women can't be friends?"

It was Logan's turn to speak now. "We're saying a single man and a woman he's become attracted to can't be friends in the purest sense of the word. I mean you can be a friend to her, but still, if you want her, you're waiting for an opportunity. It's how we're wired."

"But a winner doesn't wait for an opportunity," Ethan interjected. "He makes one."

"You know what? I don't want to talk about Rachel anymore. I have other things on my mind. In a week, we make the announcement about Carolinas United."

Ethan and Logan clapped. Logan added, "That's a sweet, man."

"It is sweet. We have a lot of work to do which is a good thing. It'll be a nice distraction." Zeke's phone rang. "It's the little woman," he said to his brothers and then answered. "Hey, Rae...what, where are you?" He frowned. "Okay. I'm on my way. Don't be silly. I'm coming."

Ethan and Logan's eyes were on him.

He stood. "Rachel had a car accident. She's in the ER at Forest Hills Medical. I'm going."

His brothers nodded, and he was out the door.

***

A nurse secured the Ace bandage on her wrist just as Zeke swept into the room like a tornado. His panic filled eyes met hers.

"Zeke, it's nothing. I told you. I'm not even hurt."

He came to stand next to her. He took her hand and tilted her head back like he was expecting to be able to get a better look. "You're in an ER."

"All I did was jar my wrist. I was planning to call a ride-share taxi if I couldn't reach someone."

"You can't..." he waited until the nurse left the room. "Rachel, you can't take a taxi. That's not cool anymore. You're married to a multi-millionaire. People get kidnapped all the time. You have to be careful."

"No one knows who I am. They certainly don't know I'm married to you."

"You don't know what people know."

"Hmmm, that's true. I did have someone call me Rachel Bennett in a restaurant a few weeks ago."

Zeke frowned.

"Serene, your old girlfriend."

His frown deepened. "She wasn't a girlfriend."

"You proposed to her."

"I did that a lot a few months ago." As if he had medical experience, inspecting her, he raised both her arms. "Are you sure you don't have any other injuries or pains?"

"I'm fine. And you didn't have to come here."

"Yes, I did. No Ubering and Lyfting. I forbid it. You need a ride you call me or one of my brothers." He paused a beat and then, "Maybe what I should do is get you a driver. I should have thought of it before. You should have a driver. I'll arrange one." He reached into his pocket for his phone.

Rachel took the phone out of his hand. "You are not getting me a driver."

"Well, a bodyguard then."

She cocked her head. "You're doing way too much right now."

He sighed. "How did this accident happen?"

"I was stopped at a traffic light, and a driver ran into me. He admitted to dropping his phone and reaching for it, so it was his fault."

She could see his temper rise. "What? He could have killed you."

Rachel glided her fingertips over the bandage. She knew the accident could have caused more damage, but the last thing she wanted was for him to get upset about it. "In stopped traffic on Hwy 81? How bad could it get?"

"I've seen people get cut out of cars on Hwy 81."

There was a knock on the door. Rachel rolled her eyes at Zeke's drama and invited them in. It was the man who hit her. *Talk about bad timing.*

"Hey, I'm all checked out. I wanted to make sure you were okay before I leave."

"Who is this?" Zeke asked, putting his body between her and the man.

"Zeke, this is John Hayes. He's the other driver."

Rachel could see his temper rising some more. "Do you make it a habit of taking your eyes off the road?" Zeke took steps toward him. Rachel jumped down from the gurney. She groaned.

Zeke turned his attention to her. "Are you okay?"

"My knee. I got down wrong."

"Did the doctor check it out?"

Once again, he was doing too much. "My knee is fine. I didn't...it's okay. I stepped down wrong."

"I apologize," John interjected. "You have my information. Please contact me about the repair and this bill."

Zeke frowned. "The bill. Do you think you can just write a check, and it's okay? You could have seriously hurt her."

"Zeke, stop it." She had to tug at his arm to keep him from jumping at John. "Please."

"We've got your number. You can go. You'll hear from my lawyer. You can count on that."

John eased out of the room.

Zeke released a long sigh, but it didn't help him release stress. Rachel could still see it all over his face. "What's wrong with you?"

He waved a hand toward the door. "He could have hurt you. I mean worse than you are." He pulled her to him and wrapped his arms around her. "You know I can't live without you."

Rachel pulled back. The warmth of his cologne sent a sharp shot to her senses. Her heart flipped. She bit her lip before saying. "It was a fender bender. I'm fine."

"We'll get you a new car. An SUV. You need something bigger anyway."

She welcomed his hug...too much. She stepped further away. "There's nothing wrong with my car. The bumper needs some work."

"Fix it, and we'll donate it to that single mom's car charity your sister works with. I'm getting you a safer one."

"So, it's okay for a single mother to have an unsafe car?" she chuckled.

He smirked. "That's not what I meant, and you know it."

She did know it, but she couldn't help teasing him.

There was another knock, right before the nurse entered the room. "You're all set. Here are your discharge papers. You can follow up with your doctor."

Rachel thanked her, and they left the hospital. "My car is right over there," she said pointing.

Zeke walked to the car, did a quick inspection, and walked back to her. "I'll get it tomorrow."

"I can drive."

He removed his keys from his pocket and said, "You have an injury."

"I have a bruised wrist."

"Rachel, this isn't up for discussion," he said pushing the key fob for his SUV and opening the door for her.

Rachel didn't get in right away. "Why are you acting so extra?"

"Extra? The guy hit you from the back because he was picking up a phone. Which by the way is illegal in this state, and you think I'm overreacting? He could have hurt you. An apology doesn't make that go away."

Rachel took a deep breath, then she got in the car. Zeke pushed her door closed, walked around to his side and did the same.

He hesitated before starting the vehicle. Rachel wasn't sure what was wrong with him, but he wasn't himself.

"Are you nervous about the Sirens?"

He turned to her. He picked up her hand and squeezed it. "No. I just...you know I love you, Rae. I'm stuck on the fact that you could have been hurt."

"But I wasn't so get over it."

He raised her hand to his lips and kissed it. "Yeah, I know." Their eyes locked for a moment. Zeke released a long breath and turned his head. "I uh…need to eat. Cook is off tonight. You want to get dinner?"

Her stomach quivered and her words came out on a shaky breath. "I'm tired. I'd prefer not to go out."

He nodded. "Cool. Is pizza okay?"

"Sure."

Zeke started the car. He placed a call for the pizza. Rachel stole snatches of him from the peripheral view. He looked super-stressed. He reached for her hand again and squeezed it. The tension in his jaw and the worry lines on his forehead disappeared. She couldn't believe he was so upset about a fender bender. The only reason she'd called him was because the nurse asked if she had. She hadn't even considered that she was married, and a married woman would call her husband after an accident. In the past, one of her sisters was available for emergencies.

"I already told the team you were designing our logo and uniforms." He glanced in her direction.

She smiled. "Finally, a benefit to marrying you."

He chuckled. "You mean other than the half a million?"

"Yes, besides that."

"They were more than happy to turn that over to me. It's the least of the things on everyone's mind right now."

"I'll start working on something."

He pulled through the security gate and stopped to ask the security guard to have someone from the concierge call him.

"The concierge. What for?" Rachel asked.

"They'll get someone to go get your car."

"Zeke, I don't need someone to get my car."

"I have a meeting in the morning. You're resting tomorrow. The hospital needs its parking spaces."

She started to say something, but he stopped her with his words. "You and I have lived in this overpriced subdivision for three years and neither one of us has ever used the concierge service. They owe us. You're resting. They'll get your car for us."

Rachel took a deep breath and held it. She wasn't used to this crazy protective side of him.

He pulled the car into the driveway and then the garage. They sat there for a few minutes, not speaking.

Rachel spoke first. "I didn't sign up for this to be told what to do."

She watched his Adam's apple bob up and down before he spoke. "I know."

She waited for him to say something else, but he didn't. He didn't look at her. The worry lines were back on his forehead and his hands were a vice around the steering wheel.

"Zeke."

He turned to her. "I need to go for a drive."

She shook her head. "What?"

"I need to...just wait for the pizza. Cook will take care of you if you need something. I'll call him."

"I don't need Cook to take care of me!" She pushed the door open. "Let the man have his day off."

Zeke grabbed her arm to hold her in the vehicle. She turned to him, before she could scream for him to let her loose, his hand was on the side of her face. His lips were on hers. The kiss was long and desperate. When it was over, she sat there stunned.

"Zeke..."

He started the car again. He stared straight ahead when he spoke. "Go in the house, Rae."

She hesitated.

"Please, I need this ride." His voice was firm, but then he cleared his throat and spoke softer. "I'll be back soon."

Rachel's eyes locked on his profile at first. She willed him to change his mind, but he didn't, so she stepped out and closed the door. He put the car in reverse and careened out of the garage as the door lowered on her heart.

Chapter 21

Zeke drove around for hours. He got as far from the Forest Hills area as he could before he stopped, but no matter how far he drove, he couldn't stop thinking about that kiss or the kiss at the wedding. But he was determined he was going to try. He went to a bar. He had a drink and flirted. The flirting paid off quickly. He had his pick of women. He tried to convince himself to take one to a hotel. Why not? Who would know? Rachel wouldn't, and it wasn't like they were having sex or ever would, but he couldn't do it. He couldn't break a promise to her. She wasn't just his fake wife. She was his friend, and he'd never lied to her. He'd never betrayed her. He asked the disappointed woman to step out of his car, and he went home.

He'd been gone nearly five hours when he entered the dark house. It was after midnight. He'd checked on Rachel a few times, via text messages to

Cook who said she was fine. He knew how many slices of pizza she ate, when she took a bath, and when she got in bed.

He stood outside her bedroom door. He wanted to knock, but he didn't want to wake her, so he went to his bedroom, showered, and changed and climbed into his own bed. After lying there for an hour, he realized he wouldn't sleep until he checked on her for himself, so he got up and entered her bedroom.

Rachel pushed herself up in the bed. She apparently hadn't been sleeping either. "What are you doing in here?"

"I wanted to check on you."

"Haven't you gotten your reports from Cook? I think he's been doing a fine job of checking on me."

"It's not his job," he said. His guilt was strong. Couldn't she see that's why he was standing here? "I shouldn't have left you."

Rachel reached for the lamp on the nightstand and clicked. A halo of light flooded the area near her. He heard the anger in her voice before, now he could see it on her face. "I'm fine, Zeke."

"But I'm not," he said. "I miss you."

"I'm right here."

"It's different, Rae. I've kissed you and I –" He struggled with saying the words on his heart.

"You what?"

"I wanted to go further than a kiss, but I don't want to hurt you."

"You don't have to hurt me."

He looked into her sweet, innocent eyes. His beautiful Rachel was a grown woman, but in many ways she was naïve. He knew that. It was one of the things he loved about her. She was different from him in that respect. But now it was a problem because she was calling to him in a way that was making their relationship difficult. "I'm no more ready to be a husband to anyone than I was on the day Uncle Oliver told me I needed to be married. I'm not even ready to be in a committed relationship."

She sighed. "I didn't ask you for a committed relationship."

"I know that, but I miss what we had." He hesitated before adding, "I'm attracted to you. I can't go back to what it was before. I'm disappointed in myself, and I'm scared."

She nodded. "It's okay to be scared."

"No, it's not because if I can't resolve these feelings, I'm not going to be able to do a year in this marriage. I was expecting us to be buddies up in here, and that's not what this is."

"Buddies," she said. "Do you want to know how I feel?"

"Honestly?" He shook his head. "Not tonight. I'm struggling with processing my own feelings."

Rachel's hurt peppered her tone. "So, you get to come in here and tell me all your feelings, and I don't get to tell you mine?"

He shook his head again. "I'm not ready for it." He stepped backward out of the room, took the door by the knob and pulled it closed. He knew that was a crap thing to do, but it was done, and he didn't have the maturity or fortitude to undo it. He had no idea how Rachel felt. Probably the same as she'd felt the day she said she'd make the deal with him and that was not something he was willing to hear her say.

Chapter 22

Rachel fidgeted when she was nervous. She bounced one knee on top of the other. Picked up and put down her phone a few times and finally opened the menu. She fought the tears that wanted to fill her eyes and forced herself to stare at the images of food rather than allow the image of Zeke's back leaving the house, yet again, return to her mind.

"Sorry, I'm late." Harper slid into the booth across from Rachel and put down her bag. "I had to wait to get the estimates for Logan's backsplash. It's going to..." Harper looked in Rachel's eyes. She stopped mid-sentence. "Forget the backsplash. How are things going with you and Zeke?"

"They're not. He's working all the time."

"Is he still traveling?"

"Sometimes. But when he's here, he leaves before seven and he doesn't come home until after ten. Sometimes later."

Harper groaned. "Heavens."

Rachel continued, "He says it takes a lot to get a soccer team started. I have no doubt about that, but I never see him. Not even on weekends." Tears fell. "This was a horrible mistake. I've lost everything. And I wish I could move back into my house. At this point, it's embarrassing for me to be in his."

Harper grabbed her hand. "Shhh, we're going to fix this."

"How? He regrets it just as much as I do, Harp. We're not even friends anymore. We don't talk to each other. I used to talk to Zeke every day, even when he was traveling. He is behaving like we're two people with no history. I hate it." Rachel reached up and swept her hands through her hair. "I feel like God is punishing me for making a joke out of the sacrament of marriage."

"God is not punishing you. He doesn't punish us. You're punishing yourself."

"Okay, so now what? What's next?" Rachel stared at her sister. She could tell Harper was clueless about what to tell her to do, but it was nice being able to talk to her.

"Let's call Lauren," Harper said.

Rachel knew she had to look pitiful if Harper wanted to call Lauren.

Harper reached into her bag for her phone. She opened the video app and propped the phone up between them and dialed Lauren's number. "Any idea what time zone she's in?"

"Kenya is seven or eight hours ahead of us. She should be getting into bed."

Lauren answered on the third ring. She was wearing an oversized bonnet and a face peel mask. "It's late here."

Harper leaned closer to the phone so Lauren could see her face. "We know, but Rachel needs help."

Lauren yawned and stretched. "What is Zeke doing or not doing?"

Rachel repeated all the details she'd just shared with Harper, minus the tears.

Lauren was silent for a minute and then she said, "You guys need face time. What can you cook that he likes?"

Rachel thought about the question for a moment. "He likes my Bourbon chicken."

"Call him, tell him you made it and ask him what time he'll be home for dinner."

"What's that supposed to do?"

"It'll get him to come home at a decent hour. When you call, tell him you need to talk to him. Tell him it's important. He's still your friend. He'll come."

"The kissing changed things. I don't know what I am anymore," Rachel said.

"You're the one he's kissing. Things have shifted, but they've shifted in your favor. You wanted him. You have him. He's like a fish on a line. You just have to reel him in."

"How do I do that?"

"Tell him how you feel."

"He doesn't feel the same way."

"I don't mean about the love stuff. About your lost friendship. Tell him you feel abandoned in his house with his things. You need him to at least come home and keep you company." Lauren yawned again. "Stand up for yourself. He's the one who got over a hundred million dollars. You did him the favor. Once he starts spending time in the house, you can get more of that kissing and everything that follows. Don't let him walk away again. Strip if you have to, but get him in bed."

"If sex hooked a man wouldn't most women have one?" Harper asked.

Lauren's eye roll sent a strong message of annoyance. "This isn't just about sex. Zeke loves her. He either doesn't know or he's running from it. Once he makes love to you, his heart will explode. He won't be able to walk away."

"I don't know," Rachel cried. "This sounds risky, Lauren."

Lauren shrugged. "Honey, it is. Love is always risky, but you're already in this. You might as well give it your all. If it goes badly and you realize it'll never get right, I'll help you come up with another plan, but right now, I'm counting on love to win this. You are the man's wife."

Rachel's eyes met Harper's. Her sister took her hand. Her smile was hopeful. "I think she's right."

Rachel laughed. "You two are agreeing. It's definitely a season for miracles."

"Yeah, yeah. I'm sleepy," Lauren said. The screen went blank.

"Grouchy heifer." Harper closed the app and placed her phone down. "It's worth a try."

The waitress came to the table for their orders. Rachel silently prayed her sisters were right.

Chapter 23

Rachel entered the house. Kicking the door behind her, she took the grocery bags to the kitchen. She'd gotten everything she needed for the chicken. On the way home, she'd called and told Cook to take the night off.

She sent Zeke a text message stating: I've decided to cook dinner.

He replied: Why?

She rolled her eyes. What kind of question was that? She responded: I'm making Bourbon Chicken. What time will you be home?

He replied: I'm working late.

Lauren told her to call him. She could see her sister was right. These text messages were getting her nowhere, so she called.

He answered. "Is everything all right?"

How could he ask her that? Rachel wondered if he lived in an alternate reality where everything was okay. "I need to talk to you. Can you please let me know what time I can expect you?"

He was silent for a moment and then said, "Seven."

They ended the call and she got busy making dinner. He would be home in less than three hours. That's what she expected. But seven came and went without even the courtesy of a text message to let her know he was running late. The garage door did not go up until a few minutes after eight.

Rachel was still sitting at the table when he entered. She could tell he felt horrible about it. She stood and went to the kitchen to remove the food from the warming oven.

They ate in silence. Rachel asked him a few questions about the team, but his brief, bothered replies made it hard for her to keep pressing. He also spent some time scrolling through his phone. He did at least have the decency to ask her about her business. He said he'd seen her new designs on Instagram. When the meal was finished, he complimented her and sat there like he was expecting whatever bomb she had been waiting to drop on him.

"You're avoiding me."

Zeke shook his head. "That's not true. I'm just busy. I didn't expect it to be so much."

Rachel bit her lip. She fought being emotional.

"Why would I be avoiding you?"

"I don't know, Zeke, but this is not what I was expecting."

Confusion clouded his face over. "What were you expecting?"

"To still have my friend." She paused and sighed. "In all the years that I've known you, you've never been late for dinner or a movie or fishing or a party or anything without calling me to let me know. You've always given me that courtesy and then tonight, you come in here after 8 p.m."

"Oh, so what, we're going to have a married couple argument?" he asked, tossing his napkin on the table.

"We're going to talk like two adults," she said, getting up her courage.

He stood and so did she.

"Since when have you regarded me so little that you couldn't text and say I'm on the way or I'm not?"

He tossed his hands up. "Okay, I'll be more considerate."

Arms folded, she walked closer to him. "What's happened to us?"

He shook his head. "Nothing. I'm just working."

"You've had projects before. You've never gone on like this. We've always talked."

"This one is different."

"It's not your work," Rachel said. "You're not being honest with me."

He inhaled deeply, then shook his head. "Are you calling me a liar?"

She noted a slight tick of his mouth to the right. Frustration. Zeke was sick of this conversation, but he was no sicker than she was. "I'm not calling you a liar. I don't think you're being honest with yourself."

"Okay, you want me to say it again? How many times do you need to hear it? Things are different, Rae. I haven't been coming home because I don't know how to change it back."

They stood there with only the beats of silence between them. And then Zeke took a step, closer. Reached up and touched her chin and lowered his head to her lips. He gave her a peck and whispered, "I need some air."

She grabbed his arm. "Different isn't always bad."

He shook his head like he was disappointed in her. "You don't know what you're saying." He shrugged her loose, turned, and walked out of the house. Moments later, she heard his car leave the garage.

Chapter 24

Zeke stood on the other side of his brother's door for a few minutes before Ethan pulled it open. He followed him into the family room. "You weren't busy with Joy were you?" Zeke asked, referring to his three-year-old niece.

"No, she's been asleep." Ethan scratched the side of his face. "Can I get you something to drink? You hungry?"

Zeke took a seat on the sofa. "No. I'm good."

Ethan sat on the other end. "So, what's up?"

"You know. Same old thing. Rachel."

Ethan sat there for a moment without speaking. Then he said, "If it's the same old thing, I've got nothing new for you, man."

Zeke expected that, but he still needed to talk to someone. He needed to dump his feelings. "I don't want to go home."

Ethan chuckled.

"You think this is funny?"

"It's not funny laughter. There's nothing funny about you hurting someone I care about. Don't treat her like this, man."

"I would never intentionally hurt her. You know that."

Ethan cocked his head in his direction. "Intent is only a part of this. It only goes so far. Your actions are what matter." Silenced stretched between them for a minute and then Ethan continued, "Have you ever thought that maybe instead of running from the change, you could try to live with it. Maybe things have changed for her too."

Zeke wished he could agree. "They haven't. She told me as much tonight. She said she wants her friend back."

"You're telling me she hasn't given you any indication that things are different?"

Zeke thought about her last words, *"Different isn't always bad."* He dismissed them. She hadn't led with that. She led with their ruined friendship. "No," he said. Even though his heart wasn't sure, he was sure he wasn't going down the relationship road with Rachel.

Ethan shook his head. "I don't believe that. You don't think she's as scared of the truth as you are, but she's waiting for you to man up and take the lead in this situation. Rachel is the woman you've been looking for all your life."

"But I haven't been looking for a woman. I've never been interested in marriage. And just because I'm attracted to Rachel doesn't mean I want to be married."

"But you are married. It may not have happened for the reasons that most people get married for, but you're in it," Ethan said. "And this is Rachel. You guys have a lot in common. Maybe this is the way it's supposed to be. I think you should stop being afraid and give it a go."

"I'm not afraid."

"You're clearly afraid."

Zeke popped to his feet and walked to the other side of the room before stopping to take up space on the wall. "I could lose her completely."

"You could also gain her completely." Ethan leaned back into the sofa. "I know I'm in the middle of a divorce, so it would seem I'm not marriage friendly right now, but that's not true. Marriage was okay. I married the wrong person, and by now, you know it was about the will."

"I'm not discounting your advice, but—"

Interrupting him, Ethan said, "Yes, you are. You're discounting everything I'm saying, and I'm telling you don't be afraid of settling down. Just because you never had it in the plan doesn't mean it shouldn't be the plan."

Zeke nodded. "I need to go home."

Ethan put a hand on his shoulder and squeezed. "Absolutely. You should. Go talk to her."

Zeke spoke over a thick knot in his throat. "I will."

"And never stop talking to her. Once you stop, it's hard to get started again." Zeke felt the pain in his brother's words. He wondered if he was talking about his ex-wife or Lauren. He sensed the ending of that relationship was a bigger loss. Ethan swayed his palm toward the door. "Get out of here."

Zeke squared his shoulders and left his brother's house. It was time for him to stop running.

***

The house was quiet when Zeke arrived. Before he lost his courage, he went upstairs to Rachel's bedroom and knocked.

She invited him in. She was sitting in bed with the comforter pulled up around her neck. The lamp was on and it was clear from the book on her bed she'd been reading.

"I need to talk to you." Zeke took slow steps to the foot of the bed. "And I'm ready to listen to you."

"That would be a nice switch." Her tone wasn't sarcastic. He heard relief in her voice.

He swallowed his fear and hesitation. "I'm sorry I ran out on you. I'm sorry I ruined your beautiful dinner, and I'm sorry I made you cry."

Rachel just stared at him. Her big brown eyes told him nothing, but her energy felt right. She wasn't angry with him.

She pushed the comforter down, and pulled her long, gorgeous legs from under it before she stood. She was wearing a white nightgown. A short one made of a sheer fabric that showed not only her curves, but the outline of her body. He couldn't stop staring. Every cell and muscle in his body was awake and aware that she was the most beautiful woman he'd ever laid eyes on.

He took a deep breath and released it. "Rae, what are you doing?"

She took a few steps toward him and replied, "I'm becoming a wife. And I want you to be my husband."

"But..."

"No, but, please. Love me, Zeke." She placed a hand on his chest. He stared at her hand like it was a foreign body before pulling it off his chest.

"I didn't come in here to take advantage of you. We need to talk."

"No, we don't. Not tonight."

"I can't," he muttered, but he knew with the way she was looking at him, and the sweet peach and vanilla scent coming off her skin, that he could.

"You've done it with other women hundreds of times." She stepped closer.

He stepped back. "You are not some random woman."

"I know that, but I am a woman," she said. "I am your wife. You said things have changed. They've changed for me too. I want you as a husband. A real one. Don't make me beg."

His defenses melted. She didn't have to beg. Not when he felt the way he felt about her. Wives didn't beg their husbands—not even the reluctant husbands. He kicked off his shoes. He pulled his shirt over his head. He saw the admiration in her eyes. Rachel had seen his chest a hundred times, but she'd never looked at him like she was looking at him right now.

The air left his lungs completely. When he could speak, he said, "You're beautiful."

Rachel leaned toward him for a kiss. "I have something to tell you." She paused for a second. "I've never done this before."

Zeke looked like he was trying to interpret her meaning, so she clarified it for him. "I'm a virgin."

He stepped back—away from her. "Why didn't you tell me this before?"

Rachel shrugged. "Like when before?"

Realizing it was a silly question, he chuckled nervously. "Now I know we need to slow this down."

"I asked you not to make me beg."

Zeke sat on the bed. "I have to think."

Rachel sat next to him. She took his hand and whispered, "You think too much. I'm not a child. We're not making mud pies."

Zeke twisted his neck in her direction. She kissed the side of his face and neck. "Treat me like a woman."

Zeke eased her into the mattress. Rachel smiled. It was the smile of a winner. He realized their mud pie making days were long behind them. He couldn't fight her. He couldn't fight himself. He didn't want to fight love.

Chapter 25

Rachel's eyes fluttered open. She found herself alone in bed. Zeke left a note stating he'd gone to work. She groaned. It was Saturday. He didn't have to work. He'd chosen to work. She'd wanted him to stay home. She was no expert, but she thought last night was pretty amazing. But then she got self-conscious. Maybe it wasn't. Maybe that's why he left so early. Maybe he was disappointed in her. Zeke had had so many women that he wasn't used to someone as inexperienced as she was. He probably would never have married a virgin and now he was stuck with one.

Rachel had no idea what to do. She couldn't undo all the waiting she'd done. She couldn't undo her years of inexperience. And she wasn't going to regret anything that she did for God. Her faith in God was the reason she'd waited.

She got out of bed and ran a hot bath. She climbed in and soaked. She cried through her disappointment. Her heavy feelings were not about last night, or even her current situation. She was crying because she didn't want to be a disappointment to him. He was stuck with her for seven more months, but more importantly, she'd done all of this wrong. She'd manipulated a marriage when she knew this was not what God wanted. The Scripture says: *He who finds a wife finds a good thing.* It wasn't the other way around and it certainly wasn't he who marries for money finds a good thing.

Rachel finished bathing, moisturized her skin, and came out of the bathroom. She heard footfalls on the stairs. Moments later, Zeke was standing in the doorway with two lattes and a bag. She knew there were bagels inside because they'd had those lattes and bagels a thousand times. Her heart smiled.

He put the food down on the dresser. "I don't want to be in the office. I don't want to be apart from you." He pulled her close and ran his fingers under the thick mass of curls at the back of her neck.

Rachel's heart melted. "I thought maybe you had regrets."

He pressed his lips to hers. "I'd be lying if I didn't tell you I had thoughts this morning. I hadn't planned on this."

"This was my idea," Rachel insisted. "I asked you to treat me like a woman."

Zeke sighed. "I've already taken too much from you. Taking your virginity felt like robbery." She opened her mouth to protest, but he raised a hand to halt her. "Let me finish." He placed his hands around her waist. "But then I realized I didn't take from you. I made love to you last night because you gave yourself to me." He tilted her chin up and kissed her again. "I'm in love with you, Rae. I'm home because there's no place I'd rather be."

Rachel fought to keep her emotions under control. He was spinning a web with his words that she would never untangle herself from. She prayed God had answered her prayers, that He had fixed her hot mess, that this wasn't temporary. "I love you too," she said. She wrapped her arms around his neck and squeezed tight, hoping he would never let her go.

Chapter 26

"You've been married for six months, and you haven't taken your wife on a honeymoon." Cole Bennett stepped out of the fitting room in his tuxedo and up onto the step stool. He was being fitted for their cousin, Jacob Bennett's, wedding. "You, sir, are already failing in the newlywed husband department." The tailor rushed to him with his chalk and tape measure. "Rachel deserves better."

"Maybe he's training her to not have high expectations," Stone said. He was standing on the other step stool in the room. "I for one think it's a great way to start a marriage."

"If Stone thinks it's a great idea, you'd better go on a honeymoon quick," Logan said. "In fact, skip this wedding and save your own marriage."

All of the men laughed except Ethan. Zeke noticed he'd been pretty quiet today. Ethan declined being in the wedding party. He was only with them for the fitting because he wanted to hang out. When all of the Bennett men were in town, they tried to see each other. Stone lived in north Georgia—in the mountains on his horse ranch and Logan traveled back and forth to the hotels in the chain he'd acquired a few years ago. The fitting and the lunch that would follow was an opportunity for them to get together.

"I've been busy with Carolina United. You all know that and so does Rachel," Zeke said, inspecting a tie in his vicinity. "But…" he added before they could come down on him. "Since we'll be traveling to St. John for Jacob's big day, we're going to stay on the island for another week. Instant honeymoon."

Jacob stepped out of the fitting room. He pulled the jacket of his Morning Coat tuxedo together, he nodded. "That's a plan. Once I let my wife up for air, we can have dinner." He smiled and ran his finger across the rim of the top hat on his head. "Just get me to the church on time."

"You guys are completely killing the Bennett cool," Stone interjected. "I mean you're all getting married like old men."

Zeke couldn't disagree with that. It seemed like it was just yesterday that he'd walked down the aisle with Rachel and now just five months after meeting his fiancée, Jacob was getting married.

"Well, some of us are getting divorced." Ethan took a glass of champagne from the tray the young man serving them offered. "Or rather we are divorced, as of yesterday."

The group all turned to Ethan. They watched as he emptied the champagne flute and then picked up another. "Everyone take a glass. Let's toast to my news."

The server passed the tray to each of them. They all took a glass.

Stone stepped down from the alteration stoop. "Me first." He paused and then said, "Ethan, I'm sorry about your divorce, but I propose we drink to your newfound singleness. Welcome back to the best club on the earth. May you never let another woman get her hooks in you or your money or your time again." He raised the glass and took a sip. Stone didn't care that no one was drinking with him, and he didn't seem to care that Ethan didn't look happy.

"Never is a long time." Ethan hesitated but raised his glass. "I'll drink to the legal stuff being over and to having custody of my daughter."

Logan said, "Here's to having custody of my niece." They all drank.

"So, any chance you'll be trying to see if you can rekindle things with Lauren?" Cole asked.

The Adam's apple in Ethan's throat moved like he'd swallowed a grapefruit. He shook his head. "I'm not pursuing anything right now. And besides, things with Lauren ended badly and a long time ago."

"Hasn't stopped you from wanting her," Zeke said.

Stone walked closer to Ethan. "Look, the man just got a divorce. Stop trying to saddle him up with another woman…Lauren Ingram of all people. He's rode that horse."

"Could you please stop with the cowboy metaphors," Cole said laughing. "My God, you're a walking cliché." The men laughed.

Stone didn't. He said, "The Ingram sisters have cast a spell on you all. Zeke's married to Rachel and Logan's strung out on Harper. It's just a matter of time for the two of them."

Logan interrupted. "Don't bring me into this. Harper and I are in business together."

"You forgot about you and Addison." Cole tilted his glass in Stone's direction. They laughed again. "That's four out of the six of them."

Stone frowned. "What do you mean about me and Addison? The only use I'd have for her would be to get her in my bed for a weekend. You suckers are playing for keeps."

Zeke raised a finger. "Hold on now. She's my sister-in-law. I won't have any of that kind of talk."

"Don't worry," Cole said. "Addison is too smart to fall for the likes of Stone." The tailor was done with him. He stepped down and walked into the fitting room.

Once they were done, they went to Fontana's for a late lunch.

Zeke called Rachel from the car. "Are you finished shopping?"

"I just walked into the house with my bags. I'm going to put them in the suitcase right now and then I'll be done packing."

Zeke closed his eyes to the sound of her voice. He'd always loved talking to Rachel, but he couldn't discern when hearing her talk made everything in his world feel better than it had the minute before. "Good. Don't pack too many clothes. We won't need them."

She chuckled. "I would like to see the island, sir."

"Yeah, you'll see it all right. It's small. That won't take but a day."

"You're incorrigible."

He pulled the car into the parking lot of Fontana's and turned off the engine. "I may be, but it's more likely that you, Rachel Bennett, have cast a spell on me." He opened the car door and stepped out. "I'm here."

"Have fun," Rachel said.

"You're welcome to join me."

"And interrupt an all-male Bennett event? I will not." He could hear a smile in her voice.

"You could come in sixty minutes and we could have dessert."

"Or I could pack and just see you when you get home."

"I'll bring you something then?" he offered.

"No, I've gained some weight. I'll pass."

He smiled. "Every pound is in the right places."

"I'm glad you approve but leave the cake there and see if you can't find something sweet here." He heard a smile in Rachel's voice.

"Now you're tempting me to skip this lunch all together." He waited for everyone else to get out of their cars before he ended their call. He didn't care what Stone said or what Ethan had been through—what he had with Rachel was good. He was keeping it that way.

***

Jacob's wedding to Traci Dougan went off smoothly with an exchange of vows and rings on the beach behind the upscale resort they were staying at. It was followed by a sit-down dinner on the patio and dance music played by a local band that sampled R&B hits from the 80's and 90's—all to their taste since they'd grown up during that time.

Rachel took Zeke's hand and stood. "Come on and dance with me."

She and Zeke and all the guests danced and dined late into the evening. After the bride tossed her bouquet into Harper's arms and Jacob flipped the garter at Logan, the two cut the cake. The couple had a final toast before disappearing to the honeymoon suite.

Zeke excused himself to the restroom and Rachel stepped off the patio and raised her phone to take a few pictures of the sun as it set. This was a gorgeous place. She was so glad they were staying an extra week.

"This view is something else."

Rachel turned to find Stone joining her.

"It is," she replied, lowering her phone.

"I don't think I've ever seen an Ingram sister alone."

"Were you looking for any one particular sister?" Rachel asked. "Perhaps Addison."

Stone laughed. "Addison is always a welcome sight, but I was thinking Sienna. She set up this shing-ding."

Rachel knew he was lying. He had no more interested in seeing Sienna than he had in getting married himself, but she humored him. "She was able to do all of this remotely."

Rachel heard Zeke speaking behind her. "Don't listen to a word he says." Zeke put his body between the two of them. "I did not wet the bed at eight."

Stone laughed. He raised a finger and pointed at Zeke. "You know I was just about to tell her about that."

Rachel laughed. "He was not."

Stone clapped a hand over Zeke's shoulder. "I would never tell this beautiful woman that you actually peed the bed until you were ten. That's far too embarrassing."

"I was not ten." Zeke smirked. "Get lost."

"You two enjoy the belated honeymoon. I'm headed back to my little ranch." He turned to the patio area and said, "You can tell Addison I said hello." He smiled slyly and left them.

Rachel cocked her head and gave him a little side-eye attitude. "Stone is something else. Is that where you learned all your bachelor tricks? From your cousin?"

Zeke laughed. "No. I figured that out for myself, but I've been tamed. Love has a way of straightening a man out." He reached down and picked up a covered basket Rachel hadn't noticed he placed behind her. He took her hand. "Let's go for a walk."

Rachel fell into step with him. They walked down the quiet coastline as the full moon rose. From where they stood, it looked close enough to toss a shell at. With all the stars in the sky, it was mesmerizing. The tide receded and a gentle breeze wafted through the saltwater laced air.

Rachel wasn't a stranger to beautiful beaches. She and her sisters had made several trips to Destin, Florida and other places in the Caribbean, but this beach was special. It was the beach she was sharing with her husband.

Zeke stopped walking. "This is a good spot."

"There are so many people at the resort. I'm surprised it's so quiet down here."

He raised a finger and wagged it. "That's because I reserved it for us."

Rachel frowned. "Reserved the beach?"

Zeke nodded. "Yeah, you can book a half a mile for four hours at a time."

She chuckled. "I don't think that's what God had in mind when He gave us these amazing views."

"Well, God wasn't the concierge. His name was Antonio." He put the basket down, removed the blanket and spread it out and dropped his phone and sunglasses on it. Rachel added her phone and shoes to the pile. Zeke pulled her into another kiss before saying, "I wonder how warm that water is."

Rachel rolled her neck. "Are you trying to get me to skinny dip?"

Zeke raised his hands to the side of her face. "Your suit is in the basket, but if I thought I could get you to leave it there..."

Rachel looked up and down the beach, realizing that with a half a mile of space, no one would see them. She pulled the loop of the bow behind her neck that held the halter top of her dress up. She let the dress fall to the ground. "We need to think of a punishment for the last one in." She giggled and hurriedly stripped before making a dash for the water.

Zeke was right behind her. When he caught her, he pulled her into an embrace and kissed her.

"It's warmer in here than I thought it would be." Rachel spun, making rippling waves in the water as she moved away from him. "I need to think of a something...I won. You were the last one in."

Zeke watched her for a moment and then stepped until he reached her. He pulled her close to him again. "That's where you're wrong. You're naked, Mrs. Bennett. I am the winner."

Rachel took both her hands and pushed him down into the water before swimming away.

Chapter 27

Rachel tossed the pee stick in the trash and felt relief wash over her. The test was negative. What was wrong with them? They were having way too much unprotected sex for people who weren't trying to get pregnant.

Ridiculousness.

She closed her eyes and dropped her head back. Things were good with Zeke, but there was no way he was ready for a baby. Heck, she wasn't ready. Thank God they didn't have to be.

This was the second month she'd prayed for a period. She and Zeke had been using birth control, but they'd been careless way too many times to count. She stood and walked into the bedroom. She was packing again. She finished tossing the last of the things she was taking in the suitcase, picked up her bag and took it down the stairs.

Rachel didn't like surprises. She knew it had to do with the way she found out her parents died. She and her sisters opened the door to a visit from the sheriff. He'd come to deliver the horrible news that they'd been killed in a car accident. She knew surprises were usually supposed to be a happy unexpected situation, but she equated them with anything that came out of nowhere. She avoided them at all costs, but she was taking Harper's advice and dropping in on Zeke.

She hadn't seen him in over a week. She missed him. She found out there was a screen printer's conference in Charlotte, so she decided it was the perfect excuse to be in the city with him.

The Bennetts had a jet, but she chose to fly commercial because one, she had no idea how to reserve the thing and two, she did not love flying. The idea of being alone on a plane was scary.

The uptown location of the Charlotte Viva-Millennium earned its reputation for elegance with its chandeliers, marble floors, posh furniture, artwork, and exotic plants in every corner. Rachel took a shuttle from the airport. Zeke would scream if he knew she took an Uber. She didn't want to fight with him. Not tonight. Tonight, she wanted nothing but positive energy, so she did things his way. She exited the limo, tipped the driver like the Bennett she'd become, and entered the hotel. Pulling her bag behind her, she approached the front desk.

The clerk offered her a pleasant smile. "Good afternoon. Welcome to the Viva-Millennium. How may I assist you?"

"My husband, Zeke Bennett, is staying here." She slid her driver's license across the counter.

The clerk typed. She raised her eyes to Rachel's and asked, "Is Mr. Bennett expecting you?"

Rachel shook her head. "I'm a surprise. It's our 9-month anniversary. Is that a thing?" She giggled. The clerk did not.

She slid the license back to Rachel. "Unfortunately, Mr. Bennett doesn't have you listed on his reservation, so I'm unable to give you a key to the room, but you can leave your bag with me. Once you locate Mr. Bennett, have him call and let us know to give you access to the room."

Rachel hadn't expected this, but she realized she should have. Why would they let her into his room? She retrieved her license and rolled the bag in the clerk's direction. In exchange, the woman gave her a small ticket.

She looked at the wall clock. It was almost 6 p.m. Zeke was usually headed back to the hotel around seven every night. She knew this because he called her. He also dined in the hotel restaurant with his partners.

"Is it okay if I go into the bar area?"

The clerk smiled again. "Of course, Mrs. Bennett. We also have a spa and a few shops at the first right."

Rachel knew nothing about hotels that charged five hundred dollars a night and the amenities they offered, so she was impressed. A massage sounded heavenly. She'd been stressed lately—she was missing Zeke, her period was late, and her work was getting demanding. It was good. She was getting orders—especially custom orders, but it was a lot to juggle. At Zeke's insistence, she'd finally hired a virtual assistant to handle customer service, billing, and social media marketing, but that was long overdue. She had just finished training the woman.

Rachel arrived at the spa. She was in luck, there was an open appointment. She opted to do a nourishing body treatment. It promised soft, supple, and glowing skin. She'd never had anything like it before. Since she was spending a small fortune, she decided to go for a treatment Zeke would appreciate. She showered and after sliding into the plush robe, she took a seat and enjoyed the lemonade and tasty pastries the hostess offered. Her treatment was wonderful. She felt like a million dollars as she exited the spa. Her phone rang and she was glad to see it was Zeke.

They exchanged greetings and chatted for a few minutes before Rachel asked him where he was.

"Pulling up to the hotel. Sorry I didn't call when I first got in the car, but I had to deal with some tax stuff with my attorney."

"No problem," she said. "I know you're busy. I do miss you though."

"I miss you too." He paused. "Isn't it weird saying that?"

"A little," she agreed.

"Hey, I have great news." Rachel could hear excitement in his voice. "I was going to wait until tonight to tell you, but I can't. The guys love the shirts you designed."

"Great. I can't wait until the season. Do you know how much business I'm going to get once the world knows I designed the logo for Carolina United?"

"You won't need my million." Zeke laughed.

"I already have half of it," she teased.

"Well, you don't need that either because you've got all of me."

Rachel's stomach fluttered. This sweet and romantic Zeke Bennett was an improved version, and she loved it. She walked toward the front entrance of the hotel. She watched as Zeke and his business partners got out of a limo.

"Babe, we're going to have dinner and talk more strategy. I'll call you as soon as we're done."

Rachel scooted out of sight. "Wait, honey, what's your room number?"

"Six twenty-two. Why?"

"It's our anniversary. I want to send you something."

Rachel could see the huge smile on his face. "That's sweet, but we can celebrate Friday when I get home." It warmed her heart to know he was as excited as she was.

"We'll do that too," she said. "Enjoy your dinner. Call me when you're done."

He agreed and they ended the call. Rachel watched him and his partners pass her on the way to the restaurant area.

She went back to the desk. The woman who'd helped her earlier was not there, so she decided to try her luck again.

"May I help you, ma'am?"

"Yes, I seem to have locked myself out of my room. Bennett. Room 622." She pushed her license across the desk.

The clerk typed and then asked, "Will you need turn down service this evening, Mrs. Bennett?"

"No, thank you." Within moments she had a key, and she was on her way to the room. She decided to have them bring her bag up later because if she asked for it now, the clerk would know she hadn't checked in.

Harper had been right. This was an excellent idea, or at least she thought so until she entered the room.

"Is that you?" a female voice called out from inside.

Rachel froze at the door. Her heart stopped. She forced herself further into the room.

A woman came out of the bedroom. Serene.

Rachel felt like she'd been kicked in the stomach.

"Oh, the new Mrs. Zeke, right?"

Rachel blinked. Had this...she stopped herself from thinking the word she wanted to think...called her Mrs. Zeke? "It's Mrs. Bennett."

"Right," she said, smirking. "Zeke isn't expecting you." She was definitive about the statement.

Rachel swallowed. No longer frozen, her heart was beating again, but now it was breaking. "And I wasn't expecting you."

Serene crossed her arms over her chest. "It's not what you think."

"You're in my husband's hotel room. You've just told me he wasn't expecting me."

"I shouldn't have presumed he isn't expecting you. I asked about you yesterday, and he said you were in Atlanta."

Swallowing back the bile rising in her throat, Rachel turned to leave and then she realized this was her husband's room. There was no reason to let this tramp have it a moment longer. "Serene, you should leave." *Before I snatch your throat out and end up in jail.*

The woman smiled and picked up her handbag. "I'll do that."

Rachel backed into the sofa and dropped down. She heard the door open and then she heard Zeke say, "What the devil?"

"Let me know when you get that divorce," Serene said the words like they were a plaything. "Good luck, darling."

There was silence for a moment and then Zeke called to her. "What do you mean good luck?"

Rachel stood and stepped into the opening where she could be seen. Serene had already disappeared through the door. Zeke let it close. He nearly jumped when he saw her. He placed his hand over his heart. "Rae, you startled me. What are you doing here?"

"I was trying to surprise you." Rachel tried to sound strong, but her voice cracked on every word. "But I'm the one who's surprised."

Zeke closed the space between them. He attempted to kiss her, but she turned her head.

"What's going on?" Tears the size of miniature soccer balls fell down her cheeks. "Babe, what did she say to upset you? Why were you with her?"

Rachel raised a hand to wipe her face. "Why was I with her? I wasn't with her."

Zeke squinted like he couldn't see what she'd just seen. "You're here, and she just walked out. I'm confused."

A surge of anger filled her. "No! I'm the one who's confused."

"Rachel, tell me what happened. Why were you here with her?"

"Zeke, the question is why was she here? But then that's a dumb question. It's obvious why she's here."

Zeke shook his head. "I have no idea what I just walked in on."

"Me either, dear." Rachel picked up her handbag and tried to pass him.

He grabbed her arm. "Baby, talk to me."

Although she tried, Rachel couldn't keep the sob in her throat from escaping. "I came to surprise you. I walked in, and she was here—in the bedroom. Obviously waiting for you."

Zeke shook his head again. "No, no, no. I did not let her in my room, and I did not give her permission to have access to my room."

Rachel folded her hands over her chest. "You just asked me what I was doing here. I didn't hear you ask her that."

"Rae, I was—" Zeke rolled his bottom lips in and bit it. "This is a misunderstanding."

"But you knew she was here. You talked to her yesterday."

"At the bar. It was a three-minute conversation about nothing."

"You told her we were getting a divorce."

Zeke's eyes widened. He reached for her arm. "I have no idea why she said that."

"I've known you most of my life, and I know you're too smart not to know anything." She pulled her arm out of his hand.

"Rachel, you need to listen to me. I did not invite Serene into this room."

"But you didn't tell me your ex was staying in the same hotel either."

He threw his arms up. "It's a big hotel. She's probably in Charlotte for work. I don't know. I didn't ask her."

"Oh yeah, Charlotte, North Carolina is a real fashion hub." Rachel rolled her eyes. "You're not this dumb. She's here for you." She paused. "Wait, what am I saying? I'm not this dumb. I'm not dumb enough to believe they let her in here when I had to manipulate my way in even with your name on my driver's license."

"I'm going to get to the bottom of this." Zeke took her arm again. Pulling her, he walked to the hotel phone, pushed the speaker, and dialed the front desk. "This is Zeke Bennett. I just arrived in my room, and I had a guest here."

"Hold please, Mr. Bennett."

Rachel pulled her arm out of his hand again. "Stop it! They don't have anything to do with this."

"Rachel, please. I swear. I am not sleeping with Serene."

"So, tell me what you're doing in here? You said you were having dinner with your colleagues. What was she? Dessert first?"

"Mr. Bennett, we don't —"

"Hold on!" Zeke barked at the phone. Rachel raced for the door, he followed her and pushed it closed before she could slide out.

"Let me out of this room!"

"I won't. I haven't done anything wrong."

"You're a liar and a cheat!"

He shook his head. "I'm not doing anything with Serene. I haven't been with anyone since we got married. I haven't wanted anyone other than you."

"Mr. Bennett—" the man on the phone called through the speaker.

Zeke raised a finger. "Wait, let me find out who let her in, and we can resolve this."

He walked back to the phone.

Rachel opened the door and ran out of the room. She heard Zeke call behind just as she slipped into the open elevator. She pressed the button for the lobby and the doors closed in his face.

When she reached the first floor, she went back to the spa. She didn't want to see Zeke, and she didn't want to hear his lies. She needed somewhere to hide. She knew he'd look for her in the lobby. Her phone began to ring. She sent his calls to voicemail. After three calls, she turned off the phone.

"Can I help you, ma'am?" the clerk asked.

"I was here earlier for a body treatment. I think I lost an earring."

"Could you describe it?"

"Diamond." Her voice cracked on the lie. "A stud."

"Do you remember the room you were in?"

"C," she said. "But I also took a shower in the first stall."

"I'll check those areas. Please have a seat."

Rachel hated lying like that, but she needed time. She needed to be able to sit here until Zeke was no longer hunting for her.

After a few minutes, the woman came back out. Of course, she hadn't found anything.

"Maybe I lost it in my room," Rachel said.

"I can call and ask the maid to look for you. What room is it?"

"No, it's okay. I can check later." She took a seat. "I'm waiting for a friend."

The woman cocked an eyebrow, but left her alone.

Rachel didn't know how long she'd sat there staring at the paintings on the wall and trying to escape the reality of what she'd just experienced. Zeke was a playboy. What made her think marrying him and telling him he had to be faithful would change that? She wasn't even sure she should be mad at him. She was the fool.

"Ma'am," a voice interrupted her thoughts. She looked up to see the clerk. "Your friend doesn't appear to be coming. We're closed. Perhaps you could meet in the lobby."

Rachel stood and walked out of the spa. She kept an eye out for Zeke. There was no sign of him. She retrieved her luggage and walked out the front entrance of the hotel. A taxi was there. She flagged the driver and climbed in.

"I'm going to make a hotel reservation at the airport. Just head in that direction."

As the taxi pulled away, she felt a piece of her soul leave. It stayed at the Viva-Millennium with her hopes, dreams, and the friendship she'd gambled and lost.

I'm not going to cry in the back of this taxi like some tired cliché out of a movie.

She made an online reservation and told the driver where to take her.

Rachel entered her hotel room. Even though Zeke's room at the Viva was a blur, the opulence was thick. That was missing here. Not that it mattered. She would not find comfort tonight in any room anywhere. She closed the door. She stood there for a moment, her emotions heavy, the pain in her heart overwhelming. Tears began to slide down her face again. She was finally free to let them flow. Pain shot through her abdomen. A cramp. Her period.

"Great," she cried, but she realized it was just as well. Tonight, all her illusions about her marriage had ended. At least she wasn't pregnant.

Chapter 28

"Tell me where she is."

Harper, Addison, and Sienna looked up from their menus.

Addison rolled her eyes. "Zeke, get out of here before I call your attorney and tell him she's left you."

"Really, Addison?" he said. "Is that what you're thinking of doing?"

She rolled her eyes harder.

"Don't worry. My attorney knows my wife has left me. He feels sorry for me, especially since he realizes how much I love her."

Addison snarled. "What would make him think you were telling the truth when you began this entire thing on a lie?"

"Maybe it was my tears," Zeke said smartly. "He's like an uncle. He knows when I'm hurting." He raised a hand to wash his face and ended with a clenched fist. "I've tried to be patient. I've tried to wait for her to come back on her own, but it's been a month. If you don't tell me where she is, I'm going to hire someone to find her."

Addison pointed an angry finger. "Leave her alone. She doesn't want to talk to you and neither do we."

He swallowed the words he wanted to say. These Ingram sisters stuck together. But they were sticking together for the wrong thing now. "I know you all think I cheated."

Harper chimed in. "Serene in your hotel room would indicate that."

"I didn't do anything wrong. If Rachel would talk to me, I could clear this up."

Addison waved him away. "Get lost."

He looked at Harper and Sienna. They weren't as angry as Addison, but neither was going to crack.

"I can prove it," he said.

Harper cleared her throat. "So you've said."

"Are you giving her my messages?"

"We can't." Harper was clearly breaking some truce they'd made because Addison looked like she wanted to shut her up. "We don't know where she is."

Addison cut her eyes at her sister and added, "Harper's telling the truth. We don't know."

"She's not in touch with any of you?"

Sienna shrugged. "She said she needed time alone."

"But it's been a month."

"We miss her too," Harper said. "But we can't help you."

He closed his eyes. He felt like falling through the floor. "This wasn't worth it."

"Sluts rarely are." Addison's gift for snark was making this worse.

"That's not what I mean. I'm talking about the marriage. The money." He shook his head. "I should have kept my friend."

"It was already too late for that," Harper said. "She married you because she loved you. You were too busy chasing your man parts around to see it."

Zeke nodded. "Yeah, well, do you think this is easy for me? I love her too."

The waitress approached the table.

"If you talk to her, please tell her to call me. Tell her I can prove everything. Tell her I love her. Tell her to come home."

Sienna and Addison wouldn't look at him, but Harper gave him an empathetic smile. He left them and walked out of the restaurant. Once outside, he took out his phone and placed a call.

"Yes, this is Zeke Bennett. We spoke last week. I need you to use every resource you have to find my wife."

***

The detective had a report. They knew she'd left Atlanta a few weeks after the blow up in Charlotte. Where she'd been in the city all that time, they could not say, but she'd flown to Miami. She'd taken ten-thousand dollars in cash out of her account. She was running her business by email and from a burner phone, but there were no more new orders. She had essentially stopped taking orders after she'd filled the ones she had in the pipeline.

Logan entered his family room from the kitchen. He put two sodas on the table and flipped open the box holding the pizza that had just been delivered.

"I'm concerned that she's by herself." Zeke said. He caught the look Logan and Ethan exchanged. Worry.

"If she's staying at a hotel in Miami, he'll find her," Logan said.

Zeke raised a hand and washed his face with it before crashing against the cushion behind him. "Maybe not with cash."

"She still had to register with ID. Only the seedy places don't require it. She's not going to stay in a dump," Ethan added.

"The detective is checking them." Zeke leaned forward. He planted his elbows on his thighs and dropped his head in his hands. "I shouldn't have done this. If I hadn't married her, she would be here in Forest Hills, sitting in her office making t-shirt graphics or hanging out with her sisters or even hanging out with me. Not in Miami."

"You two were happy and you'll be happy again."

"When, in the afterlife?"

"She'll come home."

"It's been five weeks."

Logan grunted. "She's hurt."

"Five weeks of not talking to me hurt?" Zeke fell back. He sank as low in the chair as he could. It didn't match how low he felt. "She's not even in touch with her sisters. I'm losing my mind."

"You'll be okay." Logan offered him a plate with two slices of pizza. He shook his head. He had no appetite.

"If I didn't have my work, I'd have already gone insane." Zeke picked up a throw pillow, squeezed his frustration into it a few times and put it down. "She could have at least waited for me to explain."

Logan nodded. "Yeah, man."

Zeke looked to Ethan for solidarity. "Right?"

Ethan didn't make eye contact with him. He was scrolling through his phone. "Look, you can't call it with women. They get emotional and draw their own conclusions."

"But she's had time to calm down."

Ethan glanced at him and nodded unconvincingly. Zeke didn't get the sense he was on his side.

He cocked an eyebrow. "Say what you have to say, E."

"No, it's just that... you know...you did have a reputation for being a player. You look guilty."

Zeke's frustration was at an all-time high. "I know that, but I can prove what Serene did. If Rachel was at least in touch, I could show her."

Logan asked, "Do you believe the sisters?"

"I'm trying to."

"Have you talked to Lauren?" Ethan asked.

"On the phone and then my detective did."

"Lauren's not likely to crack on the phone. If any of them knows where she is, it's her."

Zeke nodded. I considered that, but I can't see Lauren keeping it from the others."

"I'd keep your secret. If the situation was reversed and you swore me to secrecy, I wouldn't tell this big head." He cocked a finger at Ethan. "Maybe you should go see Lauren. Show up. Show her you mean her sister well."

Zeke nodded. Ethan was right about Lauren. She might be the key to finding Rachel.

***

The flight to Chile was nine hours. Lauren was on a new assignment in Arica photographing an annual arts festival that took place in various locations throughout the country. He'd never been to Chile. He didn't have any expectations of what it would be like but found Arica to be crowded during the festival.

Ethan was with him. Moral support, he called it, but Zeke was sure Ethan wanted to see his old girlfriend. He and Lauren had unfinished business.

Lauren was easy to find. She was a Black American female photographer. He asked and people pointed until they made their way to a historic cathedral where she was working. They hung back and watched her for a while as she took pictures of the last of a group of dancers on the tail end of a parade. As evidenced by her squint, she spotted them from a distance. She didn't look excited to see either of them, but she met them halfway in the street.

"Bennetts. We Ingrams can't escape you," she said to Zeke, and then she looked at his brother. "Ethan."

Ethan's wry smile matched hers. "How are you, Lauren?"

She held up the camera that was hanging from a strap around her neck. "Busy."

Zeke looked around at the thinning crowd and then checked his watch. "It's dinnertime isn't it? I was hoping you would dine with us."

"Dinner won't get you what you want. You wasted your time coming here."

Zeke persisted, "What about dinner anyway? You must be itching to speak English."

Lauren smirked and replied, "Mi asistente habla ingles."

Zeke chuckled. "I didn't know you had an assistant with you."

"It wasn't for you to know." She cocked her head in Ethan's direction. "Or your sidekick."

Ethan smirked and shoved his hands in his pockets.

"We're at the Apacheta," Zeke said, advising her of their hotel.

She nodded. "So am I, but of course you know that." She hesitated for a moment. "Let's go. I know you rich boys have a driver. You'll save me cab fare."

Ethan sent a text to the driver they'd hired and within five minutes, he was opening the door to the car for them. They went back to the hotel, showered, and met Lauren in the lobby and traveled to a restaurant.

They dined on French inspired, local foods that included lamb and rock fish and plantain and wine—really good wine.

"Do you ever plan to stop traveling?" Ethan tossed his napkin on his empty plate.

Lauren raised her glass and took a drink. "I like my work. No reason to stop."

Dinner had been nice, but Zeke thought it prudent to interrupt before Ethan pissed Lauren off or vice versa. The two had a history of doing that. "Can I just..." Zeke paused. "I need to know if you know anything about where Rachel is."

Lauren released a long breath. "I told you, you wasted your time coming here. I told you over the phone —"

"Yeah, I know what you told me. I believe Harper and Addison and Sienna and Zoe. I do, but I don't believe your sister disappeared off the face of the earth without you knowing where she is."

Lauren rolled her eyes.

"I am begging you, Lauren, please."

"Why should I tell you anything? You hurt her."

"I didn't hurt her. She only thinks I did." Zeke removed his phone from his pocket and pulled up a file to show her.

She looked and then glanced at Ethan like she was expecting him to tell her whether or not it was credible.

Zeke reached for her hand and squeezed it. He wanted her to feel his desperation. "Please, tell me where she is. I'm losing my mind."

Lauren's heart softened right before his eyes. "I'll talk to her."

"When?"

"Soon. She'll call me."

"You can't call her?"

Lauren seemed to lose her appetite. She put down her fork and placed her napkin on the plate. The rims of her eyes told her story; she was sad too. "I can't call her. She deserves her privacy. For all I know, you have my phone records."

"I wouldn't disrespect you that way."

"Zeke, you're going to have to be patient. She calls me. When she does, I'll tell her."

He bit his lip. He knew the answer to his question, but he asked anyway. "So, she's not here—in Chile?"

Lauren shook her head. "You know she didn't enter this country. Her passport would have been too easy to trace."

Lauren was right. His detective told him that much, but he had to ask. Desperation was making him stupid and angry. He wanted to scream, curse, cry, or throw something, but he kept his emotions under control. "Thanks, Lauren."

The waitress came to the table with a dessert tray. Zeke stood. He was full, exhausted, and frustrated. "I'm going to go back to the hotel. Enjoy dessert." He didn't wait for them to reply. He sailed out of the restaurant leaving Ethan and Lauren to either make love or war like they always did.

Zeke and Ethan stayed in the capital city of Santiago for a few days. They watched soccer games and Zeke scouted out local talent in the high school and community. He'd just touched down in Charlotte when a text came through on his phone.

I'll be home next week.

He dropped his head back. Was she seriously not going to call him? Had Lauren told her he was innocent? He dropped his head in his hands. Why was she doing this to him?

A few text messages came in on his phone from his business partners. They confirmed one of the MLS Cup playoff games would be held in their new stadium on Zeke's one-year anniversary. He'd prayed the date would work out that way, so they'd have lots to celebrate. He also knew without Rachel, he would not be a part of the Sirens organization, so the date was significant.

His phone dinged a reminder. He had a meeting in ten minutes. He was grateful he had his work to keep him busy.

Chapter 29

Rachel turned the key in her door. She released a long breath. Home. She couldn't believe she'd been gone for almost four months. She pushed the door closed and pulled her suitcase inside. She dropped her keys on the foyer table and kicked her shoes off. The house looked exactly as she'd left it. She was grateful for the housekeeper she'd hired to keep the dust bunnies away.

She passed the family room and noted the empty space over the fireplace. Her precious print was hanging in Zeke's house—what had been their house, but wasn't anymore. She opened the refrigerator and was happy to see the items stocked that she'd asked Sienna to pick up for her, especially the orange juice because she'd been craving it. She fixed a tall glass, finished it, and then followed up with water.

"I need a nap," she whispered, noting the time was noon. She was used to sleeping at her leisure and midday naps came naturally. She blamed it on depression, but she realized that wasn't really the reason she was sleeping.

She walked past her office on the way to her bedroom. She could see the huge pile of mail on the desk, but decided she'd sift through it later. Her bills were paid online monthly, so anything else in there was probably not that important.

She entered her bedroom, stripped out of her clothes and climbed into her bed. "Home sweet home," she whispered before closing her eyes. But as she drifted off, she realized that being here and facing Zeke was going to be anything but sweet.

Hours later, she found herself turning the key in another door she hadn't entered in a long time. Zeke's house. She released a long breath before entering. It was Thursday, so she knew Cook was off. The housekeeper was also off. She went directly to the office she and Zeke shared. Her things were just as she'd left them. She thought she'd wanted to pack up her personal mementos, but she didn't have the energy for it. Napping did nothing to energize her. She'd lost too much in the horrible decision she'd made.

She left the office and went to the family room. She stopped in the door and squinted over the fireplace. Her Geneva Boseman print had been replaced. She bit her lip and walked further into the room. Her print had been placed against the wall. She touched the painting that was hanging and looked at the raised signature on the canvas.

"It's the original." Zeke's voice came from behind.

Rachel closed her eyes. She hadn't expected him to be home. "I see."

"I had to go through a lot to get it. Had to convince the owner to part with it."

Rachel opened her eyes to the original *Spirit* painting by Boseman. She knew he had to have paid a fortune for it.

"It arrived early, but I thought it would be a nice anniversary gift."

Rachel swallowed her shaky emotions before speaking. "I thought you were in Charlotte."

"Obviously," he said.

A tear fell down Rachel's cheek. She reached up to wipe it before she turned around to face him.

"But I've been expecting you so..." Zeke's mouth dropped open. He shook his head. Her belly was protruding. She was pregnant. He'd been leaning on the door jamb, but now he walked to her. She raised a hand to halt him.

"How could you do this to me?" he asked. "I've been out of my mind and now..."

"You did this to us."

"No," he shook his head again. "I didn't. I told Lauren I had proof, but you wouldn't talk to me. You wouldn't even hear me out and then to hide..." He closed the distance between them. He placed a hand on Rachel's face and then lowered it to her small belly. "You hid our baby from me?"

"My pregnancy." Tears streamed down Rachel's face.

"You made a baby...by yourself?" She watched as a full gamut of emotions ran over his face before he asked, "You didn't think I had a right to know you were pregnant?"

"I needed time alone. I needed to accept that I was doing the one thing I thought I'd never do—have a baby before marriage. I didn't keep my virginity for twenty-nine years for that."

"But you're not alone."

She blinked back tears. "I feel alone."

Zeke pulled his phone from his pocket, swiped, opened a file and handed it to her. It was a video recording. It took a moment for her to realize what it was. She played it twice before she accepted that it was Serene paying a maid to let her into Zeke's room at the Viva-Millennium.

She handed him his phone. "So you were telling the truth."

"Didn't Lauren tell you I had proof?"

"Yes."

Pushing to his feet, he walked away from her, stopping to lean on the door jamb that separated the room from the foyer. "But you still stayed an extra week."

She clasped her hands together and crushed anxiety into her palms. "I was taking a class in textile design. I wanted to finish it."

Now the only emotion on his face was frustration. "Rachel don't play with me. Were you in Chile?"

She shook her head. "No. I was in Puerto Rico."

He sighed. "Why didn't you call me after I showed Lauren my proof?"

"I needed time."

"To finish your class?" Sarcasm and frustration fell on every word he said.

"No. It wasn't just about that."

"You've been gone for six weeks. You were wrong not to let me speak. You were wrong to leave me. You were wrong to stay away so long. You were wrong to –"

She raised a hand to stop him. "I can see I was wrong about Serene." She lowered it and resigned herself to the truth. "And that makes me the only liar here."

He frowned. "What do you mean?"

"She was the reason I left, but she's not the only reason I stayed gone." She hesitated. "I had to spend some time with God to pray and repent. I also needed to get my head and my heart together."

"Rae, I don't understand. What did you lie about?"

"You don't want a baby. You didn't even want a wife."

"Now wait a minute—"

"Let me speak." She walked away from him and sat. "I manipulated you into this marriage, Zeke."

His frown deepened.

"I knew that I'd fallen in love with you. I think I've known that for years. I just pushed my feelings down every time they tried to bubble up, but then there was nowhere else in my belly for them to go. I had nowhere else to push them." Rachel's eyes filled with tears. "I asked my sisters what I should do about it. We…some of us decided I should try to seduce you. Because just telling you the truth was too much like right."

Zeke squinted. It was clear he was trying to get his brain to understand what she was saying.

"Your need for a wife to get your money became a part of my master plan. I knew you'd never marry some random woman, and I didn't think you'd marry me, but then I used the one thing we've had between us to get what I wanted…" Zeke stood there waiting for her answer. She felt terrible. "…Your trust. You married me because you knew you could trust me."

"Rae—"

"No, let me get this out. I've spent the past month trying to find the words and the last week trying to find the nerve to say them." She sighed. "I was dishonest with you. I betrayed you. I was wrong. And now my wrong has grown into more than you ever signed up for. I am ashamed of what I did to you." She stood. "Let's just finish the term of our agreement without losing any more than we already have."

She moved to walk away from him, but he caught her hand. "You are not leaving. We're not done talking. That's my baby you're carrying." Zeke placed his hands on either side of her belly. He pulled her down on his lap and said, "I don't care how we came to be together. I wouldn't care if you drugged me and pulled me down that aisle."

"But—"

Zeke raised a hand and shushed her with a warm finger against her lips. "I love you. We can't go back to being friends or neighbors and you're definitely not about to be my baby's mama."

She smiled and raised a hand to his face. "Are you sure you don't need time to think about all of this? To process it? A baby is a big deal."

He rubbed her belly. He seemed mesmerized by the small mound. "It's our big deal."

Rachel smiled. "Are you sure you feel that way? I couldn't bear it if you changed your mind."

"Rae, I know how to keep a woman from getting pregnant. Every time I made love to you without protection, I think I secretly hoped…" he paused. "I love you so much. I wanted a part me inside of you." He rested his forehead against hers. "I wanted this."

Rachel pulled back and kissed his face multiple times before wrapping her arms around his neck. "I love you so much Zachary Bennett."

"I love you too," he whispered then planted a trail of kisses to her lips. "This baby is a blessing from God."

Just then Rachel felt a flutter in her uterus. She nearly jumped off his lap. "Oh my goodness. He moved." She placed Zeke's hand over to the area where she felt it. "Here."

They were still for a moment before Rachel said, "Repeat what you said."

"My baby is a blessing from God."

It happened again. "You can't feel it. It's just a light flutter, but I'm thinking he or she felt you."

"Boy or girl?"

"I think it's too early to know." Rachel laced her fingers through his.

"How far along?"

"Seventeen weeks. I was pregnant on our honeymoon, but I didn't know. I kept getting my period."

They stared into each other's eyes for a long moment before Zeke said, "Let's go upstairs. It's time for the baby to meet daddy."

Rachel laughed and slapped his arm. "You're terrible, you know that?"

Zeke swept her hair off her shoulder. "I can't think of a lot of words to describe me right now, but suffice to say, I'm a man who's missed his wife." He smiled suggestively, stood, and pulled her up. He tugged her to his chest and folded her body into his before kissing her hair and forehead. He pulled back and stared into her eyes. Rachel thought her heart would burst. "I've got everything I want in this life," Zeke said, "All I need is you."

Rachel smiled. She pushed up on her toes and pecked him on the lips. "Me too."

Chapter 30

Opening day at the Carolina United-Sirens stadium was a flurry of activity. The Sirens were playing an exhibition game with Atlanta. Afterward, a championship cup game was being played. Rachel and her sisters traveled on the Bennett jet to Charlotte and rode in a limo to the stadium. They met the Bennetts—all of them—and the other owners' families in the owner's suite. The Sirens had renovated one of the club suite areas to make it their own.

Rachel's logo design was prominently engraved in gold on the double doors at the entrance. Once inside, her sisters' heels clicked on the marble floors. Rachel wore blinged out sneakers. She was hard pressed to walk in heels with the extra weight she was carrying. Above their heads hung a gorgeous chandelier they'd had brought in from France. Zeke told her it was made with over five hundred pieces of crystal. It was mesmerizing. Paintings of great soccer players covered the walls as did a collage of black and white photos of children playing soccer from all around the world.

Harper, Addison, and Sienna were used to the atmosphere. They'd both worked in some of the poshest places in Atlanta, but Rachel's breath left her; so did Zoe's. They entered the apartment areas of the suite. This was Zeke's personal space. Again, Rachel's breath caught. It was more beautiful than any of the hotels Zeke had taken her to over the years when they traveled. Except for his Lamborghini, Zeke was unpretentious about his money, but he was a hotel snob.

"I can't believe you married a Bennett," Zoe said. "You get to live like this all the time."

Addison placed a hand on Rachel's bulging belly and said, "And just think. She's secured the bag."

Rachel swatted her hand away. "My baby is not security."

"The heck if little he or she ain't." Addison smirked. "Your prenup does not address children born of the marriage."

"Well, let's pray I never need to address it." Rachel rubbed her belly. "Now, we do need to address my appetite, so let's eat."

They dined on gourmet food and beverages in the club restaurant and then went to the Bennett suite.

The suite was hoisted just above field level. The view was amazing. Sliding glass doors led to a seated balcony area for outside viewing. Three of the walls were covered by televisions. They were the largest Rachel had ever seen. It was pure luxury. This was how rich people viewed games. Spectacular.

Lauren entered the room. She was working as one of the photographers, capturing the highlights of the day for the team. She picked up a lemonade from a passing tray and joined Rachel's little crowd. Everyone greeted her and the extra eye contact between she and Ethan was noticed. Lauren usually tried to pretend he wasn't in a room. Rachel couldn't help but wonder what had happened between them in Chile.

"Where's your husband and his partners in crime? I need to get some pre-game pics of them up here."

"I don't know," Rachel said. She'd yet to see Zeke or his business partners. She'd texted him from the limo when they first arrived to let him know she was here. The game was starting soon. She assumed they were with their players.

She and her sisters mingled among the other guests until game time. Lauren disappeared to go to the field. The announcer invited the owners onto the field. They were each introduced. One by one, they took the microphone and said a few words about how honored and excited they were to start the franchise.

Zeke was last. When he took the microphone he said, "My partners have said it all, so I want to take the opportunity to tell my lovely wife, Rachel Bennett, Happy Anniversary. Rachel, baby, let's do the rest of our lives together!" A thunderous applause came from the stands on both sides.

Within minutes, Zeke and the other owners joined them in the suite. Zeke headed straight for Rachel. He removed a box from his pocket, tipped it open to reveal the most beautiful diamond anniversary ring Rachel had ever seen.

"New rings for a new commitment." He hesitated for a moment before saying, "A commitment for forever."

A slow smile spread across Rachel's face. She raised her hand and allowed Zeke to slide the ring on her finger. He placed the other ring in the box on his. Zeke tossed the box over his shoulder and pulled her into his arms. "The best decision I ever made in my life was to marry my best friend."

Rachel's smile widened. She couldn't agree more. Her lips met his and she knew she'd never have to look for love again. She had all she needed too.

Epilogue

Five months later...

The church was packed. Invitations had gone out a month before:

Zeke and Rachel Bennett cordially invite you to attend the dedication ceremony of their beloved son, Christopher Evan Bennett. Good Faith Church, 101 Forest Hills Lane, Forest Hills, Georgia.

The dedication was beautiful. It seemed everyone in Forest Hills was in attendance. The only person missing was the godmother—Lauren. Ethan was the godfather. Addison stood in for Lauren, who, at the last minute, called to let them know she had missed her connection in New York. She would not make it. Rachel was disappointed.

"Things happen, babe," Zeke said taking his son from her arms. "He's still dedicated, and Lauren is still his godmother."

"I know, but I wanted her here. She usually flies in early for family events to avoid this."

Zeke raised the baby and cooed words to him. "Little Guy, your godmother is like fairy dust. One moment you see her, the next you don't."

Rachel cooed at the baby. "Don't listen to your daddy."

"Maybe he'll listen to his auntie." Harper and Logan walked up on them. Harper extended her hands. "Can I have him?"

Zeke handed the baby to her. "Don't get too used to them, Christopher. This is another set of folks who are going to be missing soon."

Logan raised a hand to play with the baby's foot. "Not as soon as I thought."

Harper cocked her head in his direction. "Is there something I should know?"

"The Vegas hotel is tied up in local politics. I'll be going out there in the morning to try to work it out." Logan sighed. "I know you were ready to get going, but right now it's a mess. I've had to stop construction."

Harper nodded and smiled. Rachel could tell it was forced. Her sister was disappointed, but she said, "I have other projects I can focus on."

"Good. I hate this. A lot of people are depending on this hotel, but I'll keep you posted." Logan leaned over and kissed the baby on the forehead. He gave

Zeke a pat on the shoulder and hugged Rachel. "I've got a midnight flight. I'll see you all when I get back."

He walked away, turning one last time to look at Harper. She had been staring at his back as well. Their eyes caught for a moment. The connection did not look like hotel business.

Rachel and Zeke looked at each other. Both knew the attraction between those two was going to have to come to a head soon. They'd been there. No one knew what it looked like better than they did.

Addison joined them. "Mrs. Washington from kindergarten is here. She wants to see the baby."

Zeke and Rachel looked at each other again. Zeke said, "Really? She must be a hundred."

Addison smirked. "She's not that old, but her husband is on a walker, so Harper if you would follow me, we can introduce Christopher to them."

The two disappeared with the baby.

"We should go say hello to her," Rachel said.

Zeke stepped closer and raised his hands to her face. "We should, but I'd prefer to do this." He leaned in and kissed her on the lips, then the face, and the neck.

Rachel's heart melted. "You realize we're in a church." Zeke kissed her again. "A church full of people."

"Looks like a bunch of babysitters to me." Zeke looked behind him, nodding to a door. "There's a room through there."

Rachel laughed. "It's marked 'Pastor's Study'."

"I plan to study." Zeke grinned. "I'm going to be studying you for the rest of our lives."

Rachel puckered her lips before speaking. "You promise?"

"You better believe it. You're stuck with me, Mrs. Bennett."

He kissed her again.

Rachel was never so glad to be caught.

If you enjoyed Rachel and Zeke's story, please consider leaving a **review** and texting a friend to let them know about the story. Thank you!

Make sure to look for Harper and Logan's story, *All They Need* on *April 20, 2021.*

All They Need

*It was his second chance and nothing
was going to keep them apart.*

Harper Ingram

Harper Ingram needed the job her ex, Logan Bennett, had to offer. Without it, her design firm would be bankrupt in months. But working for Logan was proving to be more difficult than she imagined. Long hours, hot Vegas nights, and an irresistible attraction make her easy prey for his affection. Just when she's ready to risk it all, an ugly accusation leaves her wondering if she knows him at all.

Logan Bennett

Logan walked away from Harper before and he's never told her why, nor did she ask. He's determined to get her back by any means necessary. A chance meeting opens the door for opportunity that neither can resist. Can Logan convince her to trust him again, and is he willing to tell her why he broke her heart the first time?

If you missed it, check out
the other book in the series…

All She Wants

Lenise Reid has become a widow, a single parent, and a fraudulent transaction wipes out her balance at the bank leaving her with no money. Now she's homeless.

Cole Bennett is used to getting everything he wants. When Lenise ghosts him, he's determined to find out why. What he finds is a woman so wounded that even in her most desperate state, she struggles with his charity.

Lenise Reid is bleeding money and heartache. Could Cole Bennett be the bandage she needs?

Sign up for my newsletter at my website www.RhondaMcKnight.com

The Winter Reunion

Everyone knows the woman in the famous 'viral" video that hit two million views on YouTube. Humiliated, *Tamar Johnson* changed her name and disappeared behind the embarrassing video that captured her losing her virginity on prom night. But who was the guy?

NFL Running Back *Stephen Pierce* is football's darling. He's spent his entire career doing community service work with at risk kids, and endeared fans as a devoted Christian, even claiming celibacy. It's time for his high school reunion. Stephen is determined to get his EX, Tamar, to come out of hiding, even going as far as posting their prom picture on Instagram in hopes that she would accept the challenge to show up.

Tamar isn't interested in the reunion, but her boss is. She writes for a small magazine. Stephen Pierce is a big story. Tamar is going to the reunion whether she wants to or not.

With reunion activity in full swing, tension between Tamar and Stephen reaches an unbearable high. Before it's over will the world find out who the real Stephen Pierce is? Will Tamar survive spending time with the only man who's ever had her heart?

The Winter Reunion - Chapter 1

"You're fired."

I frowned. "You can't fire me."

"Actually, I can." My boss, Eva Stanford, dropped into her chair. She folded her arms over each other on the desk. That position meant business. So did the steely glare in her eyes.

"You can't." This time my voice held the question. *Could she?*

"I'm the managing editor. I can fire whomever I want."

"But I have a contract."

"You sure do. Have you looked at it since you signed it? There's a part in the legalese that says you have to do the stories that are assigned to you."

I hadn't looked at my contract in years. I never had a reason to. I was happy doing the stories that came across my desk. I didn't have aspirations of becoming some big time reporter. All I wanted to do was pay my bills and keep pecking at the novel I'd been revising for three years. But now paying my bills might become an issue.

"I can't do a story about Stephen Pierce. I don't know anything about sports."

Eva picked up her cell phone and shoved it in my direction. "You may not know sports, but you know him. I'm pretty annoyed that you kept that from me."

I took the phone and looked down at an Instagram photo of myself and Stephen. The blood drained from my face. Pain constricted my heart. He was going to be the death of me. "This is my prom picture."

"That's obvious." Eva rolled her eyes. "One of the interns brought it to my attention. He recognized you."

I squinted at the picture. My head got light. I was glad I was sitting. "I can't believe he posted this."

"He's on his way to your reunion. I guess he's feeling nostalgic."

I continued to stare at the picture — at him really. I hadn't seen this picture in years. I didn't even have my yearbook or any of the memorabilia anymore. My exasperated sigh filled the momentary quiet. "It's not my reunion. It's a thing they do. It's for all classes."

"Small school stuff. I get it." Eva unfolded her arms and pressed her back into her plush, leather chair. "You're thirty, right? So it's been eleven — twelve years since prom?"

I nodded.

"Did you go to this thing last year?"

"I don't go to my reunions." I pushed the offending phone across the desk to her.

Eva cocked her head. "I'm sure there's a story there. Does it involve Pierce? Do you ever talk to him?"

I fought hard to keep my face from telling my truth. "He was a prom date, Eva. It was a lifetime ago. I have no idea what he's doing now."

Eva extended a manicured fingernail and tapped the screen. "Hmmm…the caption over his Instagram is evidence that he's curious about what you're doing. He put the same thing on Twitter."

I sighed again. I could tell by the look in her eyes that I was not getting out of this. I harnessed my irritation. "I can't believe you're going to make me do this. I haven't been to Pine since I finished high school."

Eva reached for a lipstick-smeared, latte cup. "Stephen certainly seems to love it. It looks like he spends a lot of time there."

Easy for him to do. I resented that.

"Do you have family there?" Eva probed.

I shifted in my chair. "Some."

"They'll be glad to see you." She pushed the button to boot up her laptop. "People get old. They die. I can't stand my family either, but I visit every few years or so."

I stood. The booting up of her laptop meant I was dismissed. "Eva —"

"It's settled, Anne. I need a good story. We're going to run this for February. Try to find out if he's dating someone. Something romantic for a Valentine feature."

I shook my head. "You know how private he is. He's not going to tell me that."

Eva cocked an eyebrow. "I won't push. You know what I need for a cover story."

I turned to leave the office.

Eva called to me. "Any truth to that rumor about him? The one about the video."

I swallowed. "That old story?"

"Nothing is really old. I'll have to see if we can dig up that video. Ask him a question or two about it."

"Asking him about the video is not going to endear him to me. He really won't talk to me then."

"You're right, but you can ask. I know this isn't what you normally do, so I'll send you a few questions. You always ask the hard stuff after you get the easy stuff."

"I know how to do my job, Eva."

She lowered her eyeglasses and peered down her nose at me. "You're acting like you don't."

I resisted the urge to fight with her. She always won. "I need to take the afternoon off. I wasn't planning to go, so I don't have anything to wear."

"Fine. Expense it. Expense a trip to the hair salon, too. You need it. Donna has your itinerary and some other details."

I walked to the door, grabbed the handle, did a half turn and looked back at her. "I guess this is just as good a time as any to tell you this, because it'll probably come out now that I'm going to the reunion."

A disconcerting look came over Eva's face. "Spit it out."

"Anne Ferguson isn't my real name."

About the Author

 Even as she earned degrees in Textile Technology, Organizational Leadership and finally Adult Education, *Rhonda McKnight*'s love for books and desire to write stories was always in the back of her mind and in the forefront of her heart. Rhonda loves reading and writing stories that touch the heart of women through complex plots and interesting characters in crisis. She writes from the comfort of her South Carolina home with hot tea, potato chips and chocolate on hand. At her feet sits a snappy mixed breed toy dog. She can be reached at her website at www.RhondaMcknight.com and on social media at

http://www.facebook.com/booksbyrhonda and www.instagram.com/AuthorRhondaMcKnight and www.twitter.com/rhondamcknight and www.SistersofFaithBooks.com where she has joined with eighteen other Christian fiction authors to introduce her stories to the world. She is also a member of the board for The Christian Book Lover's Retreat. www.ChristianBookLoversRetreat.com